NEUROSCIENCE
INTELLIGENCE
UNIT

ON ASTROCYTES AND GLUTAMATE NEUROTRANSMISSION: NEW WAVES IN BRAIN INFORMATION PROCESSING

Elisabeth Hansson, Ph.D.

Institute of Neurobiology and Institute of Clinical Neuroscience
Department of Neurology
Göteborg University
Göteborg, Sweden

Torsten Olsson, Ph.D.

Department of Applied Electronics
Chalmers University of Technology
Göteborg, Sweden

Lars Rönnbäck, M.D., Ph.D.

Institute of Clinical Neuroscience
Department of Neurology
Göteborg University
Göteborg, Sweden

Springer

New York Berlin Heidelberg London Paris
Tokyo Hong Kong Barcelona Budapest

AUSTIN, TEXAS
U.S.A.

NEUROSCIENCE INTELLIGENCE UNIT
ON ASTROCYTES AND GLUTAMATE NEUROTRANSMISSION: NEW WAVES IN BRAIN INFORMATION PROCESSING

R.G. LANDES COMPANY
Austin, Texas, U.S.A.

Please address all inquiries to the Publishers:
R.G. Landes Company, 810 South Church Street, Georgetown, Texas, U.S.A. 78626
Phone: 512/ 863 7762; FAX: 512/ 863 0081

International distributor (except North America):
Springer-Verlag GmbH & Co. KG
Tiergartenstrasse 17, D-69121 Heidelberg, Germany

Springer

International ISBN: 3-540-62984-X

Library of Congress Cataloging-in-Publication Data
CIP applied for, but not received as of publication date.

Publisher's Note

R.G. Landes Bioscience Publishers produces books in six Intelligence Unit series: *Medical, Molecular Biology, Neuroscience, Tissue Engineering, Biotechnology* and *Environmental.* The authors of our books are acknowledged leaders in their fields. Topics are unique; almost without exception, no similar books exist on these topics.

Our goal is to publish books in important and rapidly changing areas of bioscience for sophisticated researchers and clinicians. To achieve this goal, we have accelerated our publishing program to conform to the fast pace at which information grows in bioscience. Most of our books are published within 90 to 120 days of receipt of the manuscript. We would like to thank our readers for their continuing interest and welcome any comments or suggestions they may have for future books.

Shyamali Ghosh
Publications Director
R.G. Landes Company

CONTENTS

EDITORS

Elisabeth Hansson, Ph.D.
Institute of Neurobiology and Institute of Clinical Neuroscience
Department of Neurology
Göteborg University
Göteborg, Sweden
chapters 1, 3, 6 and 8

Torsten Olsson, Ph.D.
Department of Applied Electronics
Chalmers University of Technology
Göteborg, Sweden
chapters 1, 6 and 7

Lars Rönnbäck, M.D., Ph.D.
Institute of Clinical Neuroscience
Department of Neurology
Göteborg University
Göteborg, Sweden
chapters 1, 7 and 8

CONTRIBUTORS

Fredrik Blomstrand, M.Sc.
Institute of Neurobiology and
  Institute of Clinical Neuroscience
Department of Neurology
Göteborg University
Göteborg, Sweden
chapters 6, 7

Peter S. Eriksson, MD, Ph.D.
Institute of Neurobiology and
  Institute of Clinical Neuroscience
Department of Neurology
Göteborg University
Göteborg, Sweden
chapter 5

Gull-Britt Hagberg, B.S.
Institute of Neurobiology and
  Institute of Clinical Neuroscience
Department of Neurology
Göteborg University
Göteborg, Sweden
chapter 4

Siamak Khatibi, M.Sc. Eng.
Department of Applied Electronics
Chalmers University of Technology
Göteborg, Sweden
chapters 6, 7

Håkan Muyderman, B.S.
Institute of Neurobiology and
  Institute of Clinical Neuroscience
Department of Neurology
Göteborg University
Göteborg, Sweden
chapter 7

Michael Nilsson, MD, Ph.D.
Institute of Neurobiology and
  Institute of Clinical Neuroscience
Department of Neurology
Göteborg University
Göteborg, Sweden
chapter 4

Thorleif Thorlin, MD
Institute of Neurobiology and
  Institute of Clinical Neuroscience
Department of Neurology
Göteborg University
Göteborg, Sweden
chapter 2

============ PREFACE ============

The literature on astroglial cells has increased considerably over the last 10 to 15 years. From having been thought of as passive, and only giving structural and metabolic support to the neurons, today astroglial cells are regarded as intimate collaborators with the nerve cells. During the late 1970s and early '80s, membrane receptors for most known neurotransmitters and neuromodulators were demonstrated on the astroglial cells. It was shown that the cells are able to register nerve cell activity, and the composition of neuroactive substances in serum as well as in the extracellular space in brain. During the last 6 to 10 years it has appeared that the cells can communicate with each other and probably also integrate the information obtained within the gap junction linked astroglial network. In the very recent years there have been indications that the astroglial network, on the basis of its functional status, can alter the ion and amino acid composition in the extracellular space, so the astroglia might be able to modulate neuronal excitability.

The aim of this book is to provide some ideas regarding how the astroglia might interact with and modulate nerve cell activity at the synaptic level but also to indicate what roles astroglia might play in brain information processing. The book is the result of an extensive collaboration between experimental neurobiology, clinical neurology and technology. Results from different laboratories including our own concerning some of those astroglial characteristics, which makes it possible for the cells to modulate the composition and concentration of neuroactive substances in the extracellular milieu are reviewed, and we also touch upon aspects on astroglial intra- and intercellular signaling. This book does not claim to be exhaustive in its details, and there are even major fields such as the area of energy metabolism or long-term potentiation (LTP), which are mentioned only very superficially if at all. For more detailed information the reader is therefore encouraged to go to the original literature, review articles or the more comprehensive textbooks. To make it possible to read each chapter separately, some repetitions occur throughout the book.

Well aware that single cells, integrated neuronal circuits and behavior represent different levels of abstraction and require different techniques to study, we include a hypothesis claiming that astroglial dysfunction might result in an organic psychosyndrome. We thus propose that an impairment of astroglial function might be one cause of stress-intolerance and fatigue upon mental activity, with decreased concentration capacity and sometimes a secondary disturbance of short-term memory and headache after long-term mentally demanding work often seen after a brain injury, stroke or brain trauma, or after infectious or inflammatory processes in brain. As we all know the brain is our most complex organ both in terms of architecture and function and we, in fact, lack knowledge of how to study very complex systems. It is, therefore, important to state that our hypotheses and thoughts about the role of astroglia in synaptic transmission on the one hand, and in integrated brain function and in higher brain function on the other, are presented within the same book not so as to appear provocative or nonscientific, but to stimulate further discussions and research on the roles of astroglia in brain information processing in physiology and pathology. One of the main challenges for glial researchers is to move towards the identification of behaviorally or clinically relevant states where astroglial dysfunction is of importance and preferably lay down the general outlines for, and probably develop, pharmacotherapy selectively directed to restoring the specific astroglial dysfunction. From that point of view, hypotheses on astroglial function at different levels, and the pathophysiological consequences of astroglial dysfunctions are important, even if they cannot be experimentally tested or properly verified at present.

Finally, we want to express our sincere thanks to Linda Schenck for proofreading all the chapters.

===== CHAPTER 1 =====

ASTROGLIA AND BRAIN FUNCTION: AN INTRODUCTION

Torsten Olsson, Lars Rönnbäck and Elisabeth Hansson

All evolution in thought and conduct must at first appear as heresy and misconduct. —George Bernard Shaw, 1856-1950

In this introduction we speculate about known and possible roles of the astroglia in medium and high-level brain functions. By matching the known properties and behavior of glial cells with needs in various processes in the brain we try to justify or validate the role of the glia in these processes. For some of these processes it is generally agreed that the glia are vital, while their role in other processes is mere speculation. In this chapter we also include a general discussion about information processing on a more philosophical level.

GENERAL INTRODUCTION

The brain consists of neurons, which rapidly conduct and transmit specific information, and glial cells, which have been considered to give structural, metabolic and functional support to the neurons. Theories on information processing in the brain are based on the observed electrical activity of neurons and the chemically transferred messages at synapses. This traditional view still holds true but it may not be the whole truth. Recent research suggests that the glial cells may communicate with each other and with the neurons. From a quantitative point of view the astroglia are the most prominent cell type in the glial cell family and this is probably one reason that astroglial research has attracted so much interest during the last 10-15 years.

The astroglial cells have long processes and form networks in which communication between the cells takes place through gap junctions. Astroglial processes encapsulate synapses, neuronal cell bodies and blood vessels, and form the blood-brain barrier together with the cells of the blood vessel walls.

On Astrocytes and Glutamate Neurotransmission: New Waves in Brain Information Processing, edited by Elisabeth Hansson, Torsten Olsson and Lars Rönnbäck. © 1997 R.G. Landes Company.

Astrocytes express a set of functional and neurochemical properties which, until a few years ago, were thought to be specific to neurons. It is now well known that astroglia express membrane receptors for most known neurotransmitters and neuromodulators. The receptors are coupled to signal transduction systems in the cell membrane. The astroglial cells have transport carriers for amino acids, and it is well known that they have a great capacity for uptake of the amino acid transmitter glutamate (Glu) from the extracellular space. The cells also have the capacity to accumulate the inhibitory transmitter γ-amino butyric acid (GABA). It has been common knowledge since the 1980s that the astroglia express ion channels, and that the cells have a membrane potential and can be depolarized although no action potential can be elicited. Instead, a Ca^{2+} based excitability was demonstrated within the astroglial network in 1990. The cells can regulate pH both inside the cells and in the extracellular space. Very importantly, the astrocytes have a great capacity to regulate their own volume. As the extracellular space in brain is relatively small, this volume regulating function of the astrocytes has a great impact in pathological states and probably even under normal conditions, as intense neuronal activity may lead to astroglial swelling. Thereby the concentration of neuroactive substances can be profoundly changed in the extracellular space.

With the state of knowledge now achieved, it thus seems probable that the astroglial cells "listen" to the activities of neurons and also sense the compositions of blood and of the extracellular milieu. The information received might be carried by the newly discovered Ca^{2+} signaling facility within the electrically

Fig. 1.1. (Opposite page) Schematic drawing demonstrating three principal astroglial functions: I) structural and metabolic support of the neurons, II) monitoring of synaptic activity and III) modulation of neuronal excitability, the latter as a probable astroglial function. Three astroglial cells are shown, two of which are linked via gap junction coupling. Furthermore, two synaptic regions with pre- and postsynaptic terminals are seen. The close relationship between the astroglia and the blood vessels are indicated by a small vessel to the left in the figure.
The glial structural and metabolic support was suspected already in the middle of the previous century, while the glial removal of K^+ and glutamate was experimentally verified during the 1960s and 1970s. The basis of the glial monitoring of synaptic activity, of neuroactive substances in the extracellular milieu, and of the serum composition has been experimentally demonstrated during the late 1970s and the early 1980s. Since 1990 Ca^{2+} based intercellular astroglial signaling is studied, and during recent years it seems probable that the astroglial syncytium can regulate ionic and amino acid homeostasis in the extracellular milieu. There are thus strong indications that astroglia can modulate pre- and postsynaptic excitability levels.
It is indicated in the figure that the astroglial network might be affected with regard to these functions and probably also the functions of synthesis and release of neurotrophic factors by interaction with astroglial receptors and/or gap junction constituents. This might be one important direction for future astroglial research to pursue.

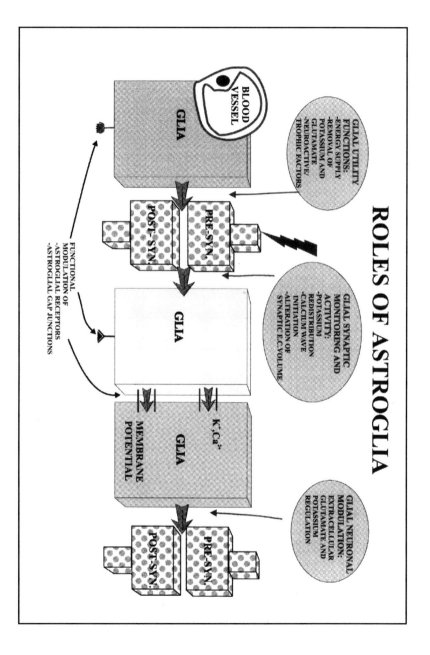

coupled astroglial network and thus different parts of the brain might be informed about the state of neuronal and environmental activities.

Very recent data show that the astrocytes can signal back to the neurons and thereby probably affect the nerve cell activity. Results from many laboratories now speak in favor of astroglial regulation of the concentrations of amino acids, ions, and other neuroactive substances in the extracellular space (Fig. 1.1). This ability places the astrocytes in the important position of changing the extracellular environment, thereby modulate the excitability of many neurons simultaneously. In addition to the fact that astrocytes can recognize and respond to impulses, it is well known that the cells can produce and release many neuroactive substances. These agents consist of amino acids, peptides, and small proteins in the form, for example, of maturating or growth factors for the neurons. They might be of importance for neuronal maturation and neuronal continuous rebuilding as an effect of synaptic activity, beyond which the growth factors may also be of importance for restoration after damage. Nerve growth factor and an agent which supports dopaminergic neurons, i.e., those neurons which degenerate in the Parkinson's disease, are produced in astroglia. The S100 protein, a calcium binding protein, is also produced in astroglia and is known to be released into the extracellular milieu where the protein has been shown to excite trophic actions. Recent research indicates that neurons and astrocytes form functional units and that interaction between these cell types are important for the plasticity of the nervous system.

To date, most knowledge about the astroglial cells is obtained from different cell culture systems although some properties of the cells have been verified in in vivo-like preparations. Important tasks for future glial cell research might be to verify the data obtained from the cell culture studies in in situ preparations. Thereafter, it might be important to develop drugs which affect the astroglial network to regulate the surrounding milieu of the neurons and thereby regulate the excitability of neurons. It should also be important to learn how to stimulate pharmacologically the production and release of trophic factors of importance for restoration processes within the CNS. In the future it might be possible to use somatic gene therapy to introduce new genetic material into the astrocytes for the synthesis, for instance, of neurotransmitters or growth factors in cases of injuries or degenerative diseases.

ABOUT SYSTEMS

Before embarking on the main subject of this book, let us turn for a moment to some more general issues about brain function in relation to signaling and information processing. Scientists aiming at a deeper and more thorough understanding of the processes involved in information handling and processing in the brain sooner or later face problems of philosophical nature. The brain is, needless to say, a complex system. There are today no general theories or well developed complete techniques to help in the study of complex systems in general. But there is an abundance of diverse knowledge and concepts to benefit from. We believe it is appropriate to highlight some of these concepts here in a modest fashion, very well aware that this is a complex matter and that we do so in a nonscientific manner. We emphasize this by referring to popular scientific rather than purely mathematical or philosophical literature. We discuss two issues, (a) the holistic versus the reductionistic approach to the study of brain function and (b) models, data and information representation in the brain.

The first issue about a holistic versus a reductionistic approach to the study of brain function is included because we believe that there is a general need to widen the scope of brain function research in many areas in order to understand the meaning and the importance of various low level phenomena to high level functions. It is certainly not only in brain research that these issues are discussed and disputed. There is also a growing interest in the more generic approach to complex system research.

Traditional neurological research is reductionistic. This is true of neuroanatomy, neurophysiology, etc. The holistic approach to brain research comes mainly from psychology. And the approaches very seldom meet. We believe that a combination of the holistic and the reductionistic approaches are required to understand how the brain functions on the levels that come close to the mental level. This is probably where the concept of information is intuitively most important, and this is where we have to seek many structurally related interactions and cooperations between lower level substructures and processes. The reductionistic approach starts off with physical and chemical observations on structures and functions. Layer after layer of knowledge and insight of structure and relations are peeled off while striving at detailed descriptions of the most basal functions. Many times this happens without any concern about why these functions exist or their role on the system level.

The holistic approach uses high level observations and tries to relate these observations to known, often well-described lower level mechanisms. In theory there are an infinite number of ways to express this relation. Functional explanations that holists pursue do not usually require a one-to-one mapping of identified biological mechanisms to behavioral or mental phenomena.

At first glance these differences may speak in favor of the reductionistic approach. It is thus easy to understand that some scientists extrapolate from physics and chemistry and claim that understanding the brain function requires techniques borrowed from quantum physics or chemistry. This is, however, questionable. There is a theorem by the mathematician Gödel that claims roughly: a system description which is logically consistent can never be made complete if complexity increases beyond a certain level. That is, it is not advisable to use one set of terms and definitions to describe basic mechanisms on the cellular level and also to use the same terms and definitions try to embrace high level mental functions completely. From this point of view there is a need for several sets of terminology and definitions to build up the various levels of functionality, and these levels can probably be linked and verified using a holistic approach. There is a highly appreciated book, *Gödel, Escher, Bach: An Eternal Golden Braid* by D. R. Hoffstadter,[1] a popular scientific-philosophical novel that treats this issue with insight and precision. To read some reflections on the matter by a neuroscientist on a similar popular level see for instance *The Making of Memory* by S. Rose.[2]

INFORMATION PROCESSING AND MODELS

Since we have introduced 'Information Processing' in the title we feel comfortable with pursuing this issue a little further. We discuss some matters in light of the concepts reductionism and holistism and give some examples of how concepts of systems theory, signal processing and computer science can be used to help form a viable set of terms and tools to advance the science relating to brain function.

First we have the term 'information'. Information has several meanings. In common language it is used to mean "something told or facts learned; news or knowledge" (Webster's Dictionary). In a scientific environment, information is used to relate data to interpretations like "Data which has been recorded, organized, related, or interpreted within a framework so that meaning emerges" *McGraw-Hill Dictionary of Scientific and Technical Terms,* 5th ed.[3]

When Cornell-Bell, Finkbeiner, Cooper et al[4] first reported about possible glial cell communication they used the term signal ("... Long-Range Glial Signaling"). It is very common to see phrases like 'extract information from signals or data' which implies that there is a difference between the two concepts. We believe that keeping this distinction in mind is important in a consistent concept-forming process. Thus signals or data should be used for observations which are used to study the phenomenon and information should be used to emphasize meaning. The meaning can be expressed in many different ways depending on the abstraction level. On the cellular level, a calcium wave can belong to the information concept when describing the action on the receptor level. However on a higher level, a memory-making process, say, the possible *information* related content of the calcium wave may be quite different if it is detectable at all.

The second word 'processing' implies that the information content is handled. Here, too, it is preferable to distinguish between signal or data processing and information processing when ever possible. For instance, carrying or coding data can be done without any regard to the information content.

This is data or signal processing. On the other hand, without knowledge of how information is encoded in the data or signal we lack important knowledge to approach the information and thus to study the information processing. Again it is vital to consider the abstraction level on which the actual study and reasoning are done. On the cellular level, data or observations about ion channel reactions may contain information on what causes the reactions. The information processing can be expressed in terms of ion channel sensitivities, etc. But this information processing knowledge may not be transferred to higher functional levels such as the motor control system. The information processing in this system must be expressed and studied using other terms and concepts. If we try to build up a model of something as complex as the human motor control system using only cell related terms and concepts, Gödel's Incompleteness theorem will predict that there will most likely be inconsistencies and errors. On the other hand, a holistic attempt to directly relate motor actions to the cellular level will also fail because there is no way to verify that we have selected the 'true' solution from an infinite number of possible solutions. The plausible way out of this dilemma is to use a number of concept layers and to relate each layer to layers below and above. Thus both reductionistic and holistic approaches are combined and the whole system may eventually be described and understood.

We argue that there is an urgent need to develop reasonable context layers to help develop functional neuroscience. There is some progress being made in the study of the motor system. The concept of motor program has been introduced,[5] but unfortunately without a proper definition. And of course the term process is frequently used in contexts like the memory making process and the pattern recognition process in the vision system. But the use of 'process' in these contexts also lacks definition and precision.

Before turning to the glial cells we put forward some ideas of how such a layered system could be built and how established techniques in the fields of information theory, computer science, system engineering and others can be used as tools. Computers are often compared with the brain. Many of these comparisons have been criticized and are irrelevant, but some are informative. Refer, for instance, to the above discussion about the reductionistic and holistic paradigms. Using a computer as an example instead of the brain, we can state that it is impossible to describe the function of a computer only in terms of its circuitry. The circuitry carries no information of how the data are coded and reveals no knowledge about how the various resources are recruited and used. One also needs knowledge of what is normally referred to as software. And software cannot be described using the same terms as are used to describe hardware. But hardware can be modeled and simulated in software and software modules can be implemented in hardware. A computer user or application programmer does not know what is executed by the hardware or the software.

One possible and obvious way to approach the concept-forming process is to use a modular approach. The morphological mapping of the brain is part of this process. There are often associations to functional levels when naming and describing these modules, but there is also a need for a set of morphologically unrelated functional modules, as well as a need for a meta-level to describe the modules unrelated to specific functionality. It is far beyond the scope of this book to suggest a set of such modules but we mention a few properties of such a system concept that are useful as we proceed. On the meta-level it is important to recognize a module representing a processing 'engine' and the fact that this 'engine' processes data or information. The engine may be of a general purpose type. The fact that it is active does not reveal information about what data are processed. On a low abstraction level the signaling properties of the astrocytes may be put into this engine category.

On a much higher level we can mention the gait process. The gait process certainly includes an engine that can be started by a command. It is distributed within the brain, the brain stem, peripheral nerves and muscles. This engine can be controlled and further developed.

Other examples are the "engines" used in speech and language processing. Some of these may be situated in the "lateral language area" or the "language cortex." However, there is evidence that these areas are also involved in creating novel movements.[6] Could it be that what we see is the action of general purpose sequencer engines that are equally important for combining sequences of symbols in a language context as they are for generating control codes to the motor system?

An engine needs data (or information) to function. The data can be divided into various sub-types; specifically we have parameter data and data to be processed. Parameter data are often persistent and can be retrieved from memory. They may also result from another process. When we talk in a noisy environment we raise our voices by adjusting our voice level parameter, while the voice data are continuously processed by the engine. Remember, however, this is a description using a functional concept and does not tell which lower level functions or processes are involved.

Let us relate the various terms we use. On each level of abstraction the process is the most far-reaching term. A process may have engines, programs, and data, and include other processes. The process performs a function.

Why do we include this reasoning here? We believe it is important to identify possible needs in such engines or processes that may benefit from being controlled or modulated through glial networks and exclude those that cannot possibly be implemented based on, or heavily dependent on, glial networks.

Technical systems are generally specified by response times, dynamic ranges and similar terms. There are several universally useful tools and methods to help to specify systems. Some of these lend themselves to some of the brain functions on a lower level. The glial activities including signaling are slow as compared to neuronal activities and neuronal signaling. Thus we should focus on process properties in this slower range when we look for glial contributions. Indeed, there are plenty of such properties, well known, but not well described in terms of neural activities or other known components of brain function. Let us speculate about the noisy environment example described above. What would be the properties of an efficient control mechanism for such behavior? First some adaptive steps are taken to adjust the hearing process. Filter properties are continuously adapted to increase the signal-to-noise-ratio, that is the noise components are suppressed and unique components in the sounds from our conversation partners are enhanced. These are active processes and continuously adapted to changes in the environment. We all know they are there: just remember what happens when you enter a room with noisy ventilation. After a short while you do not notice the fan or moving air noise, but, if it is switched off you experience an immediate relief (an indication that this is probably an active process). To keep the parameters set in this filter process, relatively persistent mechanisms are needed. Neural activities are primary but when a pattern is established, a footprint of this pattern could be maintained by less energy-demanding means. These may be localized enhanced signal-substance concentrations maintained by a process in which astrocytes may play an active and specific role. The response time of the astrocyte processes fits into that role, while the filter itself must process incoming sound signals and must use components with neuronal properties.

The filtering process is recognized by everyone but is most easy to demonstrate in the visual system. A very spectacular and effective experiment is the following: A homogeneous dynamic noise picture is displayed on a TV screen (like what you see without a channel tuned in). Abruptly, within a circle, say, the noise characteristics are changed but with the intensity maintained. We then see a round disk very clearly for a few seconds while the perceived picture gradually returns to that of a homogeneous noisy display. When the noise pattern is switched back again the phenomenon is repeated. This demonstrates, explained in model world terms, how information about the signal (image) properties is extracted and maintained as a footprint. Deviations in properties are used to adjust the property-footprint and the fact that there is a deviation is available as useful information. Again, we can ask, do the astrocytes play an active role in this footprint making process?

Let us return to the noisy environment example. The filtering and voice detection process is local to the auditory centers. We must also tell the speech process to raise the volume. This kind of message propagation could be a candidate for a long range astrocyte signaling task, but it could also be implemented by neuronal connections or a combination of both.

With these examples we hope to encourage the search for observable high level functions that are suitable candidates for astrocytes and astrocyte network participation. In the remainder of this chapter we will expand this reasoning to a few phenomena that have already been reported and discussed in the literature.

A FUNCTIONAL SYSTEM

In order not to anticipate the upcoming chapters we continue our anecdotal style. We will add a few more useful concepts to describe process properties. A few examples are briefly mentioned, but we have no ambition to completely review these matters. Consider the evoked EEG response. Many high level brain functions are studied using this technique. A very simple stimulus like a light flash gives rise to an EEG response that extends over a period of several 100 ms recorded by scalp electrodes. The action potential has a duration of just about 1 ms. Already in 1937, Forbes, Renshaw and Rempel[7] concluded about the EEG that "All evidence indicates that the slow waves are not the summations of numbers of axon-like spikes." Very briefly, the sources of the EEG are associated with variations in postsynaptic potentials. The slow variations of these potentials are attributed to summation effects from dendrite trees. However, since astrocytes are intimately connected to the synaptic region, as is discussed in chapters below, determining their role in the forming of the various EEG-signals is an intriguing matter.

The well-known phenomenon of habituation manifests itself in the evoked potential as progressively lower amplitudes in late components of the response when the same stimulus is repeated over an extended period of time. Given the assumption that astrocytes act in a way that modulates the potentials in the synaptic region, one can postulate that the astrocytes are active in the habituation process. A holistic hypothesis that this is the case is supported by our current knowledge of astrocyte functionality and cannot be rejected on the basis of known facts.

Information coding within the nervous system is known to have both topographic and nontopographic modalities. Topographic coding has many levels of persistency—from permanently irreversible to continuously adaptable. Nontopographic coding is mostly considered to be time sequence modulation of various kinds. Processes may use a combination of different modalities, and modalities used during a time course may vary. If we continue to reason about habituation, we may suggest that the actual astrocytes involved in signal suppression form a topographic pattern which, in turn, represents a temporary code for the particular stimulus. The stimulus signal itself, as carried by neurons, is suppressed as long as it matches this code.

A good many attempts have been made to relate functional high level phenomenon to lower levels. One of these is the Hebb's Cell-assembly. William H. Calvin[6] expanded this idea with the concept of a Darwin Machine, which could model the function of this unit or engine. It is striking, though, that activities in these engines are almost always referred to as neuronal firing. The topographic pattern is a vital part of the code used by such engines and here, again, the astrocytes may play an important role.

Another brain feature studied using the evoked response technique is the ability to create expectation responses of various kinds. One simple form is to omit some stimuli in a continuous otherwise regular sequence. At the times of the omitted stimulus a different evoked response appears. The relation of this response to the habituation phenomenon is not clear. It could be an inhibitory action balanced by the activation generated by the signals, in which case the topographic pattern code also has a temporal pattern. The question arises as to whether the astrocytes could generate such a temporal pattern. There is no clear answer to this question, but the rate and amount by which the astrocytes can change ion concentration (primarily $[K^+]$) in the synaptic region does not rule out the possibility (time constants in the order of seconds and potential changes up to 70 mV).

The example above relates to the sensory system but there are far more sophisticated experiments which generate responses to mentally related activities. The origins of the potentials attributed to the response are often found in areas known to have dense astrocyte population. The effect of the synaptic environment can be described as sensitivity, gain or threshold control.

MEMORY AND MEMORY MAKING

Common sense suffices to create an idea of a layered system in which habituation is the first step in a memory forming process. Of course there are various types of memory. For instance, there are procedural or skill memory—the 'how' memory—and declarative memory—the 'that' memory. And there are short-term and long-term memory. Let us not get lost in intricacy but stay on a meta-level and suggest some further direction to search for suitable missions for the astrocytes, given the current insight to their properties. Some or all memory can be associated with a spatio-temporal pattern. Memory forming may simply be represented by the state of the active components in the brain during the procedures or the episodes that are imprinted in memory. Since the glial cells are active components they are thus part of the memory-making process in this holistic model. But keeping a record based on the state of each active component for each episode or procedure is highly inefficient, to say the least. Some kind of reduction and pruning procedures must accompany the recording procedure. The reduction procedures can identify sub-patterns already stored in memory and refer to them instead of recording them again.

We can relate back to the concept of engines here, too: the state of an engine represents a pattern or a code that could be what we retain as memory. Thus there is a very close relationship between action and memory.

Although parallel processing is a generally accepted property of brain function it is not possible to make all possible searches in flash mode: Some state-related features must remain long enough for the search engine to do its task. Astrocytes may have the ability to maintain a certain state along the active neuronal path for an extended period of time and could thus be used by the path-finder of a search engine. If we accept that the pattern is spatio-temporal, there must also be a means to regenerate temporal patterns for the search engine: The ability for the astrocytes to communicate via (calcium-related) gap junctions could be utilized in such a regeneration. Now we are fifteen fathoms deep but it must be admitted that this kind of speculative reasoning lends itself to the formulation of hypotheses to be tested on a lower level in a reductionistic manner.

The above reasoning could also be used to model what is associated with the buzzword, "plasticity." This concept is easily included as a sub-process of the general memory-making process. But there is probably something more versatile to it. Proprioceptive and other state information is continuously received and memorized on different time scales. The recognition of signal flow is part of this process. In the intermediate-to-long time frame astrocytes have properties that make them suitable to participation in this process. It is well known, and this is beautifully captured by Oliver Sacks in his novel *A Leg to Stand On*,[8] that essential parts are not hard-wired. The use of the term "state" above is deliberate. In engineering and systems theory the concepts of "state" and "state space" have proven to be very powerful. We will not be surprised if in the near future these concepts are used in relation to brain function and if the astrocytes are found to be important components in holding and carrying state information.

Observations in recent years that the astrocytes have very potent abilities to interact with neurons and have properties allowing them to communicate with each other is stimulating research in this area. We may eventually see new knowledge evolve about many brain functions and observed phenomena in which glial participation will prove to be essential. We will revisit many areas of brain research open mindedly and discover new roles of the astrocytes in view of the newly gained knowledge about them. We hope that this introduction may stimulate such revisiting. Below we describe state of the art knowledge about astrocytes with a focus on their role in glutamate-related brain functions. Where appropriate, the chapters conclude with some speculations to stimulate further penetration into the role of astrocytes in signal- and information-related processes in the brain.

REFERENCES

1. Hoffstadter DR. Gödel, Escher, Bach: An Eternal Golden Braid. New York: Basic Books, 1979.
2. Rose S. The Making of Memory. From Molecules to Mind. London: Bantam Books, 1993.
3. Parker SP, ed. McGraw-Hill Dictionary of Scientific and Technical Terms, 5th Edition New York: McGraw-Hill, 1994:1013.
4. Cornell-Bell AH, Finkbeiner SB, Cooper MS et al. Glutamate induces calcium waves in cultured astrocytes: long-range glial signaling. Science 1990; 247:470-474.
5. Keele SW. Movement control in skilled motor performance. Psychol Bull 1968; 70:387-403.
6. Calvin WH. The emergence of intelligence. Sci Am 1994; 271(4):100-107.
7. Forbes A, Renshaw B, Rempel B. Units of electrical activity in the cerebral cortex. Am J Physiol 1937; 119:309-310.
8. Sacks O. A Leg to Stand On. New York:Summit Books, 1984.

CHAPTER 2

MORPHOLOGY AND GENERAL PHYSIOLOGY OF ASTROGLIAL CELLS

Thorleif Thorlin

INTRODUCTION

The brain consists of complex networks in which neurons and glial cells are structurally and functionally interwoven. Astrocytes, the most numerous members of the glial family, were originally considered, along with the whole glial population, to be of mostly structural importance as passive support elements for the neurons.[1] They are recognized as star-shaped cells whose processes extend into the surrounding neuropil and are extensively coupled in a network, the astrocyte syncytium. Some of the processes from each cell form expansions that contact the surfaces of blood vessels with their so-called endfeet, forming part of the blood brain barrier together with the capillary endothelium. Other processes extend to the neuronal cell bodies and the astrocytes thereby serve as a connecting link between the neurons and the blood circulation. Furthermore, other processes have been shown to very closely approach the synaptic regions and ensheat the synaptic clefts (Fig. 2.1). In view of the fact that astrocytes have been proven to express a variety of ion channels, a large number of neurotransmitter receptors and several active release and uptake mechanisms for neuroactive compounds, this surrounding of the synapse gives the astrocyte the possibility of communicating with the neurons and regulating the extraneuronal milieu. In addition to these vital extensions, astrocyte processes also reach the ependymal cells, connecting them with the cerebral ventricular system, while other processes extend to the brain surface to form expansions that constitute the glial limiting membrane.

Astrocytes are the most frequent cells in the brain, constituting over 50% of the total cell number in the cerebral cortex, and their relative number is especially high in humans and other highly developed mammals.[2] The cells constitute

On Astrocytes and Glutamate Neurotransmission: New Waves in Brain Information Processing, edited by Elisabeth Hansson, Torsten Olsson and Lars Rönnbäck.

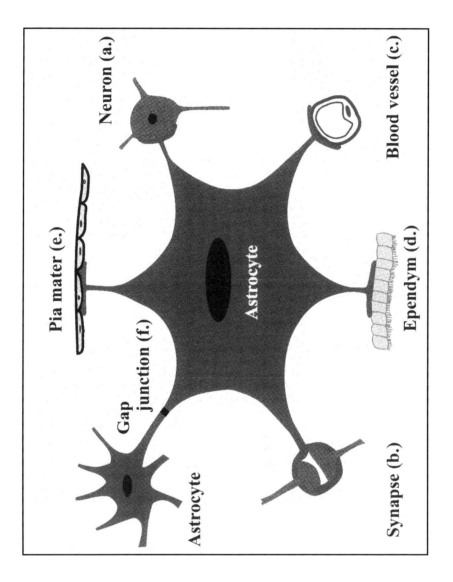

a large fraction of the volume of the mammalian brain cortex, around 20%.[3] In view of this general distribution, it seems important to explain the interrelationships between neurons and glia in the CNS.

ASTROGLIA IN VIVO

Classically, two main types of astrocytes can be identified in light microscopy using the Golgi-Rio Hortega metallic impregnation.[4] These are the fibrous and protoplasmic types, divided according to morphology and to their location in white or gray matter.[5] Fibrous astrocytes are predominantly found in the myelinated areas and have a star-like morphology with thin, usually unbranched, processes spreading out symmetrically from the cell body. The processes, rich in intermediate filaments, extend over long distances and frequently form the end-feet on blood vessels. Protoplasmic astrocytes have shorter and highly branched processes of varying dimensions that ensheat neuronal cell bodies and their processes. They form the end-feet on blood vessels and they also make contact with the pial surface. Compared with the fibrous astrocytes they contain fewer intermediate filaments and have a higher density of organelles. Transitional forms of the two types are occasionally found in the interface between white and gray matter. Whether the fibrous and protoplasmic astrocytes have distinct functional differences is not yet fully known, but subtypes with different characteristics have been detected in cultivated cells from various brain regions.[6,7]

A third cell type is the radial astrocytes which span over the whole white matter with one or sometimes a group of processes. They are thought to play an important role in the developing central nervous system (CNS) in that they guide the migrating neurons on their way from the ventricles to the gray matter.[8] The radial glia, ubiquitous in the early brain, gradually disappear during the maturation process and it is probable that these cells are transformed to both fibrous and protoplasmic astrocytes as shown in several histological

Fig. 2.1. (Opposite page) The cell in the middle of the figure shows the central position of an astrocyte and its connections to different parts of the central nervous system. Processes are seen to contact the neurons (a) and the synapses (b), where they ensheat the synaptic cleft, giving astrocytes possibilities for regulation of synaptic activity by uptake or release of ions or neurotransmitters. Processes also extend to the capillaries, on which they form the end-feet (c). This intermediate position between the blood vessels and the neurons enables the astrocytes to function as a pathway for various metabolic substances to and from the blood stream. Other astrocytic extensions contact the ependymal cells (d) which are lining the ventricles and the spinal canal, and others reach pia mater on the surface of the brain (e). The astrocytes are coupled in a network via gap junctions (f) to form the astroglial syncytium. Through the gap junctions neighboring astrocytes can exchange cytoplasmatic compounds and even signal over long distances. See text for more information.

studies.[9-11] In the living animal, they are also seen to be transformed into stellate astrocytes.[12] Different types of radial glia have been described.[13] They are referred to as tanycytes when found in the cerebral cortex or in the spine, where they are disposed in a plane perpendicular to the ventricles or to the spinal canal. In the cerebellum these astrocytes are known as Golgi epithelial cells or Bergmann glia and extend radially in the molecular layer, ensheathing the Purkinje neurons. The radial cells also include the Müller cells of retina, cells spanning the whole thickness of the retina, with their processes continuing into the nerve fiber layer.

Electron microscopic analyses have revealed nuclear and cytoplasmatic ultrastructural characteristics that are common for all these glial types and the observed differences are more of a quantitative rather than of a qualitative art. Whether the diverse astrocyte subtypes are the result of one common progenitor with the phenotype expression determined by the neuronal environment or represent independent pathways of development with certain aspects in common is an unresolved question.

Concerning this astroglial subtype genealogy two parallel theories are usually discussed. As mentioned, one line of evidence points toward the radial glia as precursors for astrocytes, and the radial cells are in turn believed to originate from immature cells of the ventricular zone. Both protoplasmatic and fibrous astrocytes are thought to arise in this way.[10,14,15] The other theory is based on data indicating that the astrocytes develop directly from cells in the germinal zone without the intermediate radial glia. Pulse-chase studies using ^{3}H-thymidine labeling of cells in the subventricular zone (SVZ) have shown that both astrocytes and oligodendrocytes originate from these cells.[16-18] Similar studies have been made with retrovirus injected into rat forebrain SVZ cells and it was showed that the injected SVZ cells principally gave rise to protoplasmatic astrocytes in the gray matter.[19] These facts indicate that both developmental pathways probably exist, but the exact origin of the defined astroglial subtypes is not yet determined.

Current studies concerning neuronal progenitors in vivo have further revealed a common immature precursor cell for both neurons and astrocytes in chick embryo spinal cord[20,21] and in rat retina[22] while results are reported from other studies showing different precursors for astrocytes and oligodendrocytes.[23-25]

ASTROGLIAL MARKERS

Through the identification of glial fibrillary acidic protein (GFAP) by Eng and co-workers[26] and Bignami and co-workers,[27] a cell-specific marker for astrocytes was detected, as both protoplasmatic and fibrous astrocytes had earlier been shown to contain gliofibrils.[28] However, numerous astrocytes in the normal brain are negative for GFAP immunohistochemistry, especially those in the gray matter.[29] Therefore, other astrocyte markers beside the intermediate filaments have been used, such as antibodies against the enzyme glutamine synthetase[30] and the calcium-binding protein S 100[31] which are both found in protoplasmatic and fibrous astrocytes. The intermediate filament vimentin has sometimes been used as a marker, especially in the early development of CNS where this is the only filament expressed, although it is not as cell specific as the other markers.[32,33]

Several other markers are used to distinguish different astroglial subtypes in vitro, and these are further described in the chapter on astrocytes in culture (see below).

FUNCTIONAL CHARACTERISTICS OF ASTROGLIA

Originally the glial cells were regarded as a passive and functionally static substance with the primary purpose of filling the space between the neurons as "nervenkitt" or nerve glue.[34] This view was partly due to the astrocytes absence of electrical excitability, considered to be necessary for active function in the brain. The ability of these cells to fill the space of succumbed neurons through the formation of glial scars after brain injury also supported this theory. Later Golgi[35] proposed, based on the observation that glial cells were interconnected to both neurons and capillaries, that astrocytes had supporting functions and supplied nutrients to the cell bodies and axons of the nerve cells. In 1889, His further suggested that the embryonic glial cells guided the migration of developing neurons.[36] This somewhat passive functional role has predominated the view of glial cells throughout the history of neuroscience and it was not until the last two decades that a growing mass of evidence was collected that pointed toward a substantially more active and dynamic role of astrocytes in the CNS.

Astrocytes were long thought to be lacking voltage-gated ion channels. However, during the last ten years they have been shown to express almost the same voltage-dependent channels as found on neurons (i.e., for K^+, Na^+, Cl^- and Ca^{2+}) (for reviews see refs. 37,38), although they have not been found to have the capacity for electrical excitability. The reason for the late discovery of these glial ion channels was due to the use of somewhat improper techniques. Early studies were made with microelectrodes on cells in culture or in situ where the extensively electrical coupled glial syncytium tended to disperse the injected currents and obscure the presence of voltage-gated channels. It was not until the use of patch clamp techniques, which preferably work with single isolated cells, that the expression of voltage-gated ion channels on glia could be proven.

The densities of the K^+ channels are approximately the same as for neurons, whereas the Na^+ and Cl^- channels are considerably lesser expressed in comparison with neurons.[37,39] This, together with the high resting conductance found in glia, is in accordance with the nonexcitability of the cells. The glial voltage-dependent Na^+ channels also need a more negative potential to open at depolarization, and they open at a slower rate than those of the neurons.[40] It is, therefore, not clear whether the glial and neuronal Na^+ channels represent the same proteins.

Astrocytes have also been found to possess ligand-activated ion channels, e.g., for Ca^{2+} or Cl^- [41,42] and most of the known second messenger systems, e.g., cAMP, cGMP, inositol trisphosphate, diacylglycerol, protein kinase C and Ca^{2+}.[43,38] These systems are activated on glia by receptors for a variety of agonists including the amino acids glutamate and γ-amino butyric acid (GABA), neuroactive peptides such as vasointestinal peptide (VIP), bradykinin and substance P, monoamines like noradrenaline, dopamine and serotonin, several cytokines, purines, eicosanoides and hormones (for reviews see refs. 44-46).

In addition to the ability to react on different neurotransmitters, the astrocytes have several mechanisms that indicate an active role in regulating the neuronal microenvironment. They have the capacity to synthesize and release a number of neuroactive molecules including the amino acids glutamate and aspartate,[47] the neuropeptides enkephalin and somatostatin[48,49] or arachidonic acid.[50] They also have active mechanisms for the uptake and degradation of molecules such as amino acids and monoamines.[51] The enzyme glutamine synthetase, for example, is present in many astrocytes and catalyzes the degradation of glutamate to glutamine.[30] Astrocytes can also buffer ions from the extracellular fluid,[52,53] and experimental evidence from in situ studies indicates that glia is essential for the regulation of the extracellular K^+ accumulated during neuronal activity.[54-56]

All these glial activities, i.e., responsiveness to neurotransmitters and mechanisms for production, release and uptake of physiologically active substances and ions, have led to theories of neural-glial interactions. In these models the spatial organization of the glial elements in close contact with and ensheathing the neurons and synapses, and their central position between the neurons and the capillaries is emphasized.[57] For example, transmitter induced astroglial Ca^{2+} uptake from the synaptic junction could reduce extracellular Ca^{2+}, leading to a decrease in transmitter release.[58] Even minute changes in the amount of ions or molecules absorbed will have considerable effects on the resulting concentration because of the small volumes in the synaptic cleft; 0,002 mm^3 over a 10 mm^2 area.[59]

A number of studies demonstrate a marked regional heterogeneity in the receptor expression and the synthesis of neurotransmitters and degradative enzymes among the astrocytes. Most of these studies were performed in culture systems. For example higher levels of cAMP were detected after β-adrenergic stimulation of astrocytes derived from cerebral cortex and striatum than in those from brain stem[60] and others have found somatostatin mRNA and peptides only in cerebellar astrocytes, whereas proenkephalin mRNA and enkephalin peptides were detected in cortical, striatal and cerebellar astrocytes.[61] (For reviews see references 6,7).

These local differences can be a reflection of an interplay between astrocytes and the surrounding neurons as coculture with neurons are found to influence the presence of neurotransmitter receptors[62] and neurotransmitter degradative enzymes.[63]

The astroglia have long processes which have contact with each other, forming a network, the astrocyte syncytium, where there is communication of small substances via gap junctions. The gap junctions are plaques of intercellular channels that allow the passage of ions and small molecules between coupled cells. The maximum channel diameter is about 1.6-2.0 nm.[64] It allows for the passage of charged and uncharged molecules with molecular weights below 1 kDa, which permits the exchange of current-carrying ions such as K^+, second messenger molecules such as cAMP, Ca^{2+}, inositol 1,4,5-trisphosphate (IP_3) or various metabolites. Gap junctions are impermeable to macromolecules such as large peptides and oligonucleotides. The molecular substrate of these astrocyte-astrocyte gap junctions is a protein, connexin 43, which is localized on the perikarya as well as on the processes, with particular concentration on subpial and perivascular endfeet.[65] Some neurotransmitters and second messengers are capable of modulating the junctional coupling,[66] thereby giving plasticity in the glial syncytium.

A large part of the contact between astrocytes and neurons seems to take place via the extracellular fluid. This space is very narrow, approximately 200 nm, and forms about 25% of the brain's total volume. Astroglia and neurons bathe in this extracellular fluid and they can be affected by neuroactive substances released far from the site of action and transported in this liquid, i.e., volume transmission.[67] Furthermore, as the astroglia are able to release substances into the extracellular fluid, they can, at least theoretically, modulate this fluid and influence the excitability of the surrounding neurons.[68,69]

During recent years another communication, Ca^{2+} based excitability, has been recognized where intracellular Ca^{2+} increases move as oscillations and waves from one cell to another. This intercellular calcium signaling, which propagates to many cells within the astrocytic syncytium, can be elicited by neuronal stimuli or by direct activation of the astrocytes themselves with, for example, glutamate.[70] Calcium variations within the cells are known to have numerous effects on the cell functions, e.g., cell migration, exocytosis, ion transport, neurotransmitter release and gap junction regulation[71] and the calcium signaling can thus be interpreted as a way of controlling and coordinating the activity in the astrocyte network. It is also possible that the spread of calcium waves across the astrocytes could influence the neurons either through astrocyte-neuronal gap junctions[69] or by affecting the glutamate neurotransmission between astrocytes and neurons.[68] These recent findings may imply that the astrocytes have a role in the brain's information processing and that we have to modify our present understanding of how the brain works.

MODEL SYSTEMS; ASTROGLIA IN CULTURE

Techniques for maintaining highly enriched astrocytes in dissociated primary culture have been successfully developed during the last 25 years.[72,73] These preparations consist of actively proliferating cells, isolated from prenatal, neonatal, or postnatal animals, and by different means they can be enriched in one specific cell type. The primary cultures originate from cells, tissues, or organs taken directly from the organism and are regarded as primary until subcultivated. Such cultures provide the option of choosing the brain region and age of the animal at seeding. However, it should be emphasized that cell and tissue cultures are model systems, and whatever is discovered in culture must also be demonstrated in vivo.

Using astroglial cell primary cultures, originally from the optic nerve, two morphologically and antigenically distinct astroglial cell types have been observed.[74-76] One is a polygonally shaped flat cell with few processes that forms a confluent bed layer in the culture dish. These cells have been called type 1 astrocytes and the overwhelming majority of astrocytes in primary culture are of this type. Whatever their morphology, fibrous or protoplasmatic, they are strongly GFAP-immunoreactive (Fig. 2.2a and in co-culture with neurons, Fig. 2.2b) and positive for the rat neural antigen-2 (Ran-2).[77] A second cell type that exhibits a central body with numerous short processes grows on top of the bed layer cells. They have been called type 2 and are most commonly detected immunocytochemically by A2B5, a monoclonal antibody against an extracellular ganglioside antigen[78,79] (Fig. 2.3). Type 1 astrocytes are devoid of A2B5 immunoreactivity. Type 2 astrocytes are derived from a precursor cell, the oligodendrocyte-type 2 astrocyte progenitor (O-2A progenitor), which is in a stage

Fig. 2.2a. (Opposite page, top) Astrocytes in primary cultures derived from newborn Sprague-Dawley rats and cultivated for 10–14 days in serum containing medium. The cells are stained for the astrocyte glial fibrillary acidic protein (GFAP) and visualized with FITC-conjugated secondary antibodies (green). The total cell number are estimated by staining the nucleus with Hoechts 33258 (blue). See color figure in insert.

Fig. 2.2b. (Opposite page, bottom) Astrocytes cocultivated with neurons seen after seven days in culture. The neuronal influence in these systems are seen to alter the astrocyte phenotype to a presumably more differentiated stage, with for example changed ion channel expression. The astrocytes are stained for GFAP as above and the neurons (red) are showed with antibodies against microtubule associated proteins (MAP2) and rhodamine conjugated secondary antibodies. Bar 60 μm. See color figure in insert.

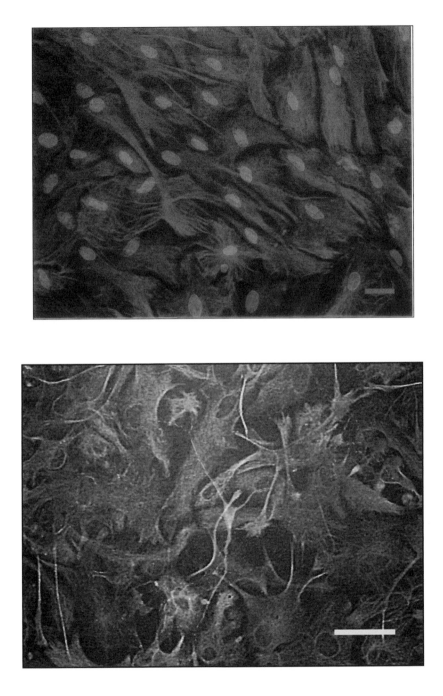

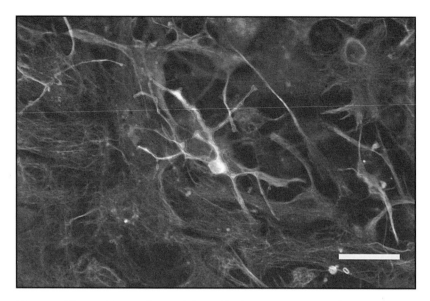

Fig. 2.3. (above) Sister culture of the cells shown in Fig 2.2a, here stained to visualize a type 2 astrocyte (red). In addition these GFAP[+] cells also label with A2B5, a monoclonal antibody against cell surface gangliosides. The majority of cultured cells are type 1 astrocytes, only expressing GFAP (green). (Rhodamine-conjugated secondary antibodies were used against A2B5. Bars 30 μm. See color figure in insert.

of plasticity and can be directed to express either oligodendroglial or astroglial cell markers.[80,81]

Several other antibodies have been used in the differentiation process of these cell types, including the anti-ganglioside antibodies R24 and LB1,[75,82] anti-chondroitin sulphate or anti-NG-2 antibodies,[83,84] and antibodies against neuromodulin (GAP-43).[85] All these antibodies selectively stain the type 2 astrocyte and the O-2A progenitor but are not found to react with type 1 astroglia. (For reviews on astroglial markers in vitro see refs. 86,87). The two cell types are also distinguished by serum and medium-dependent factors. Type 1 astrocytes will proliferate if the culture medium contains epidermal growth factor (EGF) which does not influence the O-2A lineage cells.[75] On the other hand, the O-2A progenitors can differentiate to type 2 astroglia in the presence of fetal calf serum (FCS) while they are directed to oligodendrocytes in a chemically defined medium devoid of FCS.[88] The factor in FCS responsible for type 2 maturation was found to be the cytokine ciliary neurotrophic factor (CNTF),[89] but an established type 2 phenotype expression also required the presence of an endothelial derived extracellular matrix-associated molecule.[90]

As mentioned, the culture nomenclature relates to glial cells from the optic nerve, which is a part of the central white matter, and there are problems associated with a direct transposition of this system to cells cultured from other parts of the CNS. While fairly equivalent cell types are found in white matter glia throughout the mammalian CNS,[75,91,92] astrocytes from gray matter are not as clearly classified and cannot be directly adapted to the white matter nomenclature. The morphology and antigen expression seem to differ depending on the area of the nervous system from which the cells to be cultivated are taken and the phenotypes have even been seen to vary among clonally related cells.[93] This again mirrors the extended astrocyte regional heterogeneity, indicated above, regarding the functional characteristics of astrocytes. In spite of these discrepancies, cultured gray matter glia have many similarities with type 1 astrocytes from white matter and astrocytes in cortical cultures are often referred to as "type 1-like astrocytes," as proposed by Raff.[94]

Applying in vitro nomenclature to in vivo circumstances is also problematic. First, the lack of specific in vivo markers makes a classification difficult. Many studies have been made to correlate the type 2 marker A2B5 with white matter glia in vivo but none have been successful[87] and other markers such as R24 have been used without positive results.[95,96] Second, the cells in culture display considerable morphological plasticity which depends on environmental factors such as medium composition,[97] intracellular cAMP levels[98] and coculture with neurons.[99] For example, the typical polygonal shape of type 1-like astrocytes in neuron free cultures have never been seen in vivo. The GFAP content in in vitro astrocytes is also strongly regulated[100-102] and makes any comparisons with fibrous and protoplasmatic astrocytes (the latter of which hold less GFAP in vivo) concerning their GFAP expression very difficult. The tools for comparing in vivo with in vitro have thus not yet been found, and it is questionable whether such comparisons can be made at all.

It is important to realize that the results obtained using cultured cells reflect the properties of astrocytes obtained from immature animals and maintained in the absence of their normal cellular and chemical milieu. For example, Na^+ current expression is altered during development of astrocytes in cell culture[103] and the properties of different K^+ currents show a prominent difference between acutely isolated cells and cells in culture.[104] The cell culture system also depends on many factors which are difficult and sometimes impossible to control. The composition of cell culture medium, the serum used and the growth matrix are factors known to influence the cultured cells. For example, the use of diverse serum batches affects the expression of different Ca^{2+} channels on primary astrocyte cultures.[105] Furthermore the concentration of cells in the seeding suspension when the culture is initiated could be of importance, in that a higher cell concentration will make the culture confluent faster. This gives early contact inhibition which could, in turn, alter the phenotype as compared with the effects of a more dilute initial cell concentration. It has also been shown that coculture with neurons could alter the channel expression on astrocytes.[104,106]

It seems, in spite of these difficulties, quite likely that the properties expressed by cultured astrocytes reflect the potential of astrocytes in brain and that these properties may be differentially expressed either by different groups of astrocytes in brain or at different stages of development.

ACUTELY ISOLATED ASTROGLIA AND BRAIN SLICES

The development of cultivation conditions for astrocytes during the last two decades has been the prerequisite to our present knowledge of the biochemistry and pharmacology of astrocytes. Most data on astroglial properties now available are therefore received from studies using different culture systems, and only a few investigations have been performed on astroglial cells in in vivo conditions. Extensive electrophysiological and microspectrofluorometric studies on astrocytes in primary cell culture have indicated that astrocytes express a variety of voltage-gated and ligand-activated ionic channels (reviewed in refs. 37,39), and the question has been raised as to whether these findings reflect the receptor expression and ionic channel phenotype in vivo or are mere artifacts of cellular culture conditions. To clarify these circumstances, two different techniques have been developed for in vivo studies, namely acute isolation of astrocytes from intact brains and brain slice preparations.

The acutely isolated astrocyte techniques were time consuming and complex until a few years ago, requiring centrifugation on discontinuous gradients.[107,108] In recent years, however, enzymatic dissociation techniques have been developed for isolation of mature astrocytes, where the cells are separated by trituration in Pasteur pipettes after the enzyme treatment. These dissociation techniques have been utilized to investigate the electrophysiological properties of several vertebrate glia including Schwann cells,[109] retinal Müller cells,[110] ependymal cells[40] and hippocampal astrocytes.[111] There are, however, some disadvantages associated with the enzyme treatment of the cells. If an expected receptor is not detected in the isolated cells, or only low amplitude responses are obtained, this could be due to the possibility that the enzyme has inactivated the receptor by cleavage of some vulnerable part of the protein. For example, enzyme treated rat hippocampal neurons are devoid of NMDA activated ionic currents.[112] To partly guard against this, the receptor resistance to the enzyme used is tested in a well-known system, e.g., a cell culture, although this does not totally exclude the possibility of cleavage because receptors in vivo could react differently from receptors on cultured cells. Some investigators have also had problems with the lack of processes which were sheared off during the dissociation procedure and which could uniquely contain certain channel types and/or receptor types.[113,114] This problem can be avoided by using an enzymatic method called tissue print dissociating technique in which the processes are relatively well-conserved.[104]

We have recently developed a new method for nonenzymatic dissociation of astrocytes,[115] which was originally used to isolate neurons.[116] Thin slices are cut from rat brains and are then hydrodynamically dissociated using a vibrating microelectrode (Fig. 2.4a). This relatively uncomplicated method gives astrocytes with considerably well-preserved processes (Figs. 2.4b and c), and the absence of enzymatic treatment yields fresh cells without the possible enzyme receptor cleavage. These cells have been tested for their reaction on depolarization with high extracellular K^+ concentrations and were found to respond with elevated intracellular Ca^{2+} concentrations (Fig. 2.5), which is in accordance with previous results.[117,118]

The electrophysiological studies on astrocytes in vivo or in situ on *isolated brain slices* have been limited because these cells form an electrically coupled network whose membrane potential cannot be uniformly controlled by

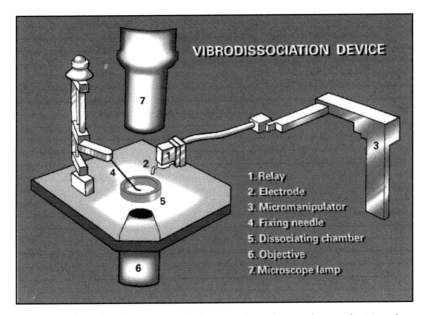

Fig. 2.4a. The vibrodissociation device consists of an ordinary electric relay with a fireshaped glass electrode attached on the moving part of the relay and vibrating at 50 Hz. The vibrating glassball was positioned just above the slice and gently lowered down until it was close to the tissue but not touching it. The electrode should never come in contact with the cells and it is the hydrodynamic forces created that are dissociating the tissue. The vibratory procedure takes 15-30 sec. and during a successful dissociation there is a white cloud of cells and intercellular material sprouting out from the vibrated area. The yield can be controlled directly after each vibration period by an inverted microscope and it is possible to treat the same slice several times until a satisfactory number of cells is obtained. See color figure in insert.

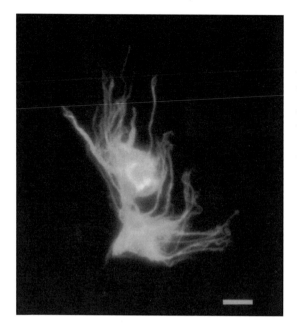

Fig. 2.4b. Acutely vibro-dissociated astrocytes positive for the astrocyte specific marker GFAP, visualized with fluorescin conjugated IgG. None of the GFAP+ cells were positive to A2B5 or the oligodendrocytic marker GalC. Bar, 12 µm. See color figure in insert.

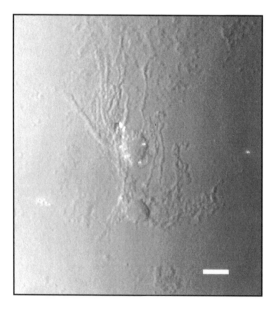

Fig. 2.4c. The figure shows differential interference contrast (DIC) micrographs of the astrocytes seen in Figure 2.4b, displaying the characteristic astrocyte morphology with multiple processes and smaller cell bodies as compared with the neurons.

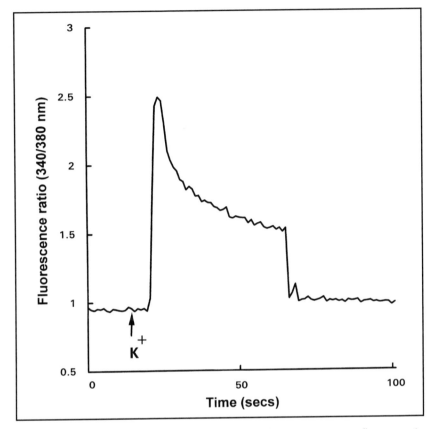

Fig. 2.5. Potassium evoked Ca^{2+} influx seen with a microspectrofluorometric technique, using the calcium sensitive dye fura-2/AM. The acutely isolated astrocytes were found to respond with sharp rises in intracellular calcium levels when depolarized with high extracellular potassium concentrations. The first elevations in $[Ca^{2+}]_i$ were detected at 20 mM $[K^+]_o$ and maximal effect was seen at 55 mM $[K^+]_o$

conventional microelectrodes.[37,119] One way to overcome this problem is to work with ion-sensitive fluorescent probes combined with ultrathin brain slices. However, very few receptor studies have been carried out to date using this technique, partly because of the high costs still associated with the confocal imaging equipment needed. This method is also complicated by the presence of the neurons in the slice, that are in close contact with the astrocytes and could mediate a neuronal originated receptor signal to the glial cells, although these techniques use different substances to block neuronal function (for example the Na^+ channel blocker TTX).[120]

Until recently, these methods have not been used to any greater extent in astroglial research, but they will probably be of increasing importance in the coming years since the in vivo properties of astrocytes is an urgent area of investigation.

CONCLUSIONS

When Virchow identified the astroglial cells at the end of the 19th century, he proposed that these cells give structural and metabolic support to the neurons. In many respects he seems to have been right. The last 20 years of very rapid progressing research on the nature and function of astroglial cells has demonstrated, on the one hand details of the neuronal-glial interactions and thereby details about the "helping function" of the astroglia toward the neurons. On the other hand, recent research has also shown that this helping function is not just passive, i.e., the astroglia do not seem to be standing as just passive supporters to the neurons but instead there is an astroglial network collaborating with the neurons in a functional way.

It is important to remark that almost all functional characteristics of astrocytes are achieved from cell culture systems. One of the urgent areas in the upcoming glial research is therefore to confirm and extend these results in more in vivo-like systems. For this purpose, techniques using brain slices and acutely isolated cells seems to be the most feasible direction of research.

Acknowledgments

Supported by grants from the Swedish Medical Research Council (project no. 12X-06812) and the Faculty of Medicine, Göteborg University. The skillful technical assistance of Barbro Eriksson, Ulrika Johansson and Armgard Kling was greatly appreciated.

References

1. Virchow RZ. Über das granulierte Ansehen der Wandungen der Gehirnventrikel. Allgemeine Zeitschrift für Psychiatrie und psychisch-gerichtliche. Medicin 1846; 3:242-250.
2. Bass NH, Hess HH, Pope A et al. Quantitative cytoarchitectonic distribution of neurons, glia, and DNA in rat cerebral cortex. Comp Neurol 1971; 143:481-490.
3. Pope A. Neuroglia: Quantitative aspects. In: Schoffeniels E, Franck G, Tower DB et al, eds. Dynamic properties of glia cells. Oxford and New York:Pergamon Press, 1978:13-20.
4 Cajal SR. Algunas concideraciones sobre la mesoglía de Robertson y Río Hortega. Trab La Invest Biol Univ Madrid 1920; 18:109-127.
5. Peters A, Palay SL, Webster H de F. The fine structure of the nervous system: Neurons and their supporting cells. 3rd ed. New York: Oxford University Press, 1991:276-285.

6. Hansson E. Regional heterogenity among astrocytes in the central nervous system. Neurochem Int 1990; 3:237-245.

7. Wilkin GP, Marriott DR, Cholewinski AJ. Astrocyte heterogeneity. Trends Neurosci 1990; 13:43-46.

8. Rakic P. Neuron-glia relationship during granule cell migration in developing cerebellar cortex: A Golgi and electron microscopic study in Macacus rhesus. J Comp Neurol 1971; 141:282-312.

9. Cajal SR. Histologie du systeme nerveux de l'homme et des vertebres. Paris: Maloine, 1911.

10. Schmechel DE, Rakic P. A Golgi study of radial glial cells in developing monkey telencephalon: Morphogenesis and transformation into astrocytes. Anat Embryol Berlin 1979; 156:115-152.

11. Culican SM, Baumrind NL, Yamamoto M et al. Cortical radial glia: identification in tissue culture and evidence for their transformation to astrocytes. J Neurosci 1990; 10:684-692.

12. Voigt T, Goldman JE. Development of glial cells in the cerbral wall of ferrets: direct tracing of their transformation from radial glia into astrocytes. J Comp Neurol 1989; 289:74-88.

13. Privat A, Gimenez-Ribotta M, Ridet J-L. Morphology of astrocytes. In: Kettenmann H, Ransom BR, eds. Neuroglia. 1st ed. New York: Oxford University Press, 1995:7.

14. Mission J-P, Edwards MA, Yamamoto M et al. Identification of radial glial cells within the developing murine central nervous system: Studies based upon a new immunohistochemical marker. Dev Brain Res 1988; 44:95-108.

15 Cameron RS, Rakic P. Glial cell lineage in the cerebral cortex: A review and synthesis. Glia 1991; 4:124-137.

16. Altman J. Proliferation and migration of undifferentiated precursor cells in the rat during postnatal gliogenesis. Exp Neurol 1966; 16:263-278.

17. Paterson JA, Privat A, Ling EA et al. Investigation of glial cells in semithin sections III. Transformation of subependymal cells into glial cells as shown by autoradiography after ^{3}H-thymidine injection into the lateral ventricle of the brain of young rats. J Comp Neurol 1973; 149:83-102.

18. Imamoto K, Paterson JA, Leblond CP. Radioautographic investigation of gliogenesis in the corpus callosum of young rats. J Comp Neurol 1978; 180:115-138.

19. Levison SW, Goldman JE. Both oligodendrocytes and astrocytes develop from progenitors in the subventricular zone of postnatal rat forebrain. Neuron 1993; 10:201-212.

20. Galileo V, Gray GC, Owens GC et al. Neurons and glia arise from a common progenitor in chicken optic tectum: Demonstration with two retroviruses and cell-type specific antibodies. Proc Natl Acad Sci USA 1990; 87:458-462.

21. Leber SM, Breedlove SM, Sanes JR. Lineage, arrangement, and death of clonally related motoneurons in chick spinal cord. J Neurosci 1990; 10:2451-2462.
22. Turner D, Cepko C. Cell lineage in the rat retina: A common progenitor for neurons and glia persists late in development. Nature 1987; 328:131-136.
23. Luskin MB, Pearlman AL, Sanes JR. Cell lineage in the cerebral cortex of the mouse studied in vivo and in vitro with recombinant retrovirus. Neuron 1988; 1:635-647.
24. Price J, Thurlow L. Cell lineage in the rat cerebral cortex: A study using retroviral mediated gene transfer. Development 1988; 104:473-482.
25. Vaysse PJ-J, Goldman JE. A clonal analysis of glial lineages in neonatal forebrain development in vitro. Neuron 1990; 5:227-235.
26. Eng LF, Vanderhaeghen JJ, Bignami A et al. An acidic protein isolated from fibrous astrocytes. Brain Res 1971; 28:351-354.
27. Bignami A, Eng LF, Dahl D et al. Localization of the glial fibrillary acidic protein in the astrocytes by immunofluorescence. Brain Res 1972; 43:429-435.
28. Mugnaini E, Walberg F. Ultrastructure of neuroglia. Ergeb Anat Entwicklungsgesch 1964; 37:194-236.
29. Palay SL, Chan-Palay V. Cerabellar Cortex, Cytology and Organization. New York: Springer-Verlag, 1974:288-321.
30. Norenberg MD, Martinez-Hernandez A. Fine structural localization of glutamine synthetase in astrocytes of rat brain. Brain Res 1979; 161:303-310.
31. Ludwin SK, Kosek JC, Eng LF. The topographical distribution of S-100 and GFA proteins in the adult rat brain: an immunohistochemical study using horseradish peroxidase-labelled antibodies. J Comp Neurol 1976; 165:197-208.
32. Schnitzer J, Franke WW, Schachner M. Immunohistochemical demonstration of vimentin in astrocytes and ependymal cells of developing and adult mouse nervous system. J Cell Biol 1981; 90:435-447.
33. Bignami A, Dahl D. Vimentin-GFAP transition in primary dissociated cultures of rat embryo spinal cord. Int J Dev Neurosci 1989; 7:343-357.
34. Virchow RZ. Gesammelte Abhandlungen zur wissenschaftlichen Medizin. Meidinger & Sohn 1856; 889.
35. Golgi C. Sulla fina anatomia degli organi centrali del sistema nervoso. Riv Sper Fermiat Med Leg Alienazioni Ment 1885; 11:72-123.
36. His W. Die Neuroblasten und deren Entstehung im Embryonalen Mark. Abhandl Math Phys Kl Saechs Akad Wiss 1889; 15:311-373.
37. Barres, BA, Chun LLY, Corey DP. Ion channels in vertebrate glia. Annu Rev Neurosci 1990; 13:441-474.
38. Bevan S. Ion channels and neurotransmitter receptors in glia. Semin Neurosci 1990; 2:467-481.

39. Sontheimer H. Astrocytes, as well as neurons, express a diversity of ion channels. Can J Physiol Pharmacol 1992; 70 suppl:223-238.

40. Barres BA, Chun LLY, Corey DP. Glial and neuronal forms of the voltage-dependent sodium channel: characteristics and cell-type distribution. Neuron 1989; 2:1375-1388.

41. Mac Vicar BA, Tse FW. Norepinephrine and cAMP enhance a nifedipine-sensitive calcium current in cultured rat astrocytes. Glia 1988; 1:359-360.

42. Bormann J, Kettenmann H. Patch-clamp study of GABA receptor Cl channels in cultured astrocytes. Proc Natl Acad Sci USA 1988; 5:336-9340.

43. Murphy S, Pearce B. Functional receptors for neurotransmitters on astroglial cells. Neuroscience 1987; 22:381-394.

44. Kimelberg HK, ed. Glial Cell Receptors. New York: Raven Press, 1988.

45. Murphy S, ed. In: Astrocytes: Pharmacology and Function. 1st ed. San Diego: Academic Press Inc., 1993:25-136.

46. Hösli E, Hösli L. Receptors for neurotransmitters on astrocytes in the mammalian central nervous system. Progr Neurobiol 1993; 40:477-506.

47. Kimelberg HK, Goderie SK, Higman S et al. Swelling-induced release of glutamate, aspartate and taurine from astrocyte cultures. J Neurosci 1990; 10:1583-1591.

48. Hauser KF, Osborne JG, Stiene-Martin A et al. Cellular localization of proenkephalin mRNA and enkephalin peptide products in cultured astrocytes. Brain Res 1990; 522:342-353

49. Shinoda H, Marini A M, Schwartz JP. Developmental expression of proenkephalin and somatostatin genes in cultured cortical and cerebellar astrocytes. Dev Brain Res 1992; 67:205-210.

50. Glowinski J, Marin P, Tence M et al. Glial receptors and their intervention in astrocyte-astrocytic and astrocyto-neuronal interactions. Glia 1994; 11:201-208.

51. Hansson E. Astroglia from defined brain regions as studied with primary cultures. Progr Neurobiol 1988; 30:369-397.

52. Orkand RK. Introductory remarks: glial-interstitial fluid exchange. In: Cserr HE, ed. The neuronal microenvironment. Annals of the New York Academy of Science 1986; 269-272.

53. Coles JA. Functions of glial cells in the retina of the honeybee drone. Glia 1989; 2:1-9.

54. Gardner-Medwin AR. Analysis of potassium dynamics in mammalian brain tissue. J Physiol 1983; 335:393-426.

55. Newman EA. Regulation of potassium levels by glial cells in the retina. Trends Neurosci 1985; 8:156-159.

56. Walz W. Role of glial cells in the regulation of the brain ion microenvironment. Prog Neurobiol 1989; 33:309-333.

57. Laming PR. Do glia contribute to behavior? A neuromodulatory review. Comp Biochem Physiol 1989; 4:555-568.

58. Eriksson PS. Opioid receptors on neural cells in primary culture. Thesis Univ of Gothenburg 1992; 36-37.

59. van den Pol AN, Finkbeiner SM, Cornell-Bell AH. Calcium Excitability and Oscillations in Suprachiasmatic Nucleus Neurons and Glia in vitro. J Neurosci 1992; 1:2648-2664.

60. Hansson E. Primary cultures from defined brain areas; effects of seeding time on the development of β-adrenergic and dopamine stimulated cAMP activity during cultivation. Dev Brain Res 1985; 21:187-192.

61. Shinoda H, Marini A M, Cosi C et al. Brain region and gene specificity of neuropeptide gene expression in cultured astrocytes. Science 1989; 245:415-417.

62. Maderspach K, Fajazi C. Development of β-adrenergic receptors and their function in glia-neuron communication in cultured chick brain. Dev Brain Res 1983; 6:251-257.

63. Westergaard N, Fosmark H, Schousboe A. Metabolism and release of glutamate in cerebellar granule cells cocultured with astrocytes from cerebellum or cerebral cortex. J Neurochem 1991; 56:59-66.

64. Flagg-Newton JL, Loewenstein WR. Experimental depression of junctional membrane permeability in mammalian cell culture: a study with tracer molecules in the 300 to 600 dalton range. J Membr Biol 1979; 50:65-100.

65. Dermietzel R, Spray DC. Gap junctions in the brain: where, what type, how many and why? Trends Neurosci 1993; 16:186-192.

66. Dermietzel R, Hertzberg EL, Kessler JA et al. Gap junctions between cultured astrocytes: immunocytochemical, molecular, and electrophysiological analysis. J Neurosci 1991; 11:1421-1432.

67. Fuxe K, Agnati L F. Two principal modes of electrochemical communication in the brain: volume versus wiring transmission. Adv Neurosci 1991; 1:1-9.

68. Parpura V, Basarsky TA, Liu F et al. Glutamate-mediated astrocyte-neuron signaling. Nature 1994; 369:744-747.

69. Nedergaard M. Direct signaling from astrocytes to neurons in cultures of mammalian brain cells. Science 1994; 263:1768-1771.

70. Cornell-Bell AH, Finkbeiner SM. Ca^{2+} waves in astrocytes. Cell Calcium 1991; 12:185-204.

71. Tsien RW, Tsien RY. Calcium channels, stores and oscillations. Annu Rev Cell Biol 1990; 6:715-760.

72. Booher J, Sensenbrenner M. Growth and cultivation of dissociated neurons and glial cells from embryonic chick, rat and human brain in flask cultures. Neurobiology 1972; 2:97-105.

73. Kimelberg HK. Primary astrocyte cultures—a key to astrocyte function. Cell Mol Neurobiol 1983; 3:1-16.

74. McCarthy KD, deVellis J. Preparation of separate astroglial and oligodendroglial cell cultures from rat cerebral tissue. J Cell Biol 1980; 85:890-902.

75. Raff MC, Abney ER, Cohen J et al. Two types of astrocytes in cultures of developing rat white matter: differences in morphology, surface gangliosides and growth characteristics. J Neurosci 1983; 3:1289-1300.

76. Raff MC. Glial cell diversification in the rat optic nerve. Science 1989; 243:1450-1455.
77. Bartlett PF, Noble MD, Pruss RM et al. Rat neural antigen-2 (RAN-2): A cell surface antigen on astrocytes, ependymal cells, Müller cells and lepto-meninges defined by a monoclonal antibody. Brain Res 1980; 204:339-351.
78. Raff MC, Miller RH. Glial cell development in the rat optic nerve. Trends Neurosci 1984; 7:469-472.
79. McCarthy KD, Salm A, Lerea LS. Astroglial receptors and their regulation of intermediate filament protein phosphorylation. In: Kimelberg HK, ed. Glial Cell Receptors. New York: Raven Press, 1988:1-22.
80. Miller RH, David S, Patel R et al. A quantitative immunohistochemical study of macroglial cell development in the rat optic nerve: In vivo evidence for two distinct astrocyte lineages. Dev Biol 1985; 111:35-41.
81. Williams BP, Abney ER, Raff MC. Macroglial cell development in embryonic rat brain: Studies using monoclonal antibodies, fluorescence activated cell sorting and cell culture. Dev Biol 1985; 112:126-134.
82. Goldman JE, Geier SS, Hirano M. Differentiation of astrocytes and oligodendrocytes from germinal matrix cells in primary culture. J Neurosci 1986; 6:52-60.
83. Gallo V, Bertolotto A, Levi G. The proteoglycan chondrotinsulfate is present in a subpopulation of cultured astrocytes and their precursors. Dev Biol 1987; 123:282-285.
84. Levine JM, Stallcup WB. Plasticity of developing cerebellar cells in vitro studied with antibodies against the NG2 antigen. J Neurosci 1987; 7:2721-2731.
85. Deloume JC, Janet T, Au D et al. Neuromodulin (GAP 43): A neuronal protein kinase C substrate is also present in O-2A glial cell lineage. Characterization of neuromodulin in secondary cultures of oligodendrocytes and comparison with the neuronal antigen. J Cell Biol 1990; 111:1559-1569.
86. Levison SW, McCarthy KD. Astroglia in culture. In: Banker G, Goslin K, eds. Culturing nerve cells. Cambridge: MIT Press, 1991: 309-336.
87. Miller RH, ffrench-Constant C, and Raff MC. The macroglial cells of the rat optic nerve. Annu Rev Neurosci 1989; 12:517-524.
88. Raff MC, Miller RH, Noble M. A glial progenitor cell that develops in vitro into an astrocyte or an oligodendrocyte depending on culture medium. Nature 1983; 303:390-396.
89. Lillien LE, Sendtner M, Roher H et al. Type 2 astrocyte development in brain cultures is initiated by a CNTF-like protein produced by type 1 astrocytes. Neuron 1988; 1:485-494.
90. Lillien LE, Sendtner M, Raff MC. Extracellular matrix-associated molecules collaborate with ciliary neurotrophic factor to induce type 2 astrocyte development. J Cell Biol 1990; 111:635-644.

91. Raff MC, Abney ER, Miller RH. Two glial cell lineages diverge prenatally in rat optic nerve. Dev Biol 1984; 106:53-60.
92. Liuzzi FJ, Miller RH. Radially oriented astrocytes in the normal adult rat spinal cord. Brain Res 1987; 403:385-88.
93. Miller RH, Szigeti V. Clonal analysis of astrocyte diversity in neonatal rat spinal cord cultures. Development 1991; 113:353-362.
94. Raff MC. Subclasses of astrocytes in culture: What should we call them? Differentiation and functions of glial cells. Proc 12th Int Soc Neurochem. New York: Liss, 1989.
95. Le Vine SM, Goldman JE. Embryonic divergence of oligodendrocyte and astrocyte lineages in developing rat cerebrum. J Neurosci 1988; 8:3992-4006.
96. Reynolds R, Wilkin GP. Development of macroglial cells in rat cerebellum. II. An in situ immunohistochemical study of oligodendroglial lineage from precursor to mature myelinating cell. Development 1988; 102:409-425.
97. Morrison RS, de Vellis J, Lee YL et al. Hormones and growth factors induce the synthesis of glial fibrillary acidic protein in rat brain astrocytes. J Neurosci Res 1985; 14:167-176.
98. Pollenz RS, McCarthy KD. Analysis of cyclic AMP-dependent changes in intermediate filament protein phosphorylation and cell morphology in cultured astroglia. J Neurochem 1986; 47:9-17.
99. Hatten ME. Embryonic cerebellar astroglia in vitro. Brain Res 1984; 315:309-313.
100. Chiu FC, Goldman JE. Synthesis and turnover of cytoskeletal proteins in cultured astrocytes. J Neurochem 1984; 42:166-174.
101. Shafit-Zagardo B, Kume-Iwaki A, Goldman JE. Astrocytes regulates GFAP mRNA levels by cyclic AMP and protein kinase C-dependent mechanisms. Glia 1988; 1:346-354.
102. Le Prince G, Copin M-C, Hardin H et al. Neuron-glia interactions: Effect of serotonin on the astroglial expression of GFAP and of its encoding message. Dev Brain Res 1990; 51:295-298.
103. Sontheimer H, Ransom BR, Cornell-Bell AH et al. Na$^+$-current expression in rat hippocampal astrocytes in vitro: Alterations during development. J Neurophysiol 1991; 65:3-19.
104. Barres BA, Koroshetz WJ, Chun LLY, Corey DP. Ion channel expression by white matter glia: The type-I astrocyte. Neuron 1990; 5:527-544.
105. Barres BA, Chun LLY, Corey DP. Calcium currents in cortical astrocytes: Induction by cAMP and neurotransmitters and permissive effects of serum factors. J Neurosci 1989; 9:3169-3175.
106. Corvalan V, Cole R, de Vellis J et al. Neuronal modulation of calcium channel activity in cultured rat astrocytes. Proc Natl Acad Sci USA 1990; 87:4345-4348.
107. Hamberger A, Sellström Å. Techniques for separation of neurons and glia and their application to metabolic studies. In: Berl S, Clarke DD,

Schneider D. eds. Metabolic compartmentation and neurotransmission. New York: Plenum Publishing Corp., 1975:145-166.

108. Farooq M, Norton WT. A modified procedure for isolation of astrocyte- and neuron-enriched fractions from rat brain. J Neurochem 1978; 31:887-894.

109. Wilson GF, Chiu SY. Potassium channel regulation in Schwann cells during early developmental myelinogenesis. J Neurosci 1990; 5:1615-1625.

110. Nilius B, Reichenbach A. Efficient potassium buffering by mammalian retinal glial cells is due to cooperation of specialized ion channels. Plfuegers Arch 1988; 411:654-660.

111. Tse FW, Fraser DD, Duffy S et al. Voltage-activated K^+ currents in acutely isolated hippocampal astrocytes. J Neurosci 1992; 12:1781-1788.

112. Allen CN, Brady R, Swann J et al. N-Methyl-D-aspartate (NMDA) receptors are inactivated by trypsin. Brain Res 1988; 458:147-150.

113. Newman EA. Regional specialization of retinal glial cell membrane. Nature 1984; 309:155-157.

114. Brew H, Gray PTA, Mobbs P et al. End feet of retinal glial cells have higher densities of ion channels that mediate K buffering. Nature 1986; 324:466-468.

115. Thorlin T, Eriksson PS, Rönnbäck L et al. Vibrodissociation: A new nonenzymatic method for acute isolation of astrocytes. Submitted for publication.

116. Vorobjev VS. Vibrodissociation of sliced mammalian nervous tissue. J Neurosci Meth 1991; 38:145-150.

117. MacVicar BA. Voltage-dependent calcium channels in glial cells. Science 1984; 226:1345-1347.

118. Duffy S, MacVicar BA. Potassium-dependent calcium influx in acutely isolated hippocampal astrocytes. Neurosci 1994; 61:51-61.

119. Burnard DM, Crihcton SA, MacVicar BA. Electrophysiological properties of reactive glial cells in kainate-lesioned hippocampal slice. Brain Res 1990; 510:43-52.

120. Porter JT, McCarthy KD. Adenosine receptors modulate [Ca^{2+}] in hippocampal astrocytes in situ. J Neurochem 1995; 65:1515-1523.

CHAPTER 3

ASTROGLIAL GLUTAMATE AND MONOAMINE RECEPTORS: CROSS-TALK AMONG cAMP AND CA^{2+} DEPENDENT INTRACELLULAR SIGNALING

Elisabeth Hansson

INTRODUCTION

The brain is composed of electrically excitable cells, or neurons, and cells which are not electrically excitable, or glial cells. Neurons are assumed to be responsible for major brain functions such as encoding and processing information and generating behavior. The astroglial cells, or astrocytes, which constitute one major type of the cell population within the glial cell family, have been regarded as more passive and as functioning mostly in physical, trophic and metabolic support of the neurons. Astroglia have a great impact on brain energy metabolism, as the cells regulate the glucose availability for the neurons. They form a syncytium wherein the cells have physical contact with each other through gap junctions and exchange information through Ca^{2+} based excitability. This arrangement underlies to an even larger extent the capacity of the glial syncytium to cooperate with the neurons, probably over large brain areas. The prerequisites thus exist for the astroglial syncytium to participate as an integrated part in neuronal activity. It has recently been established that there is extensive interaction between neurons and astroglia, where the neurons may be subject to both a supportive and a modulatory influence from the astroglial cells.[1-3]

Astroglia express a large number of membrane receptors for most known neurotransmitters and neuromodulators which in in vitro and even in some in vivo experimental sets have been shown to be coupled to signal transduction

On Astrocytes and Glutamate Neurotransmission: New Waves in Brain Information Processing, edited by Elisabeth Hansson, Torsten Olsson and Lars Rönnbäck. © 1997 R.G. Landes Company.

systems and effector systems such as energy metabolism, membrane potential and cell volume regulation.[4]

Glutamate (Glu) is the main excitatory neurotransmitter in the brain. Released mainly at the presynaptic terminal, it can activate different types of receptors on the neuronal postsynaptic membranes. Glu has been implicated in higher cortical processes such as learning and memory. A large array of different Glu receptors were cloned during recent years and great efforts have been made to clarify the signal transduction systems coupled to the receptors. The astroglial cells are shown to express Glu receptors in vitro and in situ.[5-7] Both neurons and astroglia express ionotropic Glu receptors (iGluRs) of the kainate and AMPA types and metabotropic Glu receptors (mGluRs), which are composed of a number of subunits.[8]

The monoamine systems use the catecholamines, dopamine and noradrenaline (NA), or the indolamine serotonin (5-hydroxytryptamine, 5-HT) as transmitters. These neuronal populations were the first in mammalian brain to be structurally and functionally defined in terms of their transmitter content. NA and 5-HT are mainly released from fibers extending from the brain stem over the entire cerebrum and cerebellum. These fibers do not display classical synapses, but varicosities, from which the released neurotransmitters diffuse into the surrounding tissue to reach even distant targets and exert desynchronized and sustained influences on vast neuronal ensembles. The proportion of astrocytes around these varicosities is quite high.[9] It can be assumed that in addition to neurons, astrocytes are targets for NA and 5-HT transmission, where NA and 5-HT, by affecting astroglial functions, may be important counterparts in the intimate interaction between astrocytes and neurons. The astrocytes express membrane receptors for both NA and 5-HT. It might be appropriate to consider the possible functions these innervations might serve.

ASTROGLIA, GLUTAMATE AND MONOAMINES

GLUTAMATE RECEPTORS

Glu receptors can be categorized into two distinct groups: ionotropic receptors (iGluRs) and metabotropic receptors (mGluRs).[8] The ionotropic receptors are thought to gate ion channels and have been named for agonists, which they selectively activate. IGluRs can be subdivided into two main categories, the N-methyl-D-aspartate (NMDA) receptors and the non-NMDA ones. The NMDA receptor family are receptor channels, permeable to Ca^{2+} via the receptor-operated Ca^{2+} channels. Several NMDA subunits were cloned; $NMDA_1$, $NMDA_{2A}$-$NMDA_{2D}$ and $NMDA_L$.[10,11] The non-NMDA receptors α-amino-3-hydroxy-5-methylisoxazole-4-proprionic acid (AMPA) and kainate (KA), are also receptor channels. Four different AMPA subunits were cloned (Glu_1-Glu_4), as well as five different KA subunits (Glu_5-Glu_7, KA_1, KA_2).[12] The AMPA and KA receptors are stimulated by the fast excitatory effects of Glu and cause depolarization of the astrocytes by opening membrane channels permeable to Na^+ and K^+ ions. They exhibit different permeabilities for Ca^{2+}. The kainate-induced Ca^{2+} influx seems to be mediated by KA receptor channels and not by the activation of voltage-sensitive channels.[13] In freshly isolated hippocampal astrocytes from mouse brain, the iGluRs expressed were of the AMPA subtype, preferentially Glu_2 and Glu_4.[14] Studies of brain slices and primary neuronal and glial cultures suggest to date that neurons and glia share the same types of iGluRs, except for the NMDA receptor, which is not found on glia in culture.[15] However, in recent years the NMDA receptor has been demonstrated on astrocytes in in vivo preparations.[16]

The mGluRs are both functionally and pharmacologically different from the iGluRs. The mGluRs are linked to G proteins. Their stimulation generates the formation of second messengers and/or regulates ion channel function by mediating intracellular signal transduction. Cloning experiments reveal that there are at least eight subtypes, $mGluR_1$-$mGluR_8$.[17-26] Amino acid sequence identity varies within the mGluRs family. This has led to a classification into three classes:[19] *Class I* comprises $mGluR_1$ and $mGluR_5$. $MGluR_1$ is primarily coupled to phosphoinositide (PI) hydrolysis/Ca^{2+} signal transduction[18,20] as are also $mGluR_{5a}$ and $_b$.[17,22] *Class II* comprises $mGluR_2$ and $mGluR_3$, and *class III* comprises $mGluR_4$, $mGluR_{6-8}$. Classes II and III inhibit the formation of cyclic AMP.[19,20,21,23-25] They differ, however, in their pharmacological profile against specific agonists. $MGluR_{4a}$ is potently activated by L-1-amino-4-phosphonobutanoic acid (L-AP4), which suggests that the $mGluR_{4a}$ receptor is a possible candidate for L-AP4 on astrocytes.[5,21] L-AP4 seems ineffective against class I and class II mGluRs.[21] $MGluR_3$ and $mGluR_5$ have been detected by antibody staining and by in situ hybridization in hippocampal astrocytes.[7,27] $MGluR_1$ has been found on glia of the optic nerve, analyzed by PCR.[28]

5-HT Receptors

Several different subtypes of 5-HT receptors have been recognized with different effector pathways, activated by the various 5-HT receptors. Most results are derived from neuronal preparations. The 5-HT_1 receptor, subdivided into 5-$HT_{1A, 1B, 1D, 1E}$ and $_{1F}$, inhibits adenylyl cyclase (AC), while the 5-HT_2 receptor, subdivided into 5-$HT_{2A, 2B}$ and $_{2C}$, activities the PI hydrolysis/Ca^{2+} signal transduction system. The 5-HT_3 receptor is directly ion channel-coupled, and the 5-HT_4 receptor is positively coupled to AC[29,30] as well as the 5-HT_6 receptor[31] and the novel 5-HT_7 receptor.[32]

Hertz and co-workers[33] were the first to report a serotonin-binding site for astroglial cells in primary culture. Later Pearce and co-workers[34] identified a

5-HT receptor coupled to the PI system. It was early found that the $5\text{-}HT_{2A}$ receptor induced the formation of PI leading to an increase in inositol (1,4,5)-trisphosphate (IP_3).[35-37] Different techniques have been used to verify the astroglial expression of the receptor, including immunohistochemistry with anti-idiotypic antibodies and in situ hybridization,[37] quantification of second messengers such as phosphoinositides and cyclic AMP.[38] In other cell systems it was shown that activation of the G protein-coupled $5\text{-}HT_{2A}$ receptor results in phospholipase C (PLC)-mediated PI hydrolysis which liberates the second messengers diacylglycerol (DAG) and IP_3.[39] The 5-HT-evoked Ca^{2+} transients were pertussis toxin (PTX)-insensitive and were suppressed by the PLC inhibitor neomycin. These data indicate that in cultivated astroglia the $5\text{-}HT_{2A}$ receptors are linked to G_q proteins coupled to PLC. In the regional expression obtained from cell culture studies it was found that the receptors were more abundant in the cerebral cortex and brain stem than in the hippocampus and striatum.[35]

Furthermore, it is suggested that the maturational state and conditions under which the astroglial cultures are maintained may have direct effects on receptor expression and density. There is thus indirect evidence for the expression of the $5\text{-}HT_{1A}$ receptor on astrocytes at least in culture and the $5\text{-}HT_{1A}$ and even the $5\text{-}HT_{2C}$ receptors could be demonstrated prenatally.[40] The Whitaker-Azmitia group demonstrated that the development of serotonergic neurons might be regulated by the S100β protein produced by astrocytes, and that the release of this factor might be stimulated by the activation of the $5\text{-}HT_{1A}$ receptor.[41] Recently this group published an article further supporting $5\text{-}HT_{1A}$ receptors on astroglia.[42] The $5\text{-}HT_7$ receptor has also been demonstrated on astrocytes.[43]

ADRENOCEPTORS

Adrenoceptors can be subdivided into several distinct categories, based on pharmacological specificity and physiological actions. They can be divided into α_1-, α_2-, β_1- and β_2-adrenergic receptor subtypes.[44] They show a specificity for coupling to different G proteins and thereby to different second messengers. The β-adrenoceptors stimulate the enzyme AC, which is mediated by the G protein G_s, which, in turn, leads to an increase in cyclic AMP. Agonist activation of the α_2 receptor leads primarily to inhibition of AC via G_i. α_1-receptor activation leads to generation of the second messengers DAG and IP_3 by stimulating the enzyme PLC. This pathway is mediated by a PTX insensitive G protein, G_q.[45] Receptor stimulation of G protein-coupled adrenoceptors or generation of these various second messengers can activate a cascade of events leading to the activation of specific kinases and subsequent phosphorylation of proteins, protein kinase A (PKA) and protein kinase C (PKC), release of intracellular Ca^{2+} stores, activation of ion channels or pumps, release of arachidonic acid and gene transcription.

It is well established that astroglial cells in primary culture respond to NA with an increase in the intracellular levels of cyclic AMP.[46,47] It was also demonstrated that the β-adrenoceptor is responsible for the increasing levels of cyclic AMP and coupled to a G_s protein.[48,49] By immunocytochemistry, in combination with receptor autoradiography, it was confirmed that $β_1$-adrenoceptors are expressed on cultured astrocytes.[50] There is heterogeneity among astrocytes with respect to the expression of the receptors. Astrocytes derived from the cerebral cortex and the striatum showed a more prominent cyclic AMP accumulation than cells from, e.g., brain stem.[47] McCarthy and collaborators[51] demonstrated the presence of β-adrenoceptor binding sites on type 1 but not on type 2 astrocytes. Furthermore, they found that all polygonal astroglia expressed the $β_1$-receptor.[52] It has also been shown that the astrocytes contain a preponderance of AC-coupled β-adrenoceptors in slices of the rat forebrain[53] and in bulk-isolated astrocytes.[54]

Stimulation of the $α_2$-adrenoceptors inhibits AC in astrocytes.[46,55,56] The $α_2$ receptor is coupled to the PTX sensitive G_i protein. It is likely that both $α_2$- and β-adrenoceptors are expressed on the same astrocyte[57] and that both receptors contribute to the modulation of intracellular cyclic AMP levels.

The $α_1$-receptors are expressed by both type 1 and type 2 astrocytes but not by all astrocytes, indicating that there is heterogeneity among astrocytes with respect to the expression of these membrane receptors.[58] The precise function of the $α_1$-receptor in brain is uncertain, although there is a high density of this subtype in most brain regions.[59]

SECOND MESSENGER SYSTEMS

CYCLIC AMP

The cyclic AMP cascade is the best studied signal transduction system.[60] Cyclic AMP is formed by the enzyme adenylyl cyclase (AC) which is linked to many different plasma membrane receptors via G proteins.[61,62] G proteins serve as signal transducers, linking extracellularly oriented receptors to membrane-bound effectors. These G proteins are heterotrimers comprising αβγ subunits, each of which exists in multiple isoforms. Upon interaction with an activated receptor, the subunits dissociate into an α subunit and a βγ moiety. During this process the α subunit hydrolyzes guanosine trisphosphate (GTP), at which point it is again inactive. The G proteins linked to AC could be positive regulators, $G_{αs}$, or negative regulators, $G_{αi}$. Cyclic AMP can then activate PKA, which phosphorylates specific proteins at serine and threonine residues. Cyclic AMP is broken down by cyclic nucleotide phosphodiesterases.

PHOSPHOINOSITIDE SYSTEM

Inositol $(1,4,5)$-trisphosphate (IP_3) is a second messenger that controls many cellular processes by generating internal calcium signals. In response to neurotransmitters, hormones and growth factors, IP_3 and DAG are formed by the hydrolysis of an inositol lipid precursor stored in the plasma membrane. The membrane-transducing units controlled by G protein linked receptors are characterized by having seven membrane-spanning domains connected to one another by extracellular and intracellular loops.[63] The G protein family can be divided into two different proteins, depending on whether or not they are sensitive to PTX. G_q is a PTX insensitive G protein and G_p is a PTX sensitive G protein.[64,65] The activation of PLC linked receptors is known to induce the formation of IP_3 and DAG from the cleavage of membrane inositol lipid, phosphatidylinositol 4,5-bisphosphate (PIP_2).[66] DAG activates protein kinase C (PKC) and IP_3 releases Ca^{2+} from intracellular organelles possessing IP_3 receptors, such as the endoplasmatic reticulum.[67] Ca^{2+} ions serve as a second messenger in all eukaryotic cells. The transient fluctuations of $[Ca^{2+}]_i$, which occur between resting levels and cellular excitation, trigger or regulate various intracellular events. The generation of cytoplasmic Ca^{2+} signals is determined by the interaction of external Ca^{2+} entry and Ca^{2+} release from intracellular stores. These stores accumulate Ca^{2+} via an ATP-dependent Ca^{2+} pump functioning across an intracellular membrane, and extracellular Ca^{2+} is necessary to replenish the cytoplasmic Ca^{2+} pool.[68-70] There are both IP_3- and ryanodine-sensitive calcium stores, which vary considerably from cell to cell.[71]

In nonexcitable cells such as astrocytes, the production of IP_3 that diffuses to the endoplasmic reticulum and causes release of intracellularly stored calcium into the cytoplasm signals the activation of calcium entry. The signal for activation of calcium entry is less clearly understood. Evidence for the existence of a diffusible cytosolic factor, a Ca^{2+}- influx factor (CIF), released by empty stores has been presented from several laboratories.[72,73] This signal or factor which is generated activates entry of a plasma membrane Ca^{2+} channel. Data suggest that receptors linked to PI turnover and the subsequent release of calcium may be coupled to the Ca^{2+}-release-activated channel (CRAC) type or to

Fig. 3.1. (Opposite page) An astroglial cell stimulated by 5-HT. 5-HT_{2A} receptor, linked to a Gq protein, which activates PLC, was found to induce IP_3 formation and Ca^{2+} release from intracellular stores, followed by an influx of calcium through the plasma membrane. A signal or factor is generated when Ca^{2+} is free in the cytosol (CIF) and activates plasma membrane calcium entry. The Ca^{2+} influx involves two components. One activates the Na^+-Ca^{2+} exchanger in its reverse mode. The Na^+-Ca^{2+} exchanger is codistributed with the Na^+-K^+ pump on the plasma membrane. The other Ca^{2+} influx is linked to a voltage independent calcium channel of the CRAC or DOCC type. At the same time the calcium-activated K^+ channel opens, which leads to a hyperpolarization. A stretch-activated Ca^{2+} channel (SAC) might also be activated.

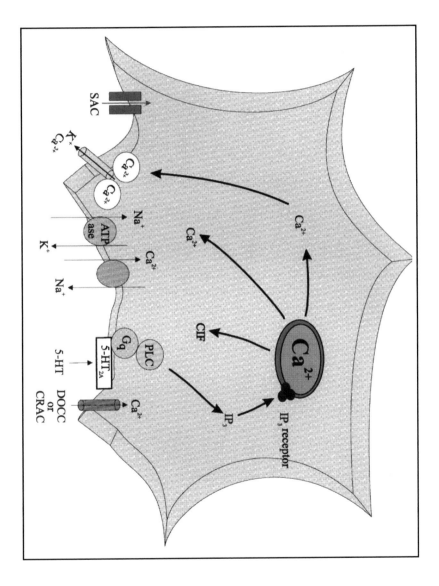

the depleted operated-channel (DOCC). It has been shown that 5-HT failed to open any Ca^{2+}-channels after (1) previous thapsigargin stimulation.[68] Thapsigargin elevates the cytosolic Ca^{2+} in various cells and inhibits the Ca^{2+}-ATPase responsible for sequestering Ca^{2+} into the IP_3-sensitive Ca^{2+} pool.[69,70] (2) Internally applied heparin (heparin blocks the release of stored intracellular IP_3-induced Ca^{2+}).[72] This indicates that the depletion of intracellular Ca^{2+}-stores is a necessity for 5-HT-induced Ca^{2+}-channel opening. However, the intracellular stores of Ca^{2+} in astrocytes seems not only to be regulated by CRACs, but also by a Na^+-Ca^{2+} exchanger.[37] The Na^+-Ca^{2+} exchanger has been demonstrated in astrocytes and mediates a net Ca^{2+} influx upon reduction of the Na^+ electrochemical gradient.[74-76] This exchanger, coupled to releasable intracellular Ca^{2+} stores might play a central role in maintaining the cytosolic Ca^{2+} concentration at a normal level both in the steady state and during active signaling by both neurons and astrocytes. The Na^+-Ca^{2+} exchanger is largely codistributed with the Na^+-K^+ pump on the plasma membrane. It may be the mechanism by which astrocytes replenish their empty Ca^{2+} stores after 5-HT_{2A} receptor stimulation (Fig. 3.1).[77]

CROSS-TALK AMONG G PROTEIN-LINKED RECEPTORS

Neurotransmitter and hormone signals are propagated via G protein- and non-G protein receptors. G proteins located in the plasma membrane interact with the cytoplasmic loops of receptor proteins, thereby transferring information to effector molecules such as AC, PLC, ion channels, as well as protein kinases and phosphatases. The molecules generate various second messengers which, in turn, induce a range of cellular physiological responses integrating the information from numerous signaling pathways. This requires "cross-talk" among different pathways, often concomitantly with mobilization of intracellular and extracellular Ca^{2+}. Different possible models for cross-talk in cellular signal transduction have been suggested.[78] Either a single receptor can activate two alternative signaling pathways through two different G proteins, different receptors that use the same G protein to produce different signals, or cross-talk can occur between two pathways through the interaction of the second messengers that are generated. Given the complexity of the regulation of cellular processes by the second messengers, cyclic AMP, Ca^{2+}, or DAG, it is not surprising that extensive cross-regulation of their levels in cells has been observed. A number of receptors in a range of cells and tissues are known to generate more than one second messenger when activated by their physiological stimuli.

During recent years many studies in different model systems have been done on interactions between the cyclic AMP and the PI systems.[79-81] The search for

Fig. 3.2. (Opposite page) Schematic drawing of interaction between the 5-HT_{2A} receptor and the adrenoceptors. See text for further details.

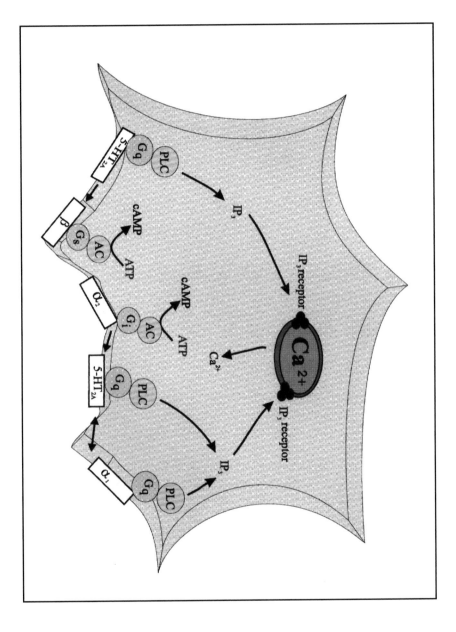

cross-regulation among metabolic and signal transduction pathways has become an important theme in many areas of research. It has been demonstrated in nonvascular smooth muscle that cyclic AMP elevating agents are effective relaxants and that cross-talk between cyclic AMP and PI signaling plays an important role in the regulation of contraction-relaxation responses. IP_3 appears to be involved in both Ca^{2+} release from the sarcoplasmic reticulum and in Ca^{2+} influx through the plasma membrane. If regulation in $[Ca^{2+}]_i$ is the underlying mechanism for cyclic AMP-mediated relaxation, an important target of cyclic AMP actions, which might take place through activation of PKA, would be either to inhibit IP_3 production or to stimulate PI inactivation.[81] For the sake of simplification, we focus on examples of receptors discussed above typifying coupling to three independent signal transduction pathways: receptors positively coupled to AC activation via stimulatory G proteins, G_s, receptors negatively coupled to AC activation via inhibitory G proteins, G_i, and receptors coupled to PLC activation via G_q proteins. Cross-talk between the stimulatory and inhibitory AC pathways and between the AC and the PLC pathways is discussed below with regard to the astroglial cells.

Interaction Between Adrenoceptors and 5-HT$_{2A}$ Receptors on Astrocytes

NA stimulates cyclic AMP production in a stimulatory way via the β-receptors and in an inhibitory way via the $α_2$-receptors. If $α_2$ and β agonists are used together, $α_2$ attenuates the AC activation by the β agonist.[82] They also showed that β-receptor stimulation decreased cyclic AMP production owing to activation of $α_1$ receptors in mixed cultures of type 1 and type 2 astrocytes, which was not seen in type 1 astroglial cultures. $α_1$ activation by NA potentiated the β-induced cyclic AMP response in mouse striatal astrocyte cultures.[83]

Recent data have demonstrated that astrocytes in primary culture respond to 5-HT as well as to agonists of the adrenoceptors $α_1$, $α_2$ and β on the same cell in a microspectrofluorometric system.[84] Using this technique it cannot absolutely conclusively be shown that several receptors are expressed on the same single cell, as the Ca^{2+} response might come from other cells after activation by the agonist some distance away and facilitated in the culture by gap junction communication. However, at our lab it has also been demonstrated that the 5-HT$_{2A}$ receptor interacts with the adrenoceptors at the second messenger level.[38] Stimulation of the 5-HT$_{2A}$ receptor, which in itself has no effect on the formation of cyclic AMP, potentiated the β-adrenergic stimulation of AC (Fig. 3.2). The PI lipid response after simultaneous stimulation with the $α_1$ agonist phenylephrine and 5-HT was found to be significantly larger than the sum of the individual phenylephrine and 5-HT effects (Fig. 3. 2). Clonidine, an $α_2$ receptor agonist, known to inhibit the formation of cyclic AMP, markedly potentiated the 5-HT$_{2A}$ stimulated formation of PI (Fig. 3. 2).[38] The cyclic AMP dependent protein kinase pathway elegantly accounts for the hormonal control of many cellular cascades including glycogenolysis, lipolysis and catecholamine biosynthesis. One of the physiological functions of the astroglial cells is to produce glycogenolysis in response to noradrenergic activation and also cause the production of neurotrophic substances.[85] There is intertwined cellular signaling by cyclic AMP and internal Ca^{2+} as it has been shown that AC is intimately associated with sites of calcium ion entry into the cell. In nonexcitable cells the route by which [Ca^{2+}]$_i$ is elevated is also critical for inhibiting Ca^{2+}-sensitive AC. The Ca^{2+} release and Ca^{2+} entry processes have been evaluated separately, and it has become clear that only Ca^{2+} entering the cell as a result of store depletion, and not Ca^{2+} released from intracellular stores, can regulate these enzymes.[86] The Ca^{2+} entry inhibits cyclic AMP accumulation in C6-2B glioma cells, which suggests that Ca^{2+}-inhibitable ACs may be functionally colocalized with sites of Ca^{2+} entry. This seems to be direct inhibition by Ca^{2+} of a type V or VI AC.[86]

In many cell types, receptor-mediated Ca^{2+} release from internal stores is followed by Ca^{2+} influx through the plasma membrane. The sustained entry of Ca^{2+} is thought to result partly from the depletion of intracellular Ca^{2+} pools. The depletion of Ca^{2+} pools induces activation of a sustained calcium inward current that was highly selective for Ca^{2+} ions over Ba^{2+}, Sr^{2+} and Mn^{2+}. This calcium current or calcium channel is voltage-inactive.[72,87] This may be the mechanism by which electrically nonexcitable cells maintain raised intracellular Ca^{2+} concentrations and replenish their empty Ca^{2+} stores after receptor stimulation.

INTERACTION BETWEEN G PROTEIN LINKED GLU RECEPTORS ON ASTROCYTES

The mGluRs recognized to date on astrocytes are coupled to the PI system mobilizing intracellular Ca^{2+} as well as to the inhibition of cyclic AMP production. The mGluR agonist trans-1-amino cyclopentane-1,3-dicarboxylic acid (1S,3R-ACPD) modifies the PI metabolism and the release of Ca^{2+} from intracellular stores.[5,88] This receptor is coupled to a PTX insensitive G protein, whereas IP$_3$ triggers the release of [Ca^{2+}]$_i$, followed by an influx of calcium via Ca^{2+} channels in the plasma membrane. The other mGluR agonist, L-AP4, which suggests that the mGluR$_{4a}$ receptor is the possible candidate,[21] is coupled to the PTX sensitive G$_i$ protein, that inhibits cyclic AMP.

Glu acting alone on astroglial cells in primary culture appears capable of generating more than one second messenger, which induces a range of cell physiological responses, concomitant with mobilization of intracellular calcium. This outlines different possible models, which might account for cross-talk between different transduction systems. Glu interacts with the mGluRs 1 and/or 5, thereby activating the G$_q$ protein coupled to PLC which subsequently induces

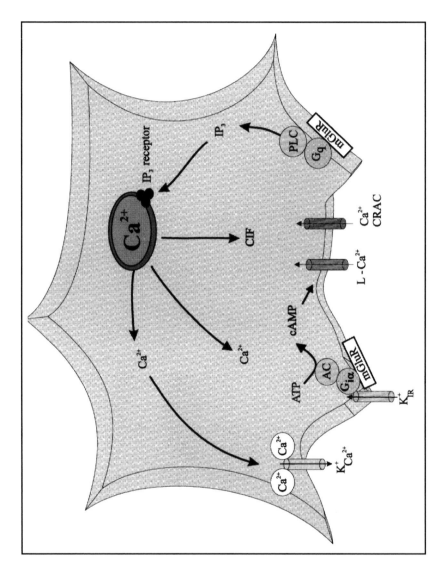

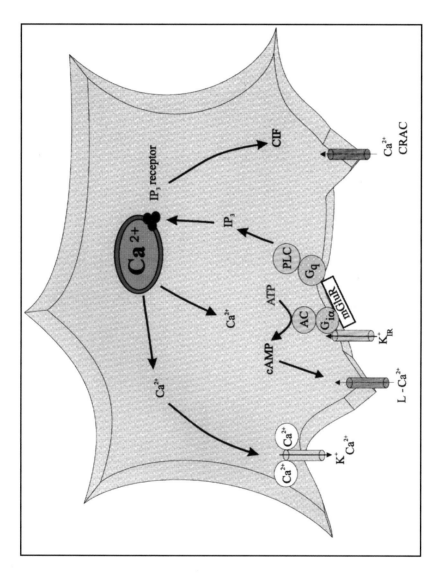

IP_3 formation and release of Ca^{2+} from intracellular organelles possessing IP_3 receptors. This leads to opening of Ca^{2+} channels and probably opening of an outward rectifying Ca^{2+}-dependent K^+ channel. Glu also interacts with at least the $mGluR_{4a}$ receptor, leading to an inhibition of AC and a decreased cyclic AMP production. This inhibition of cyclic AMP formation could lead to an opening of L-Ca^{2+} channels, through activation of a $G_{i\alpha}$ protein (Fig. 3.3a).[89] Recently Bygrave and Roberts[78] reviewed different models for cross-talk in cellular signal transduction, which can also be applied to the Glu cross-talk system in astrocytes. A hypothesis and alternative theory of G protein-linked Glu receptors might be that Glu stimulates one receptor, which might be coupled to two different G proteins such as G_q and G_i. In this case the two second messenger systems PI and cyclic AMP would be activated simultaneously, which could result in more precise and faster intracellular signal transduction (Fig. 3.3b). Stimulation of each pathway alone might not be sufficient to activate the intracellular signal transduction, but together they might provide the appropriate stimuli required, for example for Glu-induced volume regulation. (See chapter 6.)

FUNCTIONAL IMPLICATIONS OF CROSS-TALK BETWEEN MEMBRANE RECEPTORS AND SECOND MESSENGER SYSTEMS IN THE ASTROGLIAL NETWORK

Cross-talk between second messenger systems certainly plays a crucial role in the regulation of multiple signal transduction mechanisms within the cell. Cyclic AMP and PI pathways appear to share positive as well as negative modulatory interactions, leading to a final cell response.[90] The G protein-linked receptors are intimately involved in modulating both direct and indirect responses to ion channels including Ca^{2+} and K^+ channels.[91,92] This leads to activation of PLC, PLA_2, PLD, PKA and PKC.[92] Nearly all intracellular pathways are influenced by activation of PKA and/or PKC.

Stimulation of the α_1-adrenoceptors results in Ca^{2+} transients similar to the Ca^{2+} response evoked by 5-HT.[84] The α_1-adrenoceptors activate PLC via a PTX insensitive G protein. The Ca^{2+} transients consisted of one initial peak and a second sustained part. Stimulation of the α_2- and β-adrenoceptors affects the cyclic AMP system. The α_2 receptor stimulates the G_i protein, leading to a cyclic AMP inhibition and the β receptor stimulates the G_s protein, leading to an intracellular cyclic AMP increase.

Fig. 3.3a. (Previous two pages) Schematic drawing where Glu might stimulate the mGluRs coupled to the PI system, releasing intracellular Ca^{2+} on the one hand and the cyclic AMP system on the other.

Fig. 3.3b. A hypothesis whereby Glu might stimulate one mGluR, which is coupled to two G proteins, the $G_{i\alpha}$ and the G_q, which simultaneously give cyclic AMP inhibition and release of intracellular Ca^{2+}.

While it is clear that astrocytes in vitro and in vivo exhibit adrenoceptors, the role played by these receptor systems in brain function is less evident. It has, however, been shown that astrocytes may respond to adrenoceptors with the breakdown of glycogen and release of metabolic substrates to be utilized by neurons. The β-receptors stimulate the release of some neuroactive factors; for example, nerve growth factor (NGF)[93,94] and taurine,[95] which may influence the growth and differentiation of neurons. One role of these receptors may be to increase the release of these neuroactive substances in brain during development. It has also been shown that the β-receptors stimulate the opening of L-type calcium channels via the activation of PKA.[96] Furthermore, monoamine uptake by astrocytes is extremely low in comparison to Glu uptake.[97,98] The metabolism of monoamines is, however, complex and results in a variety of oxidized, deaminated, methylated, and sulfated products. Two of the principal enzymes of monoamine degradation are monoamine oxidase (MAO) and catechol-O-methyltransferase (COMT), which have been shown to be present in cultured astroglial cells[99] and in astrocytes in situ.[100,101] The morphology of the astroglia could also be affected by stimulating the adrenoceptors. Increasing the activity of PKA or protein kinase C (PKC) converts the astroglia from flat, polygonally shaped cells to process-bearing cells.[102]

Furthermore, astrocytes supply neurons with glucose,[103] which could also be controlled by NA.[104] More recently it has been demonstrated that the astrocytes release lactic acid.[105] The glycogen, which appears to be located almost exclusively in astrocytes, is also known to undergo hydrolysis in response to the activation of adrenoceptors by both exogenous and endogenous NA.[106] The role of adrenoceptors in glycogenolysis has been examined in different systems.[107,108] Activation of the β-receptors by exogenous catecholamines has been found to induce a significant increase in glycogenolysis. However, in primary astroglial cultures the response required combined stimulation of β- and α-receptors,[109] which is mediated through α$_2$- and β-receptors.[110]

5-HT INDUCES A HYPERPOLARIZATION AND NA INDUCES A DEPOLARIZATION OF THE ASTROGLIA—POSSIBLE CONSEQUENCES FOR NEURONAL ACTIVITY

It was shown that 5-HT hyperpolarizes astroglial cells in model systems obtained from leech neuropile glial cells, rat glioma cells and cultured astrocytes.[111-113] These changes in membrane potential may be a result of the activation of a calcium dependent potassium conductance suspected to be attributable to the release of intracellular calcium.[114,115]

Walz and Schule[111] argued that the 5-HT-induced hyperpolarization in at least leech glial cells could increase the cells' spatial buffering capabilities. Newman and co-workers[116] suggested that voltage dependent ion channels may function to amplify the K$^+$ currents involved with spatial buffering in amphibian retinal Müller cells. The ability of a glial cell network to adjust its ionic buffering capacity in response to a decrease in extracellular $[K^+]$ or neurotransmitter levels has important implications for ionic homeostasis in the brain.[117] This might mean that the 5-HT influence on the astroglial network might constitute one factor for the optimum clearance of the extracellular space of at least one ion and one amino acid vital to optimal neuronal function, especially when there is rapid firing of many neurons in parallel.

The stimulation of α_1 receptors results in depolarization of astroglia.[118] In different tissues, the calcium activated K^+ channels are modulated by exogenous ligands signaling through membrane receptors. This leads to depolarization by closing K^+ channels. There is only speculation to date about the physiological functions, but it has been proposed that regulatory mechanisms such as phosphorylation, interaction with GTP-binding proteins or direct modulation by intracellular second messengers are involved. So the calcium activated K^+ channels might be activated by both plasma membrane depolarization and binding of calcium at the intracellular surface of the channel.[119]

ARE ASTROGLIA TARGETS FOR NON-SYNAPTIC NA AND 5-HT NEUROTRANSMISSION? (FIG. 3.4.)

Much interest has been focused on the role of the neurotransmitter 5-HT in the etiology and treatment of neuropsychiatric disorders such as anxiety disorders, depression, alcoholism, schizophrenia, migraine, sexual dysfunction and Alzheimer's disease.[120-122] 5-HT containing neurons are concentrated in the raphe nuclei in the mammalian CNS, while 5-HT-releasing fibers project to virtually all parts of the CNS. The effects of 5-HT on neural systems are not fully understood. Results from many laboratories indicate that 5-HT acts primarily to modulate the effects of other neurotransmitters. There is a great deal of data on the interaction between the NA system and 5-HT, and at the integrated level 5-HT has been pointed out as being primarily inhibitory on the NA system.[123]

A large proportion of the 5-HT fibers from the raphe nucleus do not establish synaptic contacts with target neurons in the cerebral cortex but rather release 5-HT into the extracellular environment.[124,125] From this point of view it is of great interest that astroglial cells express 5-HT receptors and it may be assumed that astroglia, like neurons, are targets for 5-HT transmission, and that 5-HT, by affecting astroglial functions, can be an important counterpart in the intimate interaction between astroglia and neurons.

The noradrenergic system of the brain is thought to play an important role in attention processes, central responses to stress and possibly also in the mechanism of action of a number of psychotherapeutic drugs.[126] Many lines of evidence suggest that astroglia might be targets of noradrenergic innervation and that an important aspect of astroglia function may be to regulate the metabolic

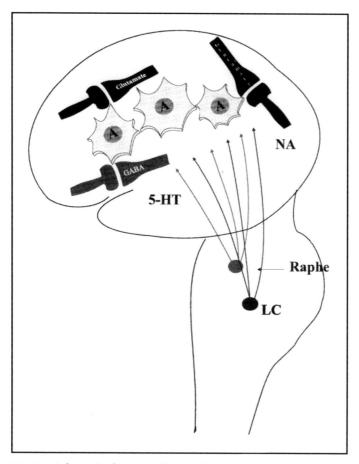

Fig. 3.4. Schematic drawing of interaction between the serotonergic (5-HT) and the noradrenergic (NA) systems at the integrated level and at the cellular level. The projections from the raphe nucleus mediate 5-HT release, and there is NA release from the locus coeruleus (LC) over large parts of the cerebral cortex. There is interaction between the systems at the nuclear level. 5-HT has been shown to exert a mainly inhibitory influence on excitatory amino acid induced LC activity. Thus 5-HT may selectively filter or gate certain afferents to the LC. 5-HT has also been shown to inhibit local NA release in the hippocampus. The interaction between 5-HT and NA second messenger systems in astroglia is demonstrated. Three astroglial cells in the cerebral cortex are shown with contacts with three synaptic regions, two Glu and one GABA. There are 5-HT induced potentiations of β-receptor induced cyclic AMP formation and of α_1-receptor induced PI formation. Furthermore, α_2-receptor stimulation enhances 5-HT$_{2A}$ receptor induced PI formation. The figure also demonstrates the projection from the basal part of the frontal cortex to the raphe nucleus and to the LC, probably forming a feed-back loop signaling the activity level of the cerebral cortex.

and trophic actions of the glia.[85,127,128] NA is present in high concentrations in the cerebral cortex.[129] The main NA source is the locus coeruleus in the brain stem. The noradrenergic innervation of the cerebral cortex is composed of fine axons, organized predominantly in a plane parallel to the pial surface and spanning a vast expanse of the cortex.[130] NA stimulates cyclic AMP formation and promotes glycogenolysis via a calcium-dependent activation of phosphorylase b.[131] Glycogenolysis in response to noradrenergic activation would provide cells with ATP and metabolic substrates in the form of glucose-6-PO_4, puruvate and lactate. The glia may require increased metabolic substrates as a result of increased neuronal activity to remove extracellular K^+ and amino acids. Activation of selected peptidergic neurons may cause potentiated cyclic AMP and glycogenolytic responses in glia.[132] Furthermore, noradrenergic action on astrocytes may also cause production of neurotrophic substances, e.g., nerve growth factor (NGF) in response to β-receptor stimulation of cyclic AMP formation.[133]

It is well known that glycogen phosphorylase is localized in astrocytes in the CNS[134] and it has recently been demonstrated that the 5-HT_{2A} receptor is involved in the breakdown of glycogen in astrocytes in culture.[135] In vivo NA enhances the rate of glucose utilization in the brain and 5-HT decreases it correspondingly.[136,137] This might suggest that there is interaction of the glycogenolysis between the noradrenergic and serotonergic systems.

FUNCTIONAL CONSEQUENCES OF ADRENERGIC AND 5-HT_{2A} RECEPTOR STIMULATION ON ASTROGLIA—PROBABLE EFFECTS FOR NEURONAL ACTIVITY

Putting the data reviewed above into a more global perspective, it might be fair to discuss the probable effects of the 5-HT and NA influence on astroglia for the astroglial support of the neurons and their possibilities to modulate and probably facilitate neuronal activity. The axonal varicosities containing NA and 5-HT release their respective transmitters, which diffuse into the surrounding tissue. The majority of these varicosities were characterized by nonsynaptic contacts (Fig. 2.3). The proportion of astrocytes around these varicosities is quite high.[9] The membranes of glial cells and neurons are separated by narrow extracellular clefts, which form an intersecting network of sheet-like spaces. This fluid space permits the diffusion of ions and small molecules between the two cell types. Thus NA or 5-HT released from the nonsynaptic varicosities may affect the astrocytes, depending on the diffusion coefficient for the particular substance in the space, the ability of the cells to modify the concentration of the substance through uptake or metabolism, the availability of receptors, and the resulting concentration of the substance at the receptor sites.[138] The extracellular concentration of NA and 5-HT could also indirectly be controlled via intercellular communication and cooperation. This led to the hypothesis that astrocytes could play a role in volume transmission with the spreading of transmitter molecules in the extracellular fluid.[9] 5-HT_{2A} receptor stimulation has been shown to induce a hyperpolarization of the astroglial network in some model systems, leading to an increased capacity for K^+ spatial buffering and Glu clearance by astroglia from the extracellular space. It has also been shown that 5-HT acts as an inhibitor of the glial fibrillary acidic protein (GFAP) expression in astrocytes.[139] A high-frequency neurotransmission will thus be facilitated, especially when there is activation of many neuronal systems simultaneously. Our group showed that in the presence of NA in astroglial cultures from the cerebral cortex, 5-HT can potentiate the cyclic AMP production caused by NA.[38] There is a complex interaction between 5-HT and NA where 5-HT has been shown to be inhibitory of NA effects. 5-HT has been shown to decrease the release of NA in the hippocampus.[140] There is also an interaction between 5-HT and the activity of the locus coeruleus (LC), the main source of NA in the cerebral cortex, where 5-HT seems to decrease the excitatory amino acid induced activation of the LC.[123] In this context our data on 5-HT and NA interactions at the level of the astroglial signal transduction systems might be especially interesting, as there might be modulation by and an innervation of 5-HT and NA of the astroglia energy metabolism and energy supply to the neurons.

5-HT_{2A} receptor induced Ca^{2+} signaling within the astroglial network might be one way for the nervous system to integrate information about the nerve cell activity level, not primarily influenced by 5-HT release, with other parts of the nervous system. This might be one way to integrate neuronal activity level over larger brain areas and might also be one way for 5-HT to exert a tonic influence upon the neuronal/astroglial activity level.

Interestingly, in states of 5-HT deficiency, there might be reduced transmission, which would be consistent with the data presented above. This is, in fact, characteristic of depressive states. The findings of a decrease in frontal cortex brain volume of 6-7% in severe depression, as reported by Coffey and co-workers,[141] is especially interesting. The 5-HT_{2A} receptor induced regulation of astrocyte function might thus be one component important to the regulation of neurotransmission and the nerve cell functional state. Given the likelihood that glial cells are targets of the noradrenergic system, it is appropriate to consider the possible functions of producing glycogenolysis in response to noradrenergic activation and also of causing the production of neurotrophic substances.[85] In any case, it now seems evident that the 5-HT and NA induced influence on the astroglial network must be taken into account when determining the neuronal activity level. It might thus be important to include astroglia in the neural circuits comprising the 5-HT and NA nonsynaptic transmission.

CONCLUSIONS

Although little is known about the interaction between different receptors, G proteins and second messengers, it should be recognized that cross-regulation between the PLC pathway and the AC pathway, can and does occur. These observations suggest that feedback and cross-system phosphorylation may represent distinct and differently regulated mechanisms for modulation of receptor function.

Evidence is now accumulating that both 5-HT and NA, by interaction with astroglia, can facilitate and modulate neuronal activity and transmission. At least two mechanisms might be involved: (1) interaction of 5-HT with adrenoceptor signal transduction systems, probably leading to modulatory effects of astroglial energy metabolism and energy supply to the neurons, (2) 5-HT induced hyperpolarization of the astroglia in some cell types with resultant possibilities for facilitation of the astroglial K^+ and Glu clearance of the extracellular space, at least in those brain regions or in those situations where the astroglial network is hyperpolarized by 5-HT. Furthermore, it might be tempting to postulate that the 5-HT and NA induced Ca^{2+} signaling within the astroglial network serves to integrate the neuronal-astroglial activity level in one brain region with other parts, not primarily reached by release of monoamines. This might be one way that neuronal activity level is integrated over larger brain areas. Since 5-HT$_{2A}$ receptors are extensively expressed on cortical astroglia, and 5-HT has been proposed to exert a tonic influence over parts of the nervous system, it might be that 5-HT also exerts a tonic influence on the astroglial network and thus, under certain circumstances, facilitates nerve cell activity in larger areas of the cerebral cortex. This influence on astroglia might be important to take into account when discussing neuronal activity level, and it might therefore be important to include astroglia in the neural circuit constituting the raphe nucleus, the cerebral cortex and the feed-back loop from the prefrontal cortex back to the raphe nucleus.

ACKNOWLEDGMENTS

This research was supported by grants from the Swedish Medical Research Council (project no 12X-06812), the Swedish Work Environment Fund (grant no 94-0214) and the Swedish Council for Work Life Research (grant no 95-0231). The skillful technical assistance of Maria Wågberg, Ulrika Johansson, Barbro Eriksson and Armgard Kling is highly appreciated.

REFERENCES

1. Nedergaard M. Direct signaling from astrocytes to neurons in cultures of mammalian brain cells. Science 1994; 263:1768-1771.
2. Parpura V, Basarsky TA, Liu F et al. Glutamate-mediated astrocyte neuron signaling. Nature 1994; 369:744-747.

3. Clapham D E. Calcium signaling. Cell 1995; 80:259-268.
4. Kimelberg HK. Glial Cell Receptors. New York: Raven Press, 1988.
5. Hansson E. Metabotropic glutamate receptor activation induces astroglial swelling. J Biol Chem 1994; 269:21955-21961.
6. v Blankenfeld G, Enkvist K, Kettenmann H. Gamma-aminobutyric acid and glutamate receptors. In: Kettenmann H, Ransom BR, eds. Neuroglia. Oxford University Press, 1995:335-345.
7. Porter JT, McCarthy KD. GFAP-positive hippocampal astrocytes in situ respond to glutamatergic neuroligands with increases in $[Ca^{2+}]_i$. GLIA 1995; 13:101-112.
8. Monaghan DT, Bridges RJ, Cotman CW. The excitatory amino acid receptors: Their classes, pharmacology, and distinct properties in the function of the central nervous system. Annu Rev Pharmacol Toxicol 1989; 29:365-402.
9. Ridet JL, Rajaofetra N, Teilhac JR et al. Evidence for nonsynaptic serotenergic and noradrenergic innervation of the rat dorsal horn and possible involvement of neuron-glia interactions. Neuroscience 1993; 52:143-157.
10. Ciabarra AM, Sullivan JM, Gahn LG et al. Cloning and characterization of χ-1: A developmentally regulated member of a novel class of the ionotropic glutamate receptor family. J Neurosci 1995; 15:6498-6508.
11. McBain CJ, Mayer ML. N-Methyl-D-aspartic acid receptor structure and function. Physiol Rev 1994; 74:723-760.
12. Steinhäuser C, Gallo V. News on glutamate receptors in glial cells. Trends Neurosci 1996; 19:339-345.
13. Récasens M, Vignes M. Excitatory amino acid metabotropic receptor subtypes and calcium regulation. In: Abood LG, Lajtha A, eds. Diversity of interacting receptors. Annals of the New York Academy of Sciences. New York, 1995:418-429.
14. Seifert G, Steinhäuser C. Glial cells in the mouse hippocampus express AMPA receptors with an intermediate Ca^{2+} permeability. Eur J Neurosci 1995; 7:1872-1881.
15. Teichberg VI. Glial glutamate receptors: likely actors in brain signaling. FASEB J 1991; 5:3086-3091.
16. Farb CR, Aoki T, LeDoux JE. Differential localization of NMDA and AMPA receptor subunits in the lateral and basal nuclei of the amygdala: a light and electron microscopic study. J Comp Neurol 1995; 362:86-108.
17. Abe T, Sugihara H, Nawa H et al. Molecular characterization of a novel metabotropic glutamate receptor mGluR5 coupled to inositol phosphate/ Ca^{2+} signal transduction. J Biol Chem 1992; 267:13361-13368.
18. Pin J-P, Waeber C, Prezeau L et al. Alternative splicing generates metabotropic glutamate receptors inducing different patterns of calcium release in Xenopus oocytes. Proc Natl Acad Sci (USA) 1992; 89:10331-10335.
19. Nakanishi S. Molecular diversity of glutamate receptors and implications for brain function. Science 1992; 258:597-603.

20. Tanabe Y, Masu M, Ishii T et al. A family of metabotropic glutamate receptors. Neuron 1992; 8:169-179.

21. Tanabe Y, Nomura A, Masu M et al. Signal transduction, pharmacological properties, and expression patterns of two rat metabotropic glutamate receptors, mGluR3 and mGluR4. J Neurosci 1993; 13:1372-1378.

22. Minakami R, Katsuki F, Sugiyama H. A variant of metabotropic glutamate receptor subtype 5: An evolutionally conserved insertion with no termination codon. Biochem Biophys Res Commun 1993; 194:622-627.

23. Simoncini L, Haldeman BA, Yamagiwa T et al. Functional characterization of metabotropic glutamate subtypes. Biophys J 1993; 64:1984.

24. Okamoto N, Hori S, Akazawa C et al. Molecular characterization of a new metabotropic glutamate receptor mGluR7 coupled to inhibitory cyclic AMP signal transduction. J Biol Chem 1994; 269:1231-1236.

25. Saugstad JA, Kinzie JM, Mulvihill ER et al. Cloning and expression of a new member of the L-2-amino-4-phosphonobutyric acid-sensitive class of metabotropic glutamate receptors. Mol Pharmacol 1994; 45:367-372.

26. Pin J-P, Duvoisin R. Review: Neurotransmitter receptors I. The metabotropic receptors: structure and functions. Neuropharmacology 1995; 34: 1-26.

27. Romano C, Sesma MA, McDonald CT et al. Distribution of metabotropic glutamate receptor mGluR5 immunoreactivity in rat brain. J Comp Neurol 1995; 355:455-469.

28. Jensen AM, Chiu SY. Expression of glutamate receptor genes in white matter: Developing and adult rat optic nerve. J Neurosci 1993; 13:1664-1675.

29. Peroutka SJ. 5-hydroxytryptamine receptor subtypes: molecular, biochemical and physiological characterization. TINS 1988; 11:496-500.

30. Humphrey PPA, Hartig P, Hoyer D. A proposed new nomenclature for 5-HT receptors. TIPS 1993; 14:233-236.

31. Monsma FJ Jr, Shen Y, Ward RP et al. Cloning and expression of a novel serotonin receptor with high affinity for tricyclic psychotropic drugs. Mol Pharmacol 1993; 43:320-327.

32. Bard JA, Zgombick J, Adham N et al. Cloning of a novel human serotonin receptor (5-HT$_7$) positively linked to adenylate cyclase. J Biol Chem 1993; 268:23422-23426.

33. Hertz L, Baldwin F, Schousboe A. Serotonin receptors on astrocytes in primary cultures: Effects of methysergide and fluoxetine. Can J Physiol Pharmacol 1979; 57:223-226.

34. Pearce B, Cambray-Deakin M, Morrow C et al. Activation of muscarinic and α_1-adrenergic receptors on astrocytes results in the accumulation of inositol phosphates. J Neurochem 1985; 45:1534-1540.

35. Hansson E, Simonsson P, Alling C. 5-hydroxytryptamine stimulates the formation of inositol phosphate in astrocytes from different regions of the brain. Neuropharmacology 1987; 26:1377-1382.

36. Deecher DC, Wilcox BD, Dave V et al. Detection of 5-hydroxytryptamine$_2$ receptors by radioligand binding, northern blot analysis, and Ca^{2+} responses in rat primary astrocyte cultures. J Neurosci Res 1993; 35:246-256.

37. Hagberg G-B, Blomstrand F, Nilsson M et al. Stimulation of astroglial 5-HT$_{2A}$ receptors opens voltage-independent Ca^{2+} channels. (Submitted).

38. Hansson E, Simonsson P, Alling C. Interactions between cyclic AMP and inositol phosphate transduction systems in astrocytes in primary culture. Neuropharmacology 1990; 29:591-598.

39. Conn PJ, Sanders-Bush E. Regulation of serotonin-stimulated phosphoinositide hydrolysis: relation to the serotonin 5 HT-2 binding site. J Neurosci 1986; 6:3669-3675.

40. Lui J, Raymond J, Tamir H et al. Embryonic glial cells express 5-HT receptors and exhibit regional differences in neuronotrophic activity in response to 5-HT. Soc Neurosci Abstr 1991; 17:Pt I, p. 745.

41. Whitaker-Azmitia PM, Clarke C, Azmitia EC. Localization of 5-HT1A receptors to astroglial cells in adult rats: Implications for neuronal-glial interactions and psychoactive drug mechanism of action. Synapse 1993; 14:201-205.

42. Azmitia EC, Gannon PJ, Kheck NM et al. Cellular localization of the 5-HT$_{1A}$ receptor in primate brain neurons and glial cells. Neuropsychopharmacology 1996; 14:35-46.

43. Hirst WD, Rattray M, Price GW et al. Expression of 5-HT$_7$ receptors coupled to cAMP production in astrocyte cultures. In: Glial Contribution to Behavior. Northern Ireland: Newcastle, 1995:63.

44. Raymond JR, Hnatowich M, Lefkowitz RJ et al. Adrenergic receptors. Models for regulation of signal transduction processes. Hypertension 1990; 15:119-131.

45. Cotecchia S, Kobilka B, Daniel K et al. Multiple second messenger pathways of α-adrenergic receptor subtypes expressed in eukaryotic cells. J Biol Chem 1990; 265:63-69.

46. McCarthy KD, deVellis J. Alpha-adrenergic receptor modulation of beta-adrenergic, adenosine and prostaglandin E$_1$ increased adenosine 3'5'-monophosphate levels in primary cultures of glia. J Cycl Nucleot Res 1978; 4:15-26.

47. Hansson E. Primary cultures from defined brain areas; effects of seeding time on the development of β-adrenergic- and dopamine-stimulated cAMP-activity during cultivation. Dev Brain Res 1985; 21:187-192.

48. Van Calker D, Hamprecht B. Effects on neurohormones on glial cells. In: Federoff S, Hertz L, eds. Advances in Cellular Neurobiology, vol. 1. New York: Academic Press, 1980:31-67.

49. Murphy S, Pearce B. Functional receptors for neurotransmitters on astroglial cells. Neuroscience 1987; 22:381-394.

50. Burgess SK, McCarthy KD. Autoradiographic quantitation of β-adrenergic receptors on neural cells in primary cultures. I. Pharmacological

studies of ^{125}I pindolol binding of individual astroglial cells. Brain Res 1985; 335:1-9.

51. McCarthy KD, Salm A, Lerea LS. Astroglial receptors and their regulation of intermediate filament protein phosphorylation. In: Kimelberg HK, ed. Glial Cell Receptors. New York: Raven Press, 1988:1-22.

52. McCarthy KD. An autoradiographic analyses of beta adrenergic receptors on immunocytochemically defined astroglia. J Pharmacol Exp Ther 1983; 226:282-290.

53. Stone EA, Sessler FM, Weimin L. Glial localization of adenylate-cyclase-coupled β-adrenoceptors in rat forebrain slices. Brain Res 1990; 530:295-300.

54. Salm AK, McCarthy KD. Expression of beta-adrenergic receptors by astrocytes isolated from adult rat cortex. GLIA 1989; 2:346-352.

55. Van Calker D, Müller M, Hamprecht B. Adrenergic α- and β- receptors expressed by the same cell type in primary cultures of perinatal mouse brain. J Neurochem 1978; 30:713-718.

56. Bylund DB, U'Prichard DC. Characterization of α_1- and α_2-adrenergic receptors. Int Rev Neurobiol 1983; 24:343-397.

57. Bockaert J, Ebersolt C. α-Adrenergic receptors on glial cells. In: Kimelberg HK, ed. Glia Cell Receptors. New York: Raven Press, 1988:35-51.

58. Lerea LS, McCarthy KD. Astroglial cells in vitro are heterogeneous with respect to expression of the α_1-adrenergic receptor. GLIA 1989; 2:135-147.

59. Johnson RD, Minneman KP. α_1-Adrenergic receptors and stimulation of ^{3}H-inositol metabolism in rat brain: Regional distribution and parallel activation. Brain Res 1985; 341:7-15.

60. Kebabian JW. The cyclic AMP cascade: a signal transduction system. Neurotransmissions 1992; 2:1-4.

61. Lefkowitz RJ, Cotecchia S, Samama P et al. Constitutive activity of receptors coupled to guanine nucleotide regulatory proteins. Trends Pharmacol Sci 1993; 14:303-307.

62. Strader CD, Fong TM, Graziano MP et al. The family of G-protein-coupled receptors. FASEB J 1995; 9:745-754.

63. Berridge MJ. Inositol trisphosphate and calcium signaling. Nature 1993; 361:315-325.

64. Ashkenazi A, Peralta EG, Winslow JW et al. Functionally distinct G proteins selectively couple different receptors to PI hydrolysis in the same cell. Cell 1989; 56:487-493.

65. Simon MI, Strathmann MP, Gautam N. Diversity of G proteins in signal transduction. Science 1991; 252:802-808.

66. Berridge MJ, Irvine RF. Inositol trisphosphate, a novel second messenger in cellular signal transduction. Nature 1984; 312:315-321.

67. Berridge MJ, Irvine RF. Inositol trisphosphates and cell. Nature 1989; 341:197-205.

68. Kimura M, Lasker N, Aviv A. Thapsigargin-evoked changes in human platelet Ca^{2+}, Na^+, pH and membrane potential. J Physiol 1993; 464:1-13.
69. Thastrup O, Cullen PJ, Drobak BK et al. Thapsigargin, a tumor promoter, discharges intracellular Ca^{2+} stores by specific inhibition of the endoplasmic reticulum Ca^{2+}-ATPase. Proc Natl Acad Sci (USA) 1990; 87:2466-2470.
70. Lo T-M, Thayer SA. Refilling the inositol 1,4,5-trisphosphate-sensitive Ca^{2+} store in neuroblastoma x glioma hybrid NG108-15 cells. Am J Physiol 1993; 264:C641-C653.
71. McPherson PS, Kim Y-K, Valdivia H et al. The brain ryanodine receptor: A caffeine-sensitive calcium release channel. Neuron 1991; 7:17-25.
72. Fasolato C, Innocenti B, Pozzan T. Receptor-activated Ca^{2+} influx: how many mechanisms for how many channels. Trends Pharmacol Sci 1994; 15:77-82.
73. Putney JW Jr. Excitement about calcium signaling in inexcitable cells. Science 1993; 262:676-678.
74. Goldman WF, Yarowsky PJ, Juhaszova M et al. Sodium/calcium exchange in rat cortical astrocytes. J Neurosci 1994; 14:5834-5843.
75. Takuma K, Matsuda T, Hashimoto H et al. Cultured rat astrocytes possess Na^+-Ca^{2+} exchanger. GLIA 1994; 12:336-342.
76. Holgado A, Beaugé L. The Na^+-Ca^{2+} exchange system in rat glial cells in culture: Activation by external monovalent cations. GLIA 1995; 9:83-104.
77. Moore EDW, Etter EF, Philipson KD et al. Coupling of the Na^+/Ca^{2+}-exchanger, Na^+/K^+-pump and sarcoplasmic reticulum in smooth muscle. Nature 1993; 365:657-660.
78. Bygrave FL, Roberts HR. Regulation of cellular calcium through signaling cross-talk involves an intricate interplay between the actions of receptors, G-proteins, and second messengers. FASEB J 1995; 9:1297-1303.
79. Port JD, Malbon CC. Integration of transmembrane signaling. Crosstalk among G-protein-linked receptors and other signal transduction pathways. Trends Cardiovasc Med 1993; 3:85-92.
80. Cooper DMF, Mons N, Karpen JW. Adenylyl cyclases and the interaction between calcium and cAMP. Nature 1995; 374:421-424.
81. Abdel-Latif AA. Cross talk between cyclic AMP and the polyphosphoinositide signaling cascade in iris sphincter and other nonvascular smooth muscle. PSEBM 1996; 211:163-177.
82. Ruck A, Kendall DA, Hill SJ. α- and β-adrenoceptor regulation of cyclic AMP accumulation in cultured rat astrocytes. Biochem Pharmacol 1991; 42:59-69.
83. Marin P, Delumeau JC, Cordier J et al. Both astrocytes and neurons contribute to the potentiation mediated by α_1-adrenoceptors of the β-adrenergic-stimulated cyclic AMP production in brain. Eur J Neurosci 1990; 2:1110-2227.
84. Nilsson M, Hansson E, Rönnbäck L. Adrenergic and 5-HT_2 receptors on the same astroglial cell. A microspectrofluorimetric study on cytoso-

lic Ca²⁺ responses in single cells in primary culture. Dev Brain Res 1991; 63:33-41.

85. Stone EA, Ariano MA. Are glial cells targets of the central noradrenergic system? A review of the evidence. Brain Res Rev 1989; 14:297-309.

86. Chiono M, Mahey R, Tate G et al. Capacitative Ca²⁺ entry exclusively inhibits cAMP synthesis in C6-2B glioma cells. J Biol Chem 1995; 270:1149-1155.

87. Felder CC, Singer-Lahat D, Mathes C. Voltage-independent calcium channels. Regulation by receptors and intracellular calcium stores. Biochem Pharmacol 1994; 48:1997-2004.

88. Miller S, Bridges RJ, Cotman CW. Stimulation of phosphoinositide hydrolysis by *trans*-(±)-ACPD is greatly enhanced when astrocytes are cultured in a serum-free defined medium. Brain Res 1993; 618:175-178.

89. Hansson E, Rönnbäck L. Astrocytes in glutamate neurotransmission. FASEB J 1995; 9:343-350.

90. DeBernardi MA, Seki T, Brooker G. Inhibition of cAMP accumulation by intracellular calcium mobilization in C6-2B cells stably transfected with substance K receptor cDNA. Proc Natl Acad Sci (USA) 1991; 88:9257-9261.

91. Gilman AG. G proteins: transducers of receptor-generated signals. Annu Rev Biochem 1987; 56:615-649.

92. Birnbaumer L, Abramowitz J, Brown AM. Receptor-effector coupling by G-proteins. Biochem Biophys Acta 1990; 1031:163-224.

93. Schwartz JP, Mishler K. β-Adrenergic receptor regulation, through cyclic AMP, of nerve growth factor expression in rat cortical and cerebellar astrocytes. Cell Mol Neurobiol 1990; 10:447-457.

94. Furukawa S, Furukawa Y, Satoyoshi E et al. Regulation of nerve growth factor synthesis/secretion by catecholamine in cultured mouse astroglial cells. Biochem Biophys Res Commun 1987; 147:1048-1054.

95. Shain W, Madelian V, Martin DL et al. Activation of beta-adrenergic receptors stimulates release of an inhibitory transmitter from astrocytes. J Neurochem 1986; 46:1298-1303.

96. Bowman CL, Kimelberg HK. Pharmacological properties of the norepinephrine-induced depolarization of astrocytes in primary culture: evidence for the involvement of an alpha1-adrenergic receptor. Brain Res 1987; 423:403-407.

97. Hansson E, Eriksson P, Nilsson M. Amino acid and monoamine transport in primary astroglial cultures from defined brain regions. Neurochem Res 1985; 10:1335-1341.

98. Kimelberg HK, Katz DM. Regional differentiation in 5-hydroxytryptamine and catecholamine uptake in primary astrocyte cultures. J Neurochem 1986; 47:1647-1652.

99. Hansson E. Enzyme activities of monoamine oxidase, catechol-O-methyltransferase and γ-aminobutyric acid transaminase in primary astroglial cultures and adult rat brain from different brain regions. Neurochem Res 1984; 9:45-57.

100. Kaplan GP, Hartman BK, Creveling CR. Immunohistochemical demonstration of catechol-O-methyltransferase in mammalian brain. Brain Res 1979; 167:241-250.

101. Levitt P, Pintar JE, Breakefield XO. Immunocytochemical demonstration of monoamine oxidase B in brain astrocytes and serotonergic neurons. Proc Natl Acad Sci USA 1982; 79:6385-6389.

102. Shain W, Forman DS, Madelian V et al. Morphology of astroglial cells is controlled by beta-adrenergic receptors. J Cell Biol 1987; 105:2307-2314.

103. Cummins CJ, Lust WD; Passonneau JV. Regulation of glycogen metabolism in primary and transformed astrocytes in vitro. J Neurochem 1983; 40:128-136.

104. Sorg O, Magistretti PJ. Vasoactive intestinal peptide and noradrenaline exert long-term control on glycogen levels in astrocytes: blockade by protein synthesis inhibition. J Neurosci 1992; 12:4923-4931.

105. Dringen R, Hamprecht B. Differences in glycogen metabolism in astroglia-rich primary cultures and sorbitol-selected astroglia cultures derived from mouse brain. GLIA 1993; 8:143-140.

106. Sorg O, Magistretti PJ. Characterization of the glycogenolysis elicited by vasoactive intestinal peptide, noradrenaline and adenosine in primary cultures of mouse cerebral cortical astrocytes. Brain Res 1991; 563:227-233.

107. Passonneau JV, Crites SK. Regulation of glycogen metabolism in astrocytoma and neuroblastoma cells in culture. J Biol Chem 1976; 251:2015-2022.

108. Quach TT, Duchemin A-M, Rose C et al. [3H]Glycogenolysis in brain slices mediated by β-adrenoceptors: comparison of physiological response and [3H]dihydroalprenolol binding parameters. Neuropharmacology 1988; 27:629-635.

109. Cambray- Deakin M, Pearce B, Morrow C et al. Effects of neurotransmitters on astrocyte glycogen stores in vitro. J Neurochem 1988; 51:1852-1857.

110. Subbarao KV, Hertz L. Effect of adrenergic agonists on glycogenolysis in primary cultures of astrocytes. Brain Res 1990; 536:220-226.

111. Walz W, Schule WR. Ionic mechanism of a hyperpolarizing 5-hydroxytryptamine effect on leech neuropile glial cells. Brain Res 1982; 250:11-121.

112. Ogura A, Amano T. Serotonin-receptor coupled with membrane electrogenesis in a rat glioma clone. Brain Res 1984; 297:387-391.

113. Hösli L, Hösli E, Baggi M et al. Action of dopamine and serotonin on the membrane potential of cultured astrocytes. Expl Brain Res 1987; 65:482-485.

114. Whitaker-Azmitia PM. Astroglial serotonin receptors. In: Kimelberg HK, ed. Glial Cell Receptors. New York: Raven Press, 1988:107-120.

115. Bartrup JT, Newberry NR. 5-HT$_{2A}$ receptor-mediated outward current in C6 glioma cells is mimicked by intracellular IP$_3$ release. NeuroReport 1994; 5:1245-1248.

116. Newman EA, Frambach DA, Odette LL. Control of extracellular potassium levels by retinal glial cell K$^+$ siphoning. Science 1984; 225:1174-1175.

117. Walz W. Role of glial cells in the regulation of the brain ion microenvironment. Prog Neurobiol 1989; 33:309-333.

118. Mac Vicar BA, Tse FW. Norepinephrine and cyclic adenosine 3':5'-cyclic monophosphate enhance a nifedipine-sensitive calcium current in cultured astrocytes. GLIA 1988; 1:359-365.

119. Knaus H-G, Eberhart A, Glossmann H et al. Pharmacology and structure of high conductance calcium-activated potassium channels. Cell Sign 1994; 6:861-870.

120. Murphy D. Neuropsychiatric disorders and the multiple human brain serotonin receptor subtypes and subsystems. Neuropsychopharmacology 1990; 3:457-464.

121. Jacobs BL, Azmitia EC. Structure and function of the brain serotonin system. Physiol Rev 1992; 72:165-229.

122. Peroutka SJ. 5-hydroxytryptamine receptors. J Neurochem 1993; 60:408-416.

123. Aston-Jones G, Akaoka H, Charléty P et al. Serotonin selectivity attenuates glutamate—evoked activation of noradrenergic locus coeruleus neurons. J Neurosci 1991; 11:760-769.

124. Soghomonian JJ, Beaudet A, Descarriers L. In: Osborne NN, Hammon M, eds. Neuronal Serotonin. Wiley, 1988:57-92.

125. Christenson J, Wallén P, Brodin L et al. 5-HT systems in a lower vertebrate model: ultrastructure, distribution and synaptic and cellular mechanisms. In: Fuxe K, Agnati LF, eds. Volume Transmission in the Brain: Novel Mechanisms for Neural Transmission. New York: Raven Press, 1991:159-170.

126. Grant SJ, Aston-Jones G, Redmond Jr E. Responses of primate locus coeruleus neurons to simple and complex sensory stimuli. Brain Res Bull 1988; 21:401-410.

127. Pentreath VW, Seal LH, Morrison JH et al. Transmitter mediated regulation of energy metabolism in nervous tissue at the cellular level. Neurochem Int 1986; 9:1-10.

128. Trimmer PA, McCarthy KD. Immunocytochemically defined astroglia from fetal, newborn and young rats express β-adrenergic receptors in vitro. Dev Brain Res 1986; 27:151-165.

129. Moore RY, Bloom FE. Central catecholamine neuron systems: Anatomy and physiology of the norepinephrine and epinephrine systems. Annu Rev Neurosci 1979; 2:113-168.

130. Foote SL, Bloom FE, Aston-Jones G. Nucleus locus ceruleus new evidence of anatomical and physiological specificity. Physiol Rev 1983; 63:844-914.

131. Magistretti PJ, Sorg O, Martin J-L. Regulation of glycogen metabolism in astrocytes: Physiological, pharmacological, and pathological aspects. In: Murphy S, ed. Astrocytes, Phramacology and Function. New York: Academic Press, 1993:243-265.

132. Magistretti PJ, Morrison JH, Shoemaker WJ et al. Vasoactive intestinal polypeptide induces glycogenolysis in mouse cortical slices: a possible regulatory mechanism for the local control of energy metabolism. Proc Natl Acad Sci USA 1981; 78:6535-6539.

133. Schwartz JP. Stimulation of nerve growth factor mRNA content in C6 glioma cells by a β-adrenergic receptor and by cyclic AMP. GLIA 1988; 1:282-285.

134. Pfeiffer B, Elmer K, Roggendorf W et al. Immunohistochemical demonstration of gylcogen phosphorylase in rat brain slices. Histochemistry 1990; 94:73-80.

135. Poblete JC, Azmitia EC. Activation of glycogen phosphorylase by serotonin and 3,4-methylenedioxymethamphetamine in astroglial-rich primary cultures: involvement of the 5-HT$_{2A}$ receptor. Brain Res 1995; 680:9-15.

136. Bloom FE, Hoffer BJ, Siggins GR et al. Effect of serotonin on central neurons: microiontophoretic administration. Fed Proc 1972; 31:97-106.

137. Waterhouse BD, Woodward DJ. Interaction of norepinephrine with cerebrocortical activity evoked by stimulation of somatosensory afferent pathways in the rat. Exp Neurol 1980; 67:11-34.

138. Nicholson C, Rice ME. Diffusion of ions and transmitters in the brain cell microenvironment. In: Fuxe K, Agnati LF, eds. Volume transmission in the brain: Novel mechanisms for neural transmission. New York: Raven Press, 1991:279-294.

139. Le Prince G, Copin MC, Hardin H et al. Neuron-glia interactions: effect of serotonin on the astroglial expression of GFAP and of its encoding message. Devl Brain Res 1990; 51:295-298.

140. Done CJG; Sharp T. Biochemical evidence for the regulation of central noradrenergic activity by 5-HT$_{1A}$ and 5-HT$_2$ receptors: microdialysis studies in the awake and anaesthetized rat. Neuropharmacol 1994; 33:411-421.

141. Coffey CE, Wilkinson WE, Weiner R.D et al. Quantitative cerebral anatomy in depression. A controlled magnetic resonance imaging study. Arch Gen Psychiatry 1993; 50:7-16.

CHAPTER 4

ASTROGLIAL POTASSIUM AND CALCIUM CHANNELS: CONTRIBUTION TO BRAIN HOMEOSTASIS AND EXCITABILITY CONTROL

Michael Nilsson and Gull-Britt Hagberg

INTRODUCTION

The cell membranes in living cells constitute a bimolecular diffusion barrier that separates the interior of the cell from the extracellular environment. Macromolecular pores in these membranes constitute ion channels. These ion channels are large integral membrane glycoproteins, ranging in molecular weight from 25 kDa to 250 kDa. All channels have a central aqueous pore that spans the entire width of the membrane. Excitation and electrical signaling within the nervous system involve the flow of various ions through these channels.[1] Na^+, K^+ and Cl^- are shown to be responsible for the dominant effects under these circumstances. Owing to methodological progress in recent years, it is now possible to study ion channels responsible for the permeation of different ions. The response of the ion channel, which is called gating, is apparently a procedure which only leads to the opening or closure of a channel. The open pore has the important property of selective permeability which makes it possible for a limited class of small ions to pass the ion channel passively via their electrochemical activity gradients. From a molecular point of view, the velocity of this event is very high ($>10^6$ ions per second). This high velocity can be used for purposes of categorizing and thereby separating different ion channel mechanisms from other ion transporting systems, e.g., the Na^+-K^+ pump.[1]

The ion channels are, in principle, identical with regard to their structure. They consist of a transmembrane-spanning protein with a water-filled pore in

On Astrocytes and Glutamate Neurotransmission: New Waves in Brain Information Processing, edited by Elisabeth Hansson, Torsten Olsson and Lars Rönnbäck.

the middle. The channel has different subunits where different regions have specific functions, e.g., a gating function and a voltage-sensor function. Many channels have recently been cloned and results from those studies show that the different ion channels (voltage and ligand-gated channels) exhibit great homology within the various group.[2] However, results show that there are many groups of ion channels, which means that every single cell type may express more than fifty different channels, and the number of channel proteins in the body might be as many as a thousand. Furthermore, identical channels have different molecular structures in different tissues.[2] This indicates that the ion channels exhibit a diversity which is comparable with the diversity of the enzymes.

Astroglial cells have been shown in a number of studies to express many of the known ion channel subtypes including classes of voltage and ligand-gated channels and also mechanically induced channels. In the present chapter, a brief introduction to ion channels in general and a description of astroglial potassium and calcium channels in particular, is presented. A theory which involves astroglial ion channels in the control of the brain microenvironment is also discussed.

TECHNIQUES FOR THE STUDY OF ION CHANNELS— A BRIEF INTRODUCTION

ELECTROPHYSIOLOGY, VOLTAGE-PATCH-CLAMP

In the mid-seventies the first successful experiments relating to ion channel activity in biological membranes were performed. Using the "patch-clamp technique," it was possible to investigate the properties of ion channels in plasma membranes of different cells and later also in the membranes of cellular organelles.[3] The patch-clamp technique is based on the establishment of a tight seal between a glass registration electrode and the cell membrane.[4] The seal has a very high resistance (10-100 gigaohm) which makes it possible to prohibit leakage of ions between the cell membrane and the electrode. The technique has a very high ability to discriminate and it is routinely possible to register currents corresponding to approximately one hundred ions. This is sufficient for registration of the very small (0.5-10 pA) and transient (<10 ms) currents which are the result of single channel opening. Thus, it is possible to observe conformation changes in *one* single channel protein, which is a superior capability of discrimination. The technique originally had four different configurations for the registration of ion channel currents: cell-attached, whole-cell, inside-out and outside-out. The basis for all patch-clamp experiments is the establishment of a cell-to-electrode contact. Through this procedure the membrane is kept structurally and functionally intact, and the ion channels are consequently exposed to a normal intracellular milieu. This basic arrangement, cell-attached, thus makes it possible to study single ion channels in a cell with an intact interior. In the next step, the whole-cell configuration, it is possible to register the ion channel activity of the whole cell. This is possible because of a rupture by suction of the membrane under the registration electrode.

Through this procedure, contact with the cell interior is obtained making it possible to control the membrane potential of the cell. Further, in the inside-out configuration, a small membrane patch is removed from the cell. After the removal, the patch still adheres to the tip of the electrode and the cytoplasmic side has turned inside-out. Then it is possible to investigate the influence of cytoplasmic regulation of the ion channels. Finally, the outside-out configuration can be obtained through the removal of the electrode from the cell after the establishment of the whole-cell arrangement. As a result, a small patch is isolated with its extracellular side in the outside position. This configuration can be considered to be a microversion of the whole-cell arrangement and is especially well suited for studies of single channels activated by extracellular receptors.

FLUOROMETRY

Using highly specific fluorescent molecules it is possible to detect various kinds of ions inside single living cells.[5] Furthermore, this technique makes it possible to see where the ions are within a single cell and how they change when the cell is stimulated. At the present time fluorochromes for many ions, including K^+ and Ca^{2+}, are available. The dyes themselves are hydrophilic and do not pass the plasma membrane easily, while the acetoxymethyl ester derivatives are highly lipophilic and pass the membrane easily. Once inside the cell the esterified forms cleave to the free dye by the action of cytosolic esterases, and the active dye is trapped inside the cell. An alternative loading technique is to microinject free dye into cells using pressure injection micro-electrodes or to dialyse cells with solutions containing the dye using whole-cell patch pipettes. Once inside the cell, the binding of the dyes to specific ions causes a shift in either the excitation spectrum (e.g., the Ca^{2+}-sensitive fura-2) or emission spectrum (e.g., the Ca^{2+}-sensitive INDO-1). The determination of this shift enables calculation of the intracellular ion concentration independently of the concentration of the dye.[6] Detection of the signals can be carried out in various set-ups. For example, ratiometric analysis is easily performed by the use of photomultipliers interfaced with a suitable computer. This is a common method for studying intracellular events with high sensitivity in single cells. Other more sophisticated techniques involve video-based digital imaging and confocal microscopy. With these techniques it is possible to study ion changes both intra- and intercellularly. With the confocal technique it is also possible to detect changes in three dimensions within the cell with good discrimination potential.

Each of these techniques provides very important knowledge about ion channels and subsequent changes in intracellular ion concentrations. The new and exciting task today is to combine the techniques and thereby obtain a powerful possibility of simultaneous qualitative and quantitative analysis of cellular ion dynamics.

DIVERSITY OF GATED ION CHANNELS

Gated channels can open or close rapidly in response to different signals. Three major signals can gate ion channels: voltage (voltage-gated channels), chemical transmitters (transmitter or ligand-gated channels) and pressure or stretch (mechanically gated channels). Individual channels in these groups are usually sensitive to only one type of signal.[7] All ion channels that open and close studied to date are allosteric proteins. Each channel protein has two or more conformational states that are relatively stable. The transition of a channel between closed and open states is called gating (see introduction). Relatively little is known about gating mechanisms, other than that they involve conformational changes in channel structure. However, several specialized allosteric control mechanisms have evolved that influence the amount of time a channel spends in each of its different conformations. Some ion channels are regulated by the noncovalent binding of chemical ligands. These ligands may be neurotransmitters or hormones in the extracellular environment that bind to the extracellular side of the channel, or they may be intracellular second messengers that are activated by transmitters.[1] The second messenger may act on the inside of the channel either directly by binding to the channel, or indirectly by initiating protein phosphorylation that is mediated by protein kinases. The result will be a covalent modification of the channel. Since ion channels are integral membrane proteins, both the electric field across the membrane and its mechanical stretch can serve as allosteric modulators of the channels. Under the influence of allosteric regulators, ion channels can enter one of three functional states: closed and activatable (resting), open (active) and closed and nonactivatable (refractory). When stimulated, the different channels use separate mechanisms to produce a change in the conformation. For voltage-gated

Fig 4.1. (Opposite page) Astrocytes express various subclasses of K^+ and Ca^{2+}-channels. Characteristics of each channel are described in the text. The following abbreviations are used: VOCC: voltage-operated calcium channel, VICC: voltage-independent calcium channel, K_{IR}: Inward rectifying K^+ channel, K_D: delayed rectifier K^+ channel, K_A: transient A-type K^+ channel, K_{Ca}: calcium-activated K^+ channel. Some of the channels in the figure may be coexpressed in one single astrocyte, but it is at present not clear if many different ion channels can simultaneously be functional in one cell. See color figure in insert.

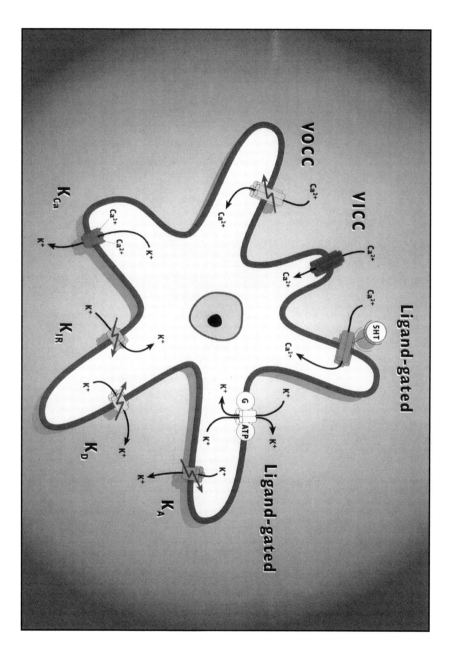

channels, such as the Na⁺-channel, the opening and closing is associated with a movement of a charged region of the channel through the electric field of the membrane. Changes in membrane voltage tend to move this charged region back and forth through the electric field, and thus drive the channel between closed and open states. For transmitter-gated channels, the change in free energy of the ligand bound to its site on the channel as compared with the ligand in solution leads to channel opening. For mechanically activated channels the energy associated with membrane stretch is thought to be transferred to the channel through the cytoskeleton. When the various channels are open, they allow channel-specific ions to pass. Ion selectivity is achieved through physical-chemical interaction between the ion and various amino acid residues that line the walls of the channel pore. From this it can be concluded that channels can be distinguished from each other on the basis of their ion selectivity and the factors that control their opening and closing.

ASTROGLIAL POTASSIUM AND CALCIUM CHANNELS

The recently discovered wealth of receptors and ion channels in the astroglial cell membrane has markedly changed the theories related to information ex-

Fig 4.2. (A) Whole-cell recordings from cortical type-1 astrocytes demonstrating K_A (transient A-type K⁺ channels) and (B) K_D (delayed rectifier K⁺ channels). Both channels are inhibited by tetraethylammonium-chloride (TEA) and 4-aminopyridine (4-AP) but astroglial A-currents are more sensitive to 4-AP than TEA.

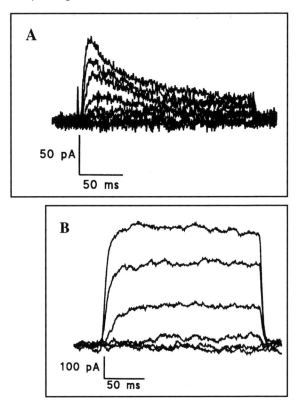

change in the brain.[8-11] Astroglial cells were previously described as "silent" cells throughout the brain, but are now known to respond in a variety of ways to both externally and internally appearing stimuli. Regarding ion channel expression, most of the ion channels found in neurons have also been confirmed for their existence in astrocytes. The different types of ion channels (voltage-, ligand- and mechanically-activated channels) have been shown to exist in the astroglial cell membrane.[9,11] Although the functional significance of the ion channels is not fully understood, a lot of data indicate important functions. For example, ion channels constitute a prerequisite for astroglial extracellular buffering, potential transmissive responses and intercellular communication. Two important and interesting classes of ion channels in this context are the potassium and calcium channels in the astrocytes (Fig. 4.1). They are expressed in different categories, have several subclasses and exhibit different characteristics.

VOLTAGE-GATED POTASSIUM CHANNELS

In comparison with neurons, astroglial cells have a more negative resting membrane potential (E_m). This results from a higher selective potassium permeability of glial cell membranes compared with neurons, and from the fact that their resting membrane potential closely follows the equilibrium potential for K^+ ions.[12,13] Numerous studies have recently demonstrated that voltage-dependent K^+ channels can be expressed in astroglial cells in vitro and in situ, most of which require transmembrane voltage changes for their activation, thereby belonging to the Shaker archetype of K^+ channels.[14-16] Using the whole-cell patch-clamp technique, it has been possible to characterize the following potassium channel phenotypes.

Delayed rectifier potassium channels (K_d)

The K_d current is present in most excitable cells and is primarily responsible for repolarization following spike discharge. In nonexcitable cells such as astrocytes, these channels have also been found.[17,18] They were the first K^+ channels described in astrocytes and have subsequently been found in all astroglial preparations studied to date.[9,11,19] Whole-cell currents mediated by K_d channels show a characteristic outward rectification with higher conductances at potentials more positive than -50 mV, and channels are largely inactive at rest or at more negative potentials (Fig. 4.2A). In astrocytes, these channels are equally inhibited by both tetraethylammoniumchloride (TEA) and 4-aminopyridine (4-AP).[18,19] Analysis of these channels in astrocytes has demonstrated a great diversity with variations in voltage-dependency, conductance (between 7 and 200 pS) and pharmacological sensitivity. It is possible that a variety of channel isoforms, each constructed of different subunits with diverse properties, contribute to the heterogeneity among the current registrations.

Transient A-type potassium channels (K_a)

A-channels are rapidly inactivating channels that mediate transient currents that require brief hyperpolarization prior to activation.[15,16] However, the resting membrane potential of glial cells is so negative (-75 to -90 mV) that it is likely that there is only little steady-state inactivation of A-type K^+ current at rest. The activation threshold is close to -40 mV. Currents exhibit a strong voltage dependence in their activation (Fig. 4.2B). A-currents are also typically superimposed on K_d currents and have to be isolated by mathematical subtraction and/or pharmacological manipulations. Astroglial A-currents are more sensitive to 4-AP than TEA.[18]

Inwardly rectifying potassium channels (K_{ir})

The most important channels for letting K^+ ions into the cell are assumed to be the inward rectifier K^+ channels (K_{ir}), through which only a minimal amount of K^+ flows outward. The conductance of this channel depends directly on the extracellular potassium concentrations and not on the relation of the extra- and intracellular concentrations.[20] K_{ir} channels are characterized by a large open probability close to and negative of the resting potential, while open probability is virtually absent at more depolarized potentials. This channel type is shown to be widely distributed in astrocytes in different model systems both in vitro and in situ.[9,15,21] As has been reported for neurons, astroglial K_{ir} channels are sensitive to external Cs^+ and Ba^{2+}, and conductance depends critically on extracellular K^+, showing increased conductances with increased $[K^+]_o$. Single-channel recordings divide glial K_{ir} channels into at least two groups with relatively small (approx. 30 pS) and intermediate to large (40-105 pS) single-channel conductances.[22,23] Astroglial K_{ir} probably plays a dominant role in setting the resting membrane potential, since it has a large open probability near the equilibrium potential for K^+. The main evidence for this is that cesium, a specific blocker of K_{ir}, virtually eliminates astroglial resting conductance in culture and in acutely isolated glia.[9] Furthermore, it has been demonstrated that K_{ir} channels are largely involved in K^+ homeostasis (see later in this chapter).

Calcium-activated potassium channels (K_{Ca})

In neurons and other nonglial cell types, two major subtypes of Ca^{2+}-activated K^+ channels (K_{Ca}) have been identified based on single-channel conductance and pharmacology.[24] The same subtypes are expressed in astrocytes from different preparations and brain areas.[15,25,26] Generally, K_{Ca} channels can be blocked by extracellular TEA but not by 4-AP.[18,25] The K_{Ca} channels are also sensitive to changes in intracellular Ca^{2+} buffering. When divided into subtypes, the maxi K_{Ca} channel (BK) is characterized by large conductance (200-300 pS) and sensitivity to charybdotoxin, whereas the mini K_{Ca} channels (SK) have conductances of only 10-14 pS and are sensitive to apamin.[24] Both classes of K_{Ca} channels have been identified in astrocytes.[18,26] However, it is not clear whether or not both channel types are expressed simultaneously in astroglial cells.

VOLTAGE-GATED CALCIUM CHANNELS

Voltage-operated Ca^{2+} channels (VOCCs) were among the first channels described in cultured astrocytes.[27] These channels are of particular importance given the ubiquitous role of intracellular calcium as a second messenger. Thus, stimuli that depolarize astrocytes sufficiently to evoke Ca^{2+} influx and concomitant increases in $[Ca^{2+}]_i$ may exert substantial influence on astroglial physiology. For example, it has been suggested that influx of Ca^{2+} via VOCCs could activate K_{Ca} and, thereby increase extracellular concentrations of K^+.[27] Activation of protein kinases in the astrocytes may also be a consequence of calcium influx through VOCCs. It is also interesting to mention the potential involvement of astroglial VOCCs in the regulation of both the uptake and release of neurotransmitters. A preceding rise in $[Ca^{2+}]_i$ has been shown to be of great importance for the neutralization of negative charges within neurotransmitter carrier complexes and this is necessary for normal function.[28] Thus, vital functions in the astrocytes may be affected by Ca^{2+} which has been allowed intracellularly through the opening of VOCCs. VOCCs are expressed widely in vitro and evidence is accumulating that such channels are normally expressed in situ.

Classification of calcium channel types

In the past few years a variety of different VOCCs have been described in a number of cell types.[29] A classification of these channels has recently been made according to electrophysiological and pharmacological criteria. It is now possible to discriminate six main categories of VOCCs, L, T, N, P, Q and R, that pass calcium ions with high selectivity. They exhibit different characteristics: (I_L) a high-threshold current that shows little inactivation and is sensitive to the dihydropyridine compounds, (I_T) a low-threshold current that is transient due to voltage-dependent inactivation and (I_N) a second high-threshold current that shows faster voltage-dependent inactivation, (I_P) a slowly inactivating, high-threshold conductance that is dihydropyridine-insensitive and is blocked by different spider and snail toxins, e.g., funnel web spider toxin and ω-Conotoxin GVIA. The recently discovered Q and R-type channels are not so well characterized. The Q-type-channel exhibits low Ca^{2+} affinity and can be blocked by ω-Agatoxin TK, while R-type currents can only be blocked by Ni^{2+}. While P, Q and R- type channels have not yet been described for astrocytes, L, T and recently, N-type currents have been observed in astrocytes in various experimental situations.[30-34] This is in line with our observations. Using patch-clamp and fluorometry, we have recently shown that rat cortical astroglial cells

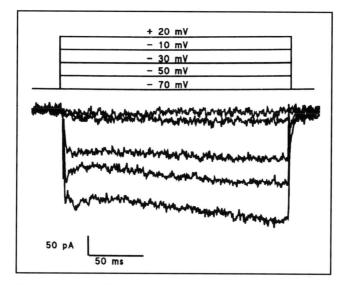

Fig 4.3. Whole-cell recording showing L-type Ca^{2+} current in a cortical type-1 astrocyte in response to depolarizing steps between -70 mV and +20 mV. Holding potential was -80 mV. This channel is inhibited by dihydropyridines such as nifedipine. A Na^+ and K^+-free and tetrodotoxin (TTX) containing bath solution was used.

in primary culture express L and N-type channels (Figs. 4.3, 4.4A,B). From the literature it is concluded that L-type calcium channels are the major channel type in cultured astroglia, because the predominant Ca^{2+} currents measured in different astroglial subtypes were high-threshold, slowly inactivating and blocked by dihydropyridines. Although the physiological relevance of these channels is questionable, L-type channel density is sufficient to both affect membrane electrophysiological properties and to significantly increase $[Ca^{2+}]_i$. Concerning the N-type channels, it is known that they are preferably localized in areas which are rich in synaptic connections.[35] It is also known that astrocytes are numerous in those areas and that a prominent astroglial function there is transmitter uptake and release. Suggestively, it is possible that Ca^{2+} influx through N-channels is necessary in the early phase of the fast transmitter uptake procedure and also for the release of transmitters via reversal of the carriers. Finally, neuronal T-type channels are suggested to be involved in the generation of pacemaker activity and excitation-response coupling, but the physiological consequences of these channels in astrocytes are less clear.

LIGAND-GATED POTASSIUM AND CALCIUM CHANNELS

Another heterogeneous group of plasma membrane ion channels are not voltage-activated. Instead these channels open in response to certain ligands,

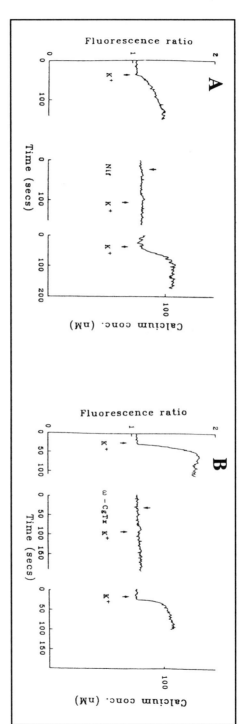

Fig 4.4. Changes in $[Ca^{2+}]_i$ as determined by the fluorescence ratio I_{340}/I_{380} were registered after depolarization with high (56 mM) K+ containing extracellular buffer. (A) The presence of L-type Ca^{2+} channels in the astrocytes were confirmed by the use of the L-channel blocker nifedipine. (B) N-type Ca^{2+} channels were also present in the astrocytes. These channels were blocked by ω-Conotoxin GVIA (ω-CgTx).

cytoplasmic agents including calcium or deformation of the plasma membrane.[36,37] For instance, K^+-channel activation by transmitters, via their G-protein coupled receptors, represents a basic mechanism of inhibitory transmission. Furthermore, the inward rectifier superfamily of K^+-channels includes ATP-sensitivity as well as G-protein coupling which means that both transmission input and metabolic status can affect these channels. In neurons, ligand-gated ion channels mediate the rapid action of neurotransmitters at the synapse. In a matter of microseconds after their release from the nerve terminal, the neurotransmitter finds the special proteins on the target cell membrane, which constitute the ion channels, binds to them and triggers a conformational change.[36] This new transient configuration of the channel creates an aqueous pathway across the membrane. Ions flow through it down their electrochemical gradients, the potential across the membrane changes and molecules of the target cell respond. The channels usually have only slight preferences among the types of ions that they allow through and so are unlike voltage-gated channels, which are strongly selective for a particular ion, and unlike gap junction channels, which are almost nonselective. For instance, the acetylcholine-, serotonin ($5-HT_3$-) and glutamate-gated ion channels at excitatory synapses create an environment that allows for the passage of cations, whereas the γ-aminobutyric acid$_A$ (GABA$_A$-) and glycine-gated ion channels, at inhibitory synapses create the same for anions.

Astroglial cells respond to a variety of neurotransmitters with changes in membrane potential.[9] Until recently, it was not clear whether any of these changes were mediated by opening of ligand-gated ion channels, or only by the activation electrogenic uptake processes and by modulation of voltage-dependent channels known to be present in astroglia. However, recent studies have demonstrated that most, if not all, astroglial cells in vitro and in vivo express one or more types of ligand-gated channels. Examples of astroglial ligand-gated channels include glutamate and GABA-gated ion channels. They are known to be present in astrocytes from various preparations in different model systems. Glutamate is shown to open ligand-gated Ca^{2+} channels, while GABA predominantly opens Cl^- channels.[38-40] In addition to neurotransmitter-gated channels, astrocytes also express many neurotransmitter receptors that activate intracellular signaling systems. For example, they mediate increase of intracellular concentrations of diacyl glycerol, inositol trisphosphate, Ca^{2+}, cAMP and cGMP which can, in turn, modulate the activity of ion channels and enzymes. Such modulation might occur at specific binding sites of different types of ion channels. However, this kind of modulation is known to preferentially involve calcium channels and especially voltage-independent calcium channels (VICCs).

Voltage-independent calcium channels (VICCs)

Results indicate that VICCs constitute a large family of proteins, with different members being expressed in excitable and nonexcitable cells, each with their own regulatory mechanisms and biological functions.[41,42] Although the classification of these channels is far from clear, it is possible to categorize some of them. First, there are second-messenger-operated calcium channels (SMOCCs), which refer to channels where the currents are unambiguously attributable to a second messenger. There are also receptor-operated calcium channels (ROCCs) which refer to channels where the receptors are integral parts of the channels. Influx via these channels occurs without the requirement of cytoplasmic messengers (see also above). Furthermore, there is evidence for channel types known as depletion-operated calcium channels or calcium-release activated channels (DOCCs or CRACs), which are sensitive to depletion of intracellular calcium stores and a simultaneous release of a "calcium-influx factor" (CIF). Finally, there are calcium channels which are sensitive to plasma membrane deformation, called stretch-activated calcium channels (SACCs).

The classification of VICCs are based on experiments performed in many cell types. Concerning astrocytes, little is known about the existence of these different calcium channel types. However, there are data supporting the presence of ROCCs and SACCs in astrocytes.[9,37] For example, glutamate analogs can open membrane calcium channels independent of voltage changes.[43] Furthermore, retinal Müller cells express calcium channels that open in response to cytosolic calcium increases[44] as well as to "stretch-activation."[45] The potential importance of these channels is unknown but involves roles in, e.g., secretion, intra/intercellular communication and cell-cycle progression.

BRAIN POTASSIUM AND CALCIUM HOMEOSTASIS—ROLE OF THE ASTROCYTES?

POTASSIUM BUFFERING

One of the essential functions of glial cells in the CNS is to buffer activity-dependent variations in $[K^+]_o$.[46-49] Neurons lose K^+ ions during activity and these accumulate in the extracellular space. The backward neuronal pumping mechanism (Na^+-K^+ ATPase) is suggested to be insufficient in preventing a build-up of extracellular K^+.[8] Therefore, astroglial cells have the important role as final determinators of $[K^+]_o$. The astrocytes can execute the task by net uptake of K^+ into the cells, by redistribution within the tissue and by "siphoning" from brain tissue into capillary blood.[50-52] For this purpose, astrocytes use different transport mechanisms including ouabain-sensitive and $[K^+]_o$-sensitive Na^+-K^+ ATPase activity,[8,53] furosemide-sensitive NaCl-KCl cotransport[8] and K^+ and Cl^- flux through voltage-gated K^+ and Cl^- channels.[9,48] The first system is an active transport system while the others work passively. The relative importance of each system is not definitely known, but they seem to be operable under different conditions. The contribution of Na^+-K^+ ATPase is greater at lower $[K^+]_o$ owing to the high sensitivity of the exchanger to relatively moderate elevations of $[K^+]_o$ (12-20 mM).[8,54] For the furosemide-sensitive NaCl-KCl cotransport the situation is the same, i.e., lower $[K^+]_o$ favors K^+ transport.[8] Furthermore, it has been proposed that simultaneous activation of both systems can occur during the "Na^+ cycle", where Na^+ influx via NaCl-KCl cotransport further increases K^+ accumulation by Na^+-K^+ exchange, as the exchanger is also sensitive to $[Na^+]_i$.[8] However, at higher $[K^+]_o$ levels, results indicate that KCl influx via K^+- and Cl^--channels is the most important uptake mechanism. At high (>50 mM) $[K^+]_o$, the K^+ uptake was to a large extent inhibited by replacing $[Cl^-]_o$ with less permanent ions or by maintaining a constant $[K^+]_o$ x $[Cl^-]_o$,[55] indicating the Cl^- dependence of the K^+ influx. Furthermore, this uptake was only slightly furosemide- and ouabain-sensitive. In this context, it should be recalled that most of the glial potassium ion channels are not activated by the degree of depolarization that would occur by the slight elevations of potassium seen during neuronal activity. The only exception is the K_{ir} channel, which is active at potentials close to the astroglial resting potential.[9,23] These channels also have increased single-channel conductance, thus letting more K^+ into the cell. Furthermore, it seems very likely that the K_{ir} channels underlies the resting potential in all glial cell types. In summary, the data speak in favor of three different K^+ homeostatic mechanisms operating in the same cell.

How Do Astroglial Cells Regulate Extracellular K^+?

An astrocyte network would appear to be especially suitable for the spatial buffering of potassium ions during neuronal activity. The concept of potassium buffering through specific ion channels was first proposed by Orkand et al[50] Potassium released by firing neurons would enter glial cells wherever the local potassium reversal potential was more positive than the resting potential of the glial cell membrane. This K^+ influx depolarizes glial cells and drives out equal amounts of current from other cell regions. This current efflux will also be conducted by K^+ because astroglial cells are principally permeable to K^+. The net efflux of this current flow is to transfer K^+ from regions where $[K^+]_o$ is lower. This process is primarily driven by a voltage gradient within a single cell, or between connected cells within a syncytium. The result is that the same amount of K^+ enters and leaves the cells. Thus, the spatial buffering mechanism does not result in an accumulation of K^+ within glial cells.

A particular kind of spatial buffering mechanism, termed potassium siphoning, has been proposed by Newman.[56] This hypothesis suggests that the site to which the elevated potassium is shunted is determined by the distribution of potassium conductance along the glial cell. As a result of this K^+ conductance localization, spatial buffering currents will be directed to specific regions of the nervous system. Instead of K^+ efflux occurring from all glial cell regions, efflux will be shunted preferentially from glial cell endfeet. This would result, at least in some tissues, e.g., retina, in a more efficient regulation of $[K^+]_o$.

Another mechanism proposed for the buffering of K^+ is K^+ accumulation.[19,57] This mechanism can operate both actively and passively (see above) and will promote local storage of K^+ within the astrocytes. The discovery that the glial resting conductance is inwardly rectifying for K^+ (driven by Donnan forces) strongly supports the possibility of local storage, since K^+ should more readily enter than leave glia.[57] A prerequisite for this mechanism is that potassium accumulation at the entry site is balanced by an anion influx, thereby neutralizing the positive charge of the potassium influx. Thus, potassium, chloride and the water that follows chloride could accumulate locally in glia near the site of the original potassium elevation. Under such conditions, low Cl^- permeability may prove to be the limiting factor in glial cell K^+ accumulation. In this respect, it is interesting to note that astroglial cell Cl^- permeability can be increased under certain conditions. Astrocyte Cl^- conductance increases as cells are depolarized.[19] This finding has led to a specific hypothesis of glial K^+ accumulation triggered by neuronal impulses that would require neuronal-to-glial signaling. According to this hypothesis, a signal substance, e.g., GABA released from neurons activates glial Cl^- channels, thus facilitating K^+ accumulation by a passive flux mechanism.[26,57] Interestingly, a functional modulation of K_{ir} has recently been found in cultured spinal cord astrocytes.[58] Here, exposure of cells to β-adrenergic receptor ligands resulted in a 50% reduction of K_{ir} currents. Thus, it is conceivable that neurons may modulate astrocytic K_{ir} channel activity and may thereby influence the ability of astroglial cells to maintain $[K^+]_o$ at suitable concentrations to support neuronal function.

As mentioned above, it is not possible at present to state definitely which of the discussed K^+ uptake mechanisms is most important for the control of $[K^+]_o$. Although there is no longer any doubt that spatial buffering does occur, it is not clear whether it is quantitatively sufficient. On the contrary, the evidence that glia buffer K^+ by accumulation in the interstitial space has become more convincing.[9,23,26,48,59] Whether this glial K^+ accumulation is in fact triggered by an impulse-mediated neuronal signal other than elevated K^+ remains to be determined.

ASTROGLIAL REGULATION OF INTERSTITIAL Ca^{2+} LEVELS?

Astroglial cells presumably take up and extrude Ca^{2+} similarly to other cell types. Data show that this uptake is influenced by fluctuating levels of various extracellular substances, e.g., neurotransmitters and various ions including Ca^{2+}

itself.[60] The uptake of Ca^{2+} also varies between different types of astrocytes.[60,61] One consequence of this may be that astrocytes in different brain regions exhibit such a function differentially. Calcium influx occurs through various types of channels (see above) under different conditions. In rat astrocytes, Ca^{2+} influx increased linearly with extracellular Ca^{2+} concentration up to 1.8 mM.[62] Extrusion of Ca^{2+} probably instead occurs through plasma membrane Na^+/Ca^{2+} exchange and ATP-dependent Ca^{2+} pumps.[61,63,64] It is shown that synaptic release of different neurotransmitters ceased when extracellular Ca^{2+} fell to approx. 0.4 mM.[65] On the basis of the astroglial ability of uptake and release of Ca^{2+}, it has been postulated that astroglial cells regulate interstitial Ca^{2+} levels and influence synaptic efficacy through neuronal Ca^{2+}-sensitive neurotransmitter release.[66] As evidence of this it has been postulated that electrical stimulation of hippocampal slices caused a drop in $[Ca^{2+}]_o$ from 2 mM to 1.4 mM.[67] Further, spreading depression (SD) induced a Ca^{2+} decrease from 2.2 mM to 0.8 mM.[68] However, no clear evidence concerning astrocytes as calcium sinkers in the interstitium exist, and many questions may be raised. One of the primary reasons for this uncertainty is the large concentration difference between $[Ca^{2+}]_i$ and $[Ca^{2+}]_o$ (nM to mM), which (according to the mM changes mentioned above) may be too much for the astrocytes to quantitatively buffer in the restricted synaptic area. However, the mechanisms underlying the interstitial Ca^{2+} shifts are far from clear. According to the above discussed mechanisms, changes in astroglial Ca^{2+} uptake can at least serve to fine-tune the $[Ca^{2+}]_o$ and may thereby strongly interfere with or activate several intracellular pathways both in surrounding neurons and in the glial network.

HYPOTHESIS ON ASTROGLIAL EXCITABILITY CONTROL

PHYSIOLOGICAL AND PATHOPHYSIOLOGICAL ASPECTS

The interposition of astroglial cells between the neurons, the geometry and the membrane properties of these cells comprise strong evidence for important roles of the astroglial cells in the homeostasis of the extracellular fluid. Failures in this normally well-controlled balance are thought to be of significance for

Fig 4.5. This figure shows a synaptic cleft with surrounding astrocytes during intense (uncontrolled) glutamatergic transmission. Suggestively, the situation may be a consequence of decreased GABA inhibition often seen in a focus of discharge. This can in turn lead to overexcitation of the postsynaptic neuron and a decreased K^+ buffer capacity of the astrocytes which will result in elevated $[K^+]_o$. The situation becomes even more complicated since astroglial cells swell as $[K^+]_o$ increases. As a consequence of glial cell expansion, the interstitial space becomes narrower and the concentrations of K^+ and other neuroactive substances such as glutamate increase. Glutamate also increases extracellularly as a consequence of the release from surrounding swelling astrocytes possibly via reversed transport through volume-sensitive anion channels. See color figure in insert.

Fig. 2.2a. Astrocytes in primary cultures derived from new-born Sprague-Dawley rats and cultivated for 10–14 days in serum containing medium. The cells are stained for the astrocyte glial fibrillary acidic protein (GFAP) and visualized with FITC-conjugated secondary antibodies (green). The total cell number are estimated by staining the nucleus with Hoechts 33258 (blue).

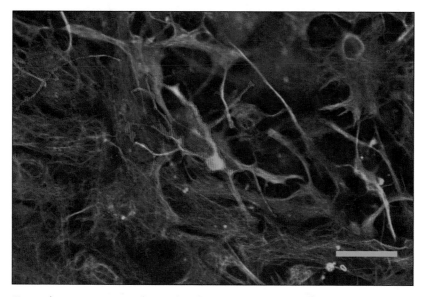

Fig. 2.2b. Astrocytes cocultivated with neurons seen after seven days in culture. The neuronal influence in these systems are seen to alter the astrocyte phenotype to a presumably more differentiated stage, with for example changed ion channel expression. The astrocytes are stained for GFAP as above and the neurons (red) are showed with antibodies against microtubule associated proteins (MAP2) and rhodamine conjugated secondary antibodies. Bar 60 μm.

Fig. 2.3. (above) Sister culture of the cells shown in Fig 2.2a, here stained to visualize a type 2 astrocyte (red). In addition these GFAP+ cells also label with A2B5, a monoclonal antibody against cell surface gangliosides. The

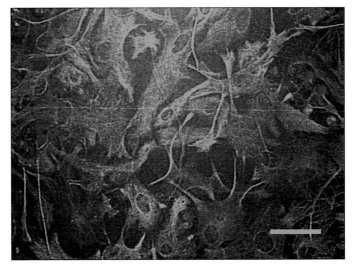

majority of cultured cells are type 1 astrocytes, only expressing GFAP (green). (Rhodamine-conjugated secondary antibodies were used against A2B5. Bars 30 µm.

Fig. 2.4a. The vibrodissociation device consists of an ordinary electric relay with a fireshaped glass electrode attached on the moving part of the relay and vibrating at 50 Hz. The vibrating glassball was positioned just

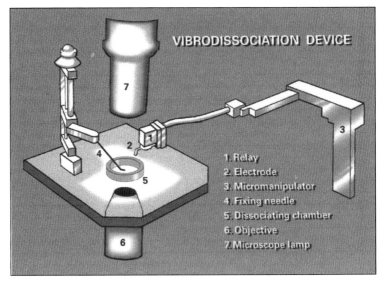

VIBRODISSOCIATION DEVICE

7

1

2

3

4

5

6

1. Relay
2. Electrode
3. Micromanipulator
4. Fixing needle
5. Dissociating chamber
6. Objective
7. Microscope lamp

above the slice and gently lowered down until it was close to the tissue but not touching it. The electrode should never come in contact with the cells and it is the hydrodynamic forces created that are dissociating the tissue. The vibratory procedure takes 15-30 sec. and during a successful dissociation there is a white cloud of cells and intercellular material sprouting out from the vibrated area. The yield can be controlled directly after each vibration period by an inverted microscope and it is possible to treat the same slice several times until a satisfactory number of cells is obtained.

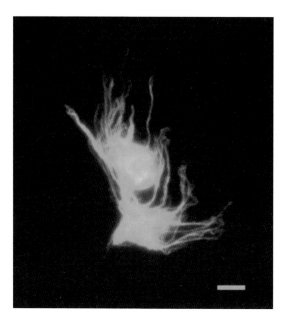

Fig. 2.4b. Acutely vibro-dissociated astrocytes positive for the astrocyte specific marker GFAP, visualized with fluor-escin conjugated IgG. None of the GFAP+ cells were positive to A2B5 or the oligodendrocytic marker GalC. Bar, 12 μm.

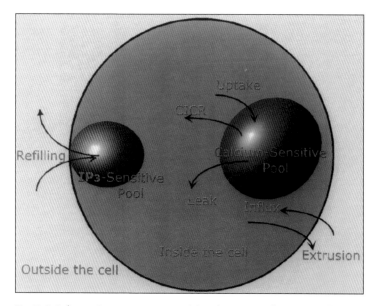

Fig. 7.6. Schematic representation of the elements in the two-pool model of Sneyd.[92] The figure shows calcium refilling of IP$_3$-sensitive pool and in- and out-fluxes of calcium to respectively from Ca^{2+}-sensitive pool.

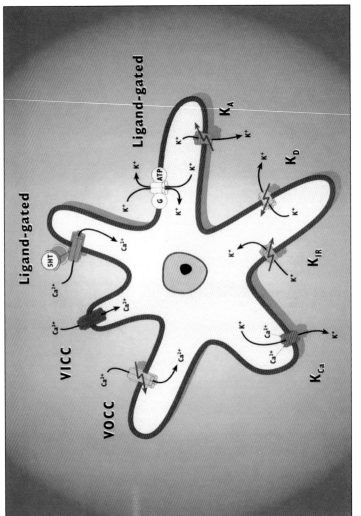

Fig 4.1. Astrocytes express various subclasses of K⁺ and Ca²⁺-channels. Characteristics of each channel are described in the text. The following abbreviations are used: VOCC: voltage-operated calcium channel, VICC: voltage-independent calcium channel, K_{IR}: Inward rectifying K⁺ channel, K_D: delayed rectifier K⁺ channel, K_A: transient A-type K⁺ channel, K_{Ca}: calcium-activated K⁺ channel. Some of the channels in the figure may be coexpressed in one single astrocyte, but it is at present not clear if many different ion channels can simultaneously be functional in one cell.

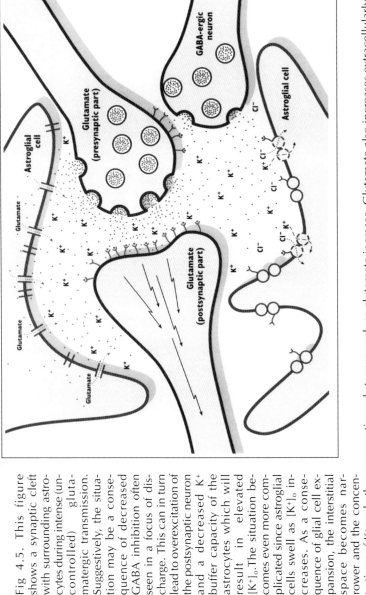

Fig 4.5. This figure shows a synaptic cleft with surrounding astrocytes during intense (un-controlled) gluta-matergic transmission. Suggestively, the situation may be a consequence of decreased GABA inhibition often seen in a focus of discharge. This can in turn lead to overexcitation of the postsynaptic neuron and a decreased K^+ buffer capacity of the astrocytes which will result in elevated $[K^+]_o$. The situation becomes even more complicated since astroglial cells swell as $[K^+]_o$ increases. As a consequence of glial cell expansion, the interstitial space becomes narrower and the concentrations of K^+ and other neuroactive substances such as glutamate increase. Glutamate also increases extracellularly as a consequence of the release from surrounding swelling astrocytes possibly via reversed transport through volume-sensitive anion channels. See color figure in insert.

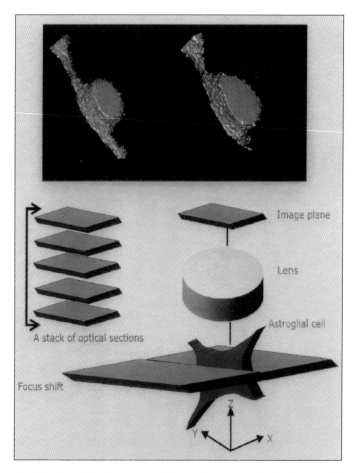

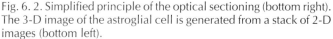

Fig. 6. 2. Simplified principle of the optical sectioning (bottom right). The 3-D image of the astroglial cell is generated from a stack of 2-D images (bottom left).
The 3-D cell reconstructions at the top represent a normal (left) and a swelling (right) astroglial cell.

Fig. 6.3. (Opposite page) Schematic drawing of the mechanisms of Glu-induced volume increase in an astrocyte. Glu interacts with metabotropic Glu receptors (mGluR) 1 and 5 (=1 in the figure), [where we have used the mGluR$_5$ agonists 1S,3R-ACPD and ibotenate (ibo)] thereby activating PLC and IP$_3$ and leading to mobilization of intracellular Ca^{2+} [Ca^{2+}]$_i$ (=2). This, in turn, induces opening of Ca^{2+} channels and opening of an outward rectifying Ca^{2+} dependent K$^+$ channel (=3).
Glu can also interact with mGluR 2,3,4,6 and 7 (=1) (where we have used the mGluR$_{4a}$ agonist L-AP4) leading to inhibition of adenylate cyclase and decreased cAMP production. This inhibition of cAMP formation could lead to opening of L-

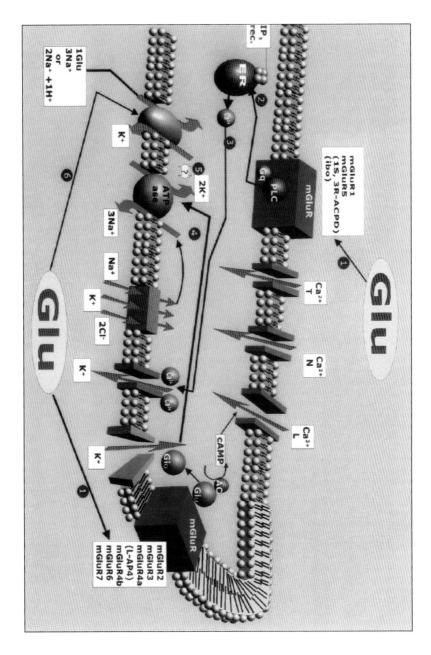

Ca²⁺ channels and, furthermore, through activation of a G protein (G_{iα}), to an opening of an inward rectifying K⁺ channel. There is also activation of the Na⁺-K⁺-2Cl⁻ cotransporter, which seems to be activated by the outward rectifying K⁺ channel complex. Na⁺-K⁺ ATPase is activated according to the figure (=4) as is also the Na⁺-dependent Glu carrier (=5), and Glu is taken up into the cell (=6).

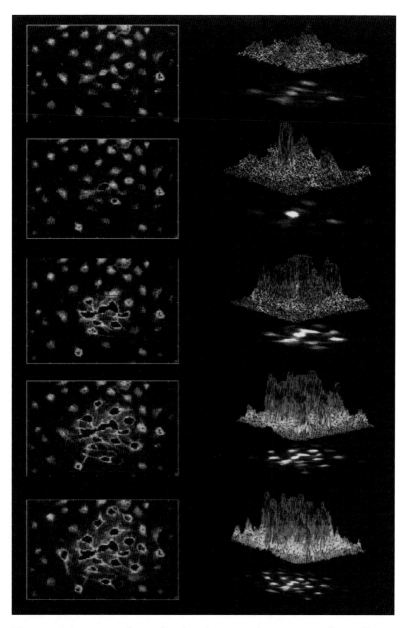

Fig. 7.3. A sequence of pseudocolored images showing a mechanically induced calcium wave in cultured astroglial cells. Time delay between each
image was 1.5 seconds. Red color corresponds to high intracellular calcium.
On the right are 3-D relief pictures of the intensity changes within the red
boxes on left pictures.

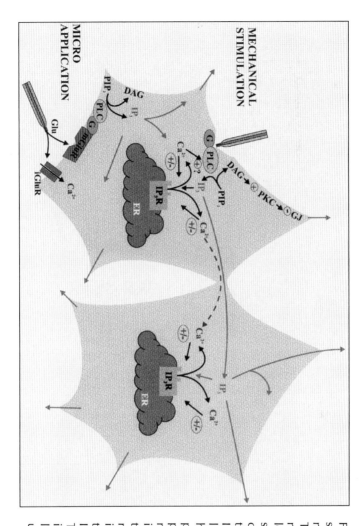

Fig. 7.4.A schematic model of a possible mechanism for the propagation of
mechanically induced calcium waves.
The mechanical deformation of the cell
membrane is thought to activate PLC
leading to an IP₃ production and a subsequent Ca²⁺ release from IP₃-sensitive
calcium stores. Ca²⁺ then diffuses
throughout the cell and can influence
IP₃R sensitivity, where an activation can
lead to CICR. However, calcium is
highly buffered in the cytosol and its
propagation to neighboring cells is
probably not very efficient. Instead the
most probable intercellular messenger
is IP₃, which diffuses through gap junctions and stimulates Ca²⁺ release in the
neighboring cells. It is not fully known
if any regeneration of IP₃ occurs along
the wave path or if all the propagating
IP₃ is derived from the stimulated cell.
The mechanisms of glutamate-induced
intercellular calcium waves upon stimulation of a single cell is to a large extent
unknown.

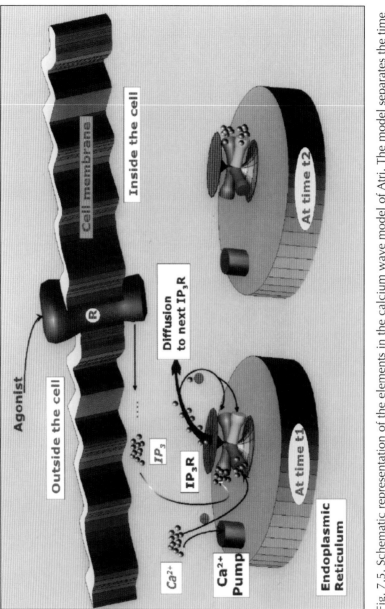

Fig. 7.5. Schematic representation of the elements in the calcium wave model of Atri. The model separates the time scales of channel activation (t1) and inactivation (t2).

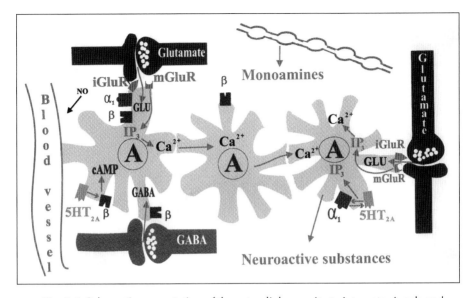

Fig. 8.4. Schematic presentation of the astroglial capacity to integrate signals and information from synapses, from the blood serum composition and from the extracellular milieu within the astroglial syncytium. The figure shows three astrocytes (=A) sharing gap junctions and forming part of a network. Astrocytic processes extend toward Glu-ergic and GABA-ergic synapses and toward a blood vessel. The astrocytes possess ionotropic and metabotropic Glu receptors (iGluRs and mGluRs) and membrane receptors for monoamines. Such substances modulate energy metabolism, ion channels, membrane properties, second messengers and amino acid uptake carriers. Interactions between the second messengers cAMP/adenylate cyclase and inositolphosphate (IP) are indicated. Glial Glu and GABA uptake carriers are shown. The arrangement with astroglial membranes encapsulating the Glu synapse makes it probable that Glu signaling induces the IP_3 formation and an intracellular Ca^{2+} release. Ca^{2+} transients are formed and propagate as waves or oscillations from cell to cell via the gap junctions. This Ca^{2+} signaling in the astroglial network might serve among others to open Ca^{2+}-activated K^+ channels, thus inducing an immediate hyperpolarization of the astroglial membrane, but, if the signaling is persistent for some time, there will be a depolarization of the astroglial syncytium and also a decreased Glu uptake capacity.

The figure also indicates the formation of nitric oxide (NO) after Glu stimulation and the probable astroglial interaction with the microcirculation, owing to the demands of neuronal activity (see text). Furthermore, the probable astroglial synthesis and release of neuroactive substances (S100, NGF, etc.) due to neuronal activity is presented.

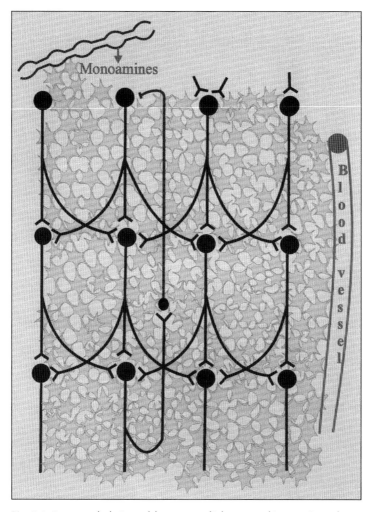

Fig. 8.6. An extended view of those astroglial-neuronal interactions shown in Figure 8.4. The astroglial network forms the background. Glu-ergic neurons (large cell bodies) and an inhibitory neuron (small cell body) is shown. Monoamine varicosities and a blood vessel are demonstrated. With this anatomical sketch and with the properties and functions of the astroglia presented in this chapter and in this book, it can be imagined that the astroglial network, by its capacity to monitor its environment and to integrate the information obtained, can modulate the neuronal excitability level in many neuronal systems simultaneously. The astroglia are probably active partners of the neurons and should be considered an active component in the neuronal circuits.

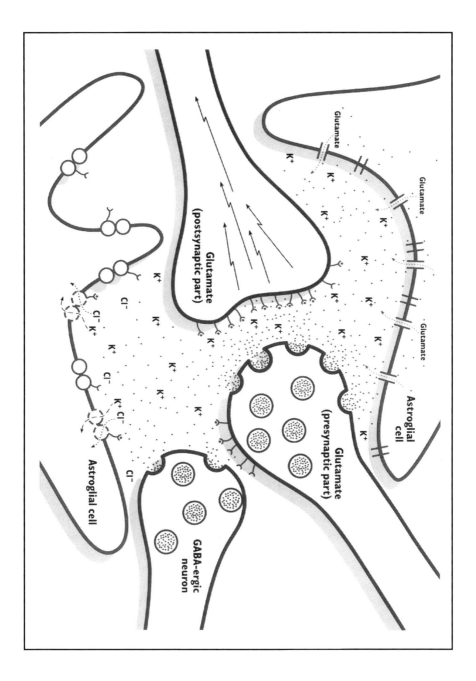

the defective excitation control that is seen within defined brain foci under certain pathological conditions such as ischemia and epilepsy. This applies particularly to malfunction of the K^+ buffering capacity of astroglial cells. Potassium is extruded from the neurons following depolarization. Persistent high K^+ levels extracellularly make the neurons hyperexcitable, which is probably the consequence of a decreased astroglial buffering capacity. It is suggested that this, in combination with the decreased neuronal inhibition of, for example, GABA which is seen in areas afflicted with deficient excitation control, can severely contribute to the ongoing processes within a focus of discharge.

The evidence that astroglia buffer K^+ by accumulation in the interstitial space has become increasingly convincing. The spatial buffering and K^+ accumulation hypotheses entail different predictions, and in most cases where these have been tested, results indicate that glial cells accumulate K^+ during neuronal activity. As mentioned earlier, this glial K^+ accumulation might be due to elevated extracellular K^+ concentration and/or impulse-mediated neuronal signaling. The central prediction of an impulse-triggered K^+ accumulation mechanism is that an extracellular K^+ elevation will not be rapidly cleared in the absence of impulse activity. This leads to speculation about whether synaptically released neurotransmitters could activate transmitter receptors on astroglial cells. Such an intercellular communication pathway might then be central in the activation of an impulse-triggered K^+ accumulation mechanism in the astrocytes. For instance, low Cl^- permeability is supposed to be a K^+ uptake limiting step. Normally, glial cells possess large-conductance Cl^- channels which are inactivated under resting conditions.[26] When a depolarizing input (increase in neuronal activity) reaches the astrocyte Cl^- influx increases. Then, under normal conditions, the astrocyte responds with an increased K^+, Cl^- and water uptake and subsequently, a repolarizing phase with a slow release of the ions and water back to the extracellular space and further on into the neurons. Interestingly, GABA is known to depolarize astroglial cells.[40,69] Astrocytes also possess Cl^- permeable $GABA_A$ receptors.[40,70] It may be concluded that GABA is a strong candidate for serving in a K^+ buffering cooperative astroglial-neuronal link. However, in a focus of discharge, GABA levels are shown to be decreased compared with the normal situation. This leads, in turn, to a less efficient opening of astroglial Cl^- channels and may cause a subsequent rise in $[K^+]_o$. In the neurons, this reduces the K^+ driving force and then leads to a decrease in the amplitude of slow $GABA_B$ inhibitory postsynaptic potentials (IPSPs).[71] The situation becomes even more complicated since astroglial cells swell when $[K^+]_o$ increases.[72] As a consequence of glial cell expansion, the interstitial space becomes narrower and the concentrations of K^+ and other neuroactive substances such as glutamate increase. Glutamate also increases extracellularly as a consequence of the release from surrounding swelling astrocytes possibly via reversed transport through volume-sensitive anion channels (Fig. 4.5).[73] This process can be ongoing until a seizure finally occurs, or the reperfusion phase starts after an ischemic event.

This hypothesis indicates the astroglial cell population is an integral part of the signaling processes in the brain. The astrocytes may also have both regulative and integrative functions during normal neurotransmission. Failure in the normally well-controlled balance between glia and neurons may underlie or complicate many pathological conditions in the brain.

ACKNOWLEDGMENTS

The authors would like to acknowledge the technical skill of Ulrika Johansson and the financial support of the following foundations : The Swedish Medical Research Council (project No 12X-06812), Axel Linders Stiftelse (Gunnar Engström's Foundation), Swedish Medical Society and Gothenburg Medical Society. The authors also want to thank Yngve Nygren for the design and production of the images included in this chapter.

REFERENCES

1. Hille B. Ion channels of excitable membranes. Sunderland: Sinauer Ass Inc, 1992:1-607.
2. Betz H. Homology and analogy in transmembrane channel design: lessons from synaptic membrane proteins. Biochemistry 1990; 29:3591-3599.
3. Neher E, Sakmann B. Single-channel currents recorded from membrane of denervated frog muscle fibers. Nature 1976; 260:799-802.
4. Hamill OP, Marty A, Neher E et al. Improved patch clamp techniques for high-resolution current recording from cells and cell free membrane patches. Pflügers Arch 1981; 391:85-100.
5. Haugland R. Intracellular ion indicators. In: Mason WT, ed. Fluorescent and luminescent probes for biological activity. New York: Academic Press, Harcourt Brace and Company Publ, 1993:34-43.
6. Grynkiewicz G, Poenie M, Tsien RY. A new generation of Ca^{2+} indicators with greatly improved fluorescence properties. J Biol Chem 1985; 260:3440-3450.
7. Siegelbaum SA, Koester J. Ion channels. In: Kandel ER, Schwartz EH, Jessel TM, eds. Principles of neural science. Norwalk: Appleton and Lange,1991:66-79.
8. Walz W. Role of glial cells in the regulation of the brain ion microenvironment. Progr Neurobiol 1989; 33:309-333.
9. Barres BA, Chun LLY, Corey DP. Ion channels in vertebrate glia. Ann Rev Neurosci 1990; 13:441-474.

10. Ritchie JM. Voltage-gated ion channels in Schwann cells and glia. Trends Neurosci 1992; 15:345-351.

11. Sontheimer H. Voltage-dependent ion channels in glial cells. GLIA 1994; 11:156-172.

12. Ransom BR, Carlini WG. In: Fedoroff S and Vernadakis A. Orlando, eds. Astrocytes: biochemistry, physiology and pharmacology of astrocytes. New York: Academic Press, 1986:1-49.

13. Barres BA. Five electrophysiological properties of glial cells. Ann NY Acad Sci 1991; 633:248-254.

14. Barres BA, Koroshetz WJ, Swartz KJ et al. Ion channel expression by white matter glia: the type-1 astrocyte. Neuron 1990; 5:527-544.

15. Tse FW, Fraser DD, Duffy S et al. Voltage-activated K+-currents in acutely isolated hippocampal astrocytes. J Neurosci 1992; 12:1781-1788.

16. Sontheimer H, Waxman SG. Expression of voltage-activated ion channels by astrocytes and oligodendrocytes in the hippocampal slice. J Neurophysiol 1993; 70:1863-1873.

17. Sonnhof U, Schachner M. Single voltage dependent K+-channels in cultured astrocytes. Neurosci Lett 1986; 64:241-246.

18. Nowak L, Ascher P, Berwald-Netter Y. Ionic channels in mouse astrocytes in culture. J Neurosci 1987; 7:101-109.

19. Bevan S, Chiu SY, Gray PTA et al. The presence of voltage-gated sodium, potassium and chloride channels in rat cultured astrocytes. Proc R Soc Lond B 1985; 225:299-313.

20. Rudy B. Diversity and ubiquity of K channels. Neurosci 1988; 25:729-750.

21. Sontheimer H, Black JA, Ransom BR et al. Ion channels in spinal cord astrocytes in vitro : I. Transient expression of high levels of Na+ and K+ channels. J Neurophysiol 1992; 68:985-1000.

22. Newman EA. Inward-rectifying potassium channels in retinal glial (Müller) cells. J Neurosci 1993; 13:3333-3345.

23. Ransom CB, Sontheimer H. Biophysical and pharmacological characterization of inwardly rectifying K+ currents in rat spinal cord astrocytes. J Neurophys 1995; 73:333-346.

24. Blatz AL, Magleby KL. Calcium-activated potassium channels. Trends Neurosci 1987; 10:463-467.

25. Quandt FN, MacVicar BA. Calcium activated potassium channels in cultured astrocytes. Neuroscience 1986;19:29-41.

26. Barres BA, Chun LLY, Corey DP. Ionic channel expression by white matter glia: I. Type-2 astrocytes and oligodendrocytes. GLIA 1988; 1:10-30.

27. MacVicar BA. Voltage-dependent calcium channels in glial cells. Science 1984; 226:1345-1347.

28. Tapia R, Salazar C. Chelation of endogeneous membrane calcium inhibits γ-aminobutyric acid uptake in synaptosomes. J Neurosci Res 1989; 24:293-298.

29. Miller RJ. Multiple calcium channels and neuronal function. Science 1987; 235:46-52.
30. Barres BA, Chun LLY, Corey DP. Calcium current in cortical astrocytes: Induction by cAMP and neurotransmitters and permissive effect of serum factors. J Neurosci 1989; 9:3169-3175.
31. Corvalan V, Cole R, de Vellis J et al. Neuronal modulation of calcium activity in cultured rat astrocytes. Proc Natl Acad Sci USA 1990; 87:4345-4348.
32. Puro DG, Mano T. Modulation of calcium channels in human retinal glial cells by basic fibroblast growth factor: A possible role in retinal pathobiology. J Neurosci 1991; 11:1873-1880.
33. Eriksson PS, Nilsson M, Wågberg M et al. Kappa-opiod receptors on astrocytes stimulates L-type channels. Neurosci 1993; 54:605-614.
34. Akopian G, Kressin K, Derouiche A et al. Identified glial cells in the early postnatal mouse hippocampus display different types of Ca^{2+} currents. GLIA 1996; 17:181-194.
35. Sher E, Clementi F. ω-conotoxin-sensitive voltage-operated calcium channels in vertebrate cells. Neuroscience 1991; 42:301-307.
36. Unwin N. Neurotransmitter action: opening of ligand-gated ion channels. Neuron 1993; 10:31-41.
37. Islas L, Pasantes-Morales H, Sanchez JA. Characterization of stretch-activated ion channels in cultured astrocytes. GLIA 1993; 8:87-96.
38. Glaum SR, Holwarth JA, Miller RJ. Glutamate receptors activate Ca^{2+} mobilization and Ca^{2+} influx in astrocytes. Proc Natl Acad Sci USA 1990; 87:3454-3458.
39. Nilsson M, Hansson E, Rönnbäck L. Agonist-evoked Ca^{2+} transients in primary astroglial cultures—Modulatory effects of valproic acid. GLIA 1992; 5:201-209.
40. MacVicar BA, Tse FWY, Crichton SA et al. GABA-activated Cl^- channels in astrocytes of hippocampal slices. J Neurosci 1989; 9:3577-3583.
41. Felder CC, Singer-Lahat D, Mathes C. Voltage-independent calcium channels. Regulation by receptors and intracellular calcium stores. Biochem Pharmacol 1994; 48:1997-2004.
42. Fasolato C, Innocenti B, Pozzan T. Receptor-activated Ca^{2+} influx : how many mechanisms for how many channels? TIPS 1994; 15:77-83.
43. Müller T, Möller T, Berger T et al. Calcium entry through kainate receptors and resulting potassium channel blockade in Bergmann glial cells. Science 1992; 256:1563-1566.
44. Puro DG. A calcium-activated, calcium-permeable ion channel in human retinal glial cells: modulation by basic fibroblast growth factor. Brain Res 1991; 548:329-333.
45. Puro DG. Stretch-activated channels in human retinal Müller cells. GLIA 1991; 4:456-460.
46. Newman EA. Regulation of potassium levels by glial cells in the retina. Trends Neurosci 1985; 8:156-159.

47. Cserr HF. The neuronal microenvironment. Ann NY Acad Sci 1986; 481:1-393.
48. Ballanyi K, Grafe K, Bruggencate G. Ion activities and potassium uptake mechanisms of glial cells in guinea-pig olfactory cortex slices. J Physiol 1987; 382:159-174.
49. Largo C, Cuevas P, Somjen GG et al. The effect of depressing glial function in rat brain in situ on ion homeostasis, synaptic transmission and neuronal survival. J Neurosci 1996; 16:1219-1229.
50. Orkand RK, Nicholls JG, Kuffler SW. Effect of nerve impulses on the membrane potential of glial cells in the central nervous system of amphibia. J Neurophysiol 1966; 29:788-806.
51. Gardner-Medwin AR. A study of the mechanism by which potassium moves through brain tissue in the rat. J Physiol 1983; 335:353-374
52. Newman EA. High potassium conductance in astrocyte end-feet. Science 1986; 233:453-454.
53. Walz W, Hinks EC. Carrier-mediated KCl accumulation accompanied by water movements is involved in the control of physiological K^+ levels by astrocytes. Brain Res 1986; 343:44-51.
54. Grisar T, Frere JM, Frank G. Effect of K^+ ions on kinetic properties of the (Na^+-K^+)-ATPase of bulk isolated glial cells, perikarya and synaptosomes from rabbit brain cortex. Brain Res 1979; 165:87-103.
55. Walz W, Mukerji S. KCl movements during potassium-induced cytotoxic swelling of cultured astrocytes. Exp Neurol 1988; 99:17-29.
56. Newman EA. Regional specialization of retinal glial cell membrane. Nature 1984; 309:155-157.
57. Barres BA. New Roles for glia. J Neurosci 1991; 11:3685-3694.
58. Roy ML, Sontheimer H. β-adrenergic modulation of glial inwardly rectifying potassium channels. J Neurochem 1995; 64:1576-1584.
59. Gray PTA, Ritchie JM. A voltage-gated chloride conductance in rat cultured astrocytes. Proc R Soc Lond B 1986; 228:267-288.
60. Finkbeiner SM. Glial calcium. GLIA 1993; 9:83-104.
61. Lazarewicz JW, Kanje M, Sellström Å et al. Calcium fluxes in cultured and bulk isolated neuronal and glial cells. J Neurochem 1977; 29:495-502.
62. Walz W, Wilson DC. Calcium entry into cultured mouse astrocytes. Neurosci Lett 1986; 67:301-306.
63. Cornell-Bell AH, Finkbeiner SM. Ca^{2+} waves in astrocytes. Cell Calcium 1991; 12:185-204.
64. Kim-Lee MH, Stokes BT, Yates AJ. Reperfusion paradox: a novel mode of glial cell injury. GLIA 1992; 5:56-64.
65. Snow RW,Taylor CP, Dudek E. Electrophysiological and optical changes in slices of rat hippocampus during spreading depression. J Neurophysiol 1983; 50:561-572.
66. van den Pol AN, Finkbeiner SM, Cornell-Bell A. Calcium excitability and Oscillations in suprachiasmatic nucleus neurons and glia in vitro. J Neurosci 1992; 12:2648-2664.

67. Benninger C, Kadis J, Prince DA. Extracellular calcium and potassium changes in hippocampal slices. Brain Res 1980; 187:165-182.

68. Kraig NT, Nicholson C. Extracellular ionic variations during spreading depression. Neuroscience 1978; 3:1045-1059.

69. Bormann J, Kettenmann H. Patch-clamp study of γ-aminobutyric acid receptor Cl⁻ channels in cultured astrocytes. Proc Natl Acad Sci USA 1988; 85:9336-9340.

70. Malchow RP, Qian H, Ripps H. γ-aminobutyric acid (GABA)-induced currents of skate Müller (glial) cells are mediated by neuron-like GABA$_a$ receptors. Proc Natl Acad Sci USA 1989; 86:4326-4330.

71. Newberry NR, Nicoll RA. A bicuculline-resistant inhibitory postsynaptic potential in rat hippocampal pyramidal cells in vitro. J Physiol 1984; 348:239-254.

72. Dietzel I, Heinemann U, Lux HD. Relations between slow extracellular potentials changes, glial potassium buffering and electrolyte and cellular volume changes during neuronal hyperactivity in cat brain. GLIA 1989; 2:25-44.

73. Bausch AR, Roy G. Volume-sensitive chloride channels blocked by neuroprotective drugs in human glial cells. GLIA 1996; 18:73-77.

CHAPTER 5

GLIAL GLUTAMATE TRANSPORTERS

Peter S. Eriksson

INTRODUCTION

One of the most important and widespread neurotransmitters is the excitatory amino acid glutamate. After release from nerve terminals, glutamate diffuses and activates postsynaptic receptors. Thereafter the transmitter is taken up into nerve terminals and astroglial cells.[1] This leads to the termination of the synaptic glutamate transmission.

Molecular cloning has recently shed light on neurotransmitter transporters in the central nervous system. Two "classes" of neurotransmitter transporters have been isolated and cloned. The first family includes transporters for γ-aminobutyric acid (GABA) biogenic amines, glycine, choline, proline and taurine.[2] These transporters couple substrate influx to the cotransport of Na^+ and Cl^- ions across the plasma membrane. Glutamate transport is probably mechanistically distinct because amino acid influx is coupled to the cotransport of Na^+ and the countertransport of K^+, with no dependence on Cl^-. Thus glutamate transporters represent a separate structural class of amino acid carriers. Three distinct complementary DNAs encoding structurally related excitatory amino acid transporters have recently been cloned and sequenced. One of the transporters, termed excitatory amino acid carrier 1 (EAAC1), is thought of as generally expressed by neuronal cells including pyramidal cells of the hippocampus.[3] The other two transporters with distribution and properties more consistent with those of the glial glutamate transporters are termed glutamate aspartate transporter (GLAST) and glutamate transporter (GLT-1).[4,5,6]

The concentration of the excitatory amino acid glutamate in the synaptic cleft is regulated by high affinity sodium-dependent glutamate transporters in surrounding glial cells and in the presynaptic nerve terminals. The properties of astroglial uptake carriers for amino acid neurotransmitters have been extensively studied in terms of kinetics.[7,8,9,10,11] Kinetic studies using model systems, e.g., bulk preparations of glial cells and cultures of glial cells gave the first firm

On Astrocytes and Glutamate Neurotransmission: New Waves in Brain Information Processing, edited by Elisabeth Hansson, Torsten Olsson and Lars Rönnbäck. © 1997 R.G. Landes Company.

indications of the existence of glutamate transporter proteins (carriers). This was later confirmed with molecular cloning and subsequent expression experiments using cloned transporter proteins.

Glial cells express receptors for a large number of transmitters including glutamate and opioid receptors.[12,13,14,15,16,17,18] Astrocytes also have the capacity of buffering potassium and possibly other ions and have therefore been postulated to uphold and regulate the microenvironment around the neighboring neurons.[19,20,21,22] These properties make the astrocytes not simply passive supportive cells but rather key players necessary for adequate neurotransmission in the brain.

Pathological astroglial properties have been proposed to be a significant factor in the etiology of some disorders in the brain, e.g., epilepsy and brain edema.[23,24] Glutamate is thought of as the key mediator of excitotoxic brain damage, e.g., cerebral ischemia or hypoglycemia.[25] Furthermore, disturbed glutamate transport has been proposed to be associated with amyotrophic lateral sclerosis.[26,27] Therefore the understanding of the regulation of glial glutamate uptake is of great potential value. This knowledge may also be used in new therapeutic strategies as discussed below.

THE DISTRIBUTION OF GLIAL GLUTAMATE TRANSPORTERS

The GLT-1 transporter has been shown to be expressed at high concentrations in the hippocampus, lateral septum, cerebral cortex and striatum.[28] The GLAST transporter, on the other hand, has a different pattern of expression with the highest abundance in the molecular layer of the cerebellum and also in the olfactory bulb. Both transporter proteins are expressed throughout the brain with similar distributions in some regions, e.g., the cerebral hemispheres and the brainstem. Areas with high density of glutamate transporters are paralleled by dense glutamatergic innervation, e.g., hippocampus. The distribution of the transporter proteins is in general agreement with the distribution of mRNA for GLT-1[29]and GLAST.[4,29] The existence of at least two glial glutamate transporters is intriguing. The partially different but in several areas overlapping distribution may be related to a very delicate fine-tuning of the glutamate uptake, where the different transporters may have different kinetic properties and/or different regulatory mechanisms. The two proteins have been shown to be expressed in the same astrocyte.[28,30] This has led these authors and others to speculate about the possibility of oligomeric proteins formed by the two transporters. The possibility of oligomeric transporters suggests an even more complex regulation of glial glutamate uptake where the relative expression of GLT-1 and GLAST would provide yet another dimension in the glial regulatory arsenal, possibly involving fine-tuning not only V_{max}, the number and subsequent capacity for glutamate uptake, but also the affinity (K_m) for glutamate uptake. Coexpression of the two transporter proteins in Xenopus oocytes might provide further insight into this interesting possibility.

DEVELOPMENTAL REGULATION OF GLIAL GLUTAMATE TRANSPORTERS

Developmental studies of the mouse brain have shown that distinct differences exist between the development of GLAST and GLT-1. In mouse E-15 a pronounced expression of GLAST is seen as early as embryonic day 15 in the primordial cerebellum, as well as in well-known proliferative zones, e.g., the ventricular zone and the olfactory bulb. This is in contrast with the expression of GLT-1, which is fairly low in this embryonic stage of development.[31] Some differences are seen during early postnatal development. Particularly notable is the difference between GLT-1 expression in the cerebral cortex with much higher levels than for the GLAST.[31]

The developmental pattern in the cerebral cortex during the postnatal stage P0 is correlated with sites of proliferation, and increased levels of expression for both GLT-1 and GLAST are associated with the lateral ventricular and subventricular proliferative zones. These sites have been associated with cell proliferation, and they are also associated with cell faith determination of immature neuroblasts and glioblasts during early postnatal CNS-development.[32] Neurons and glial cells derived from the ventricular and subventricular zones are thereafter guided toward the final destination by radial glial processes.[33,34] The expression of glutamate transporter mRNAs in this highly proliferative zone suggests that the glutamate system might be involved in the regulation of gliogenesis and/or neurogenesis.

The distribution of the glial glutamate transporter mRNAs seen in the P0 hippocampus is very similar to the distribution seen in the adult animal, although a more pronounced expression of GLT-1 compared with GLAST is seen throughout the hippocampus. In the adult hippocampus the transcript of GLT-1 is expressed abundantly in the pyramidal cells especially in CA1, CA2 and CA3, the dentate gyrus, the hilus, stratum lacunosum, molecular and radiatum.

In the rat, it has been proposed that gliogenesis occurs in the subventricular zone around the lateral ventricles of the embryonic 14 mouse brain.[35,36] The expression of both transporters coincides with gliogenesis in the subventricular zone. The abundance of GLAST subsequently decreases with the completion of cell migration, which concomitantly coincides with the decrease in mitotic activity within the subventricular zone. It is therefore possible that the expression of GLAST transcript occurs preferentially in progenitor cells and in radial glial cells. N-methyl-D-aspartate (NMDA) dependent regulation of cell proliferation has been shown. Furthermore, NMDA dependent cell migration has been demonstrated in cerebellar granular cells in vitro.[37] During later stages of embryogenesis the expression of GLAST mRNA coincides with the expression of NMDA-receptor subunit mRNA.[38] It has therefore been proposed that the expression of glutamate transporters could be involved in NMDA dependent neuronal cell migration.

Another possible mechanism for glutamate transport involvement in the regulation of early cell proliferation is the finding that membrane depolarization results in decreased mitotic activity presumably attributable to increased calcium entry and the subsequent modulation of calcium sensitive cell cycle events. This phenomenon has been attributed to the activation of voltage gated ion channels.[39] Since the glutamate transporters are highly voltage sensitive, the inhibition or even reversal of glutamate uptake may play a role in the timing and synchronization of the termination of mitotic activity in the proliferative zones of developing brain.

THE ELECTROPHYSIOLOGY OF GLIAL GLUTAMATE TRANSPORT AND ITS IMPLICATIONS FOR PATHOLOGY

Studies on the electrophysiology of glial glutamate transport have suggested that three Na^+ (or two Na^+ and one H^+) ions are cotransported into the cell, and one K^+ ion is transported out of the cell for each glutamate anion transported into the cell.[40,41] This mechanism is of particular interest since it has an inherent pathological implication, should the glial membrane potential be disturbed. Establishment of a depolarized resting membrane potential could result in decreased uptake due to the increased sodium inward current[40] and due to the strong voltage dependency, there could then be decreased effectiveness of the glutamate uptake carrier toward zero uptake. The strong electrogenic dependency of the transporter could be of significance during anoxia or ischemia when the extracellular glutamate is predicted to be significantly increased (predicted to rice to 370 mM),[42] possibly exceeding the glial cell uptake capacity. Glial cells then might inhibit their own glutamate uptake systems or even reverse the carrier, owing to two synergistic mechanisms: (1) direct glutamate-receptor mediated glial depolarization, (2) the reversal of the glutamate carrier owing to an increase in extracellular potassium, recently demonstrated (Fig. 5.1).[40] Firing neurons in the vicinity (excited by glutamate) might provide extracellular potassium to depolarize the glial cells further and thereby create a circulus vitiosus leading to glial swelling which could seal off regions with disturbed glutamate metabolism, possibly saving neighboring regions but also exacerbating the situation within the perturbed area, possibly leading to excitotoxic neuronal cell death.

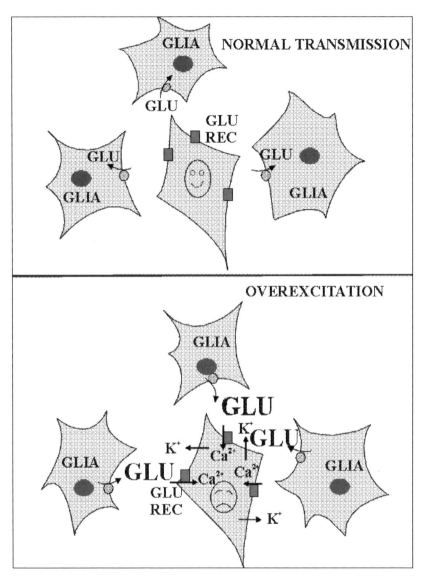

Fig. 5.1. The glial glutamate uptake systems might be inhibited owing to two synergistic mechanisms, namely glutamate-receptor mediated glial depolarization and/or reversal of the glutamate carrier by increased extracellular potassium concentration.

GLIAL GLUTAMATE TRANSPORTERS AND PATHOLOGY

Sporadic amyotrophic lateral sclerosis (ALS) was recently put forward as a disease possibly caused by defects in glutamate transport. This suggestion was originally based on the theory that impaired glutamate transport could cause neurodegeneration. In fact, pharmacological inhibition of all glutamate transporters can cause neurotoxicity,[43,44] in particular, motorneuron toxicity.[27] Studies on sporadic ALS have suggested that the functional glutamate transport is impaired.[26,45] These studies suggest that the defect in glutamate transporters is confined to neuropathologically affected regions, i.e., the motor cortex and the spinal cord. Parallel studies aimed at other neurodegenerative disorders such as Alzheimer's disease, Huntington's, or progressive muscular atrophy did not reveal similar findings, which suggests that the findings are specifically associated with ALS.[26,45] These studies could not, however, resolve the question of whether or not the defect/s were confined to neuronal or glial glutamate transport. The molecular cloning of the three glutamate transporters EAAC1[3], GLAST[4] and GLT-1[4] has facilitated the generation of specific antipeptide antibodies.[46] Additional studies using specific antipeptide antibodies have revealed that the main abnormality is the substantial loss of GLT-1 immunoreactive protein in human specimens from the cerebral motor cortex.[46] This study included both immunoblot and immunohistochemical analysis. A substantial and specific loss was seen in the motor cortex and the spinal cord in specimens from affected patients compared with age matched controls. The amount of glial fibrillary acidic protein (GFAP) was measured as a control of possible loss of astroglial cells. However, no decrease could be detected in the number of glial cells in the affected areas. On the contrary, gliosis has been described in ALS motor cortex.[46]

Furthermore, the loss of GLT-1 transporter protein has been shown to be restricted, extending from layer 2 through 5 cortex.[46] It has been speculated whether the loss of astroglial GLT-1 transporters could theoretically account for neuronal toxicity. Antisense oligonucleotide experiments have suggested that GLT-1 and GLAST are responsible for more than 80% of total glutamate transport and that loss of glial glutamate transport produces neural toxicity.[47]

An almost complete and selective loss of the astroglial GLT-1 protein, despite complete preservation of the glial population as assessed by immunoblots and histology found in sporadic ALS patients suggests that either a selective GLT-1 positive population of astroglial cells is lost or damaged or there is a selective loss of the protein from glial cells in the affected regions of the brain.[46] The loss of GLT-1 protein might be due to an anomalous receptor operated regulation of the transporter specific to the afferent agonists involved in motorneuronal activation.

One study aimed at detecting possible EAAC1 mutations in patients with sporadic ALS failed to reveal any mutations specific to patients compared with controls. The conclusion was that sporadic ALS is not caused by mutations in the coding region of the neuronal glutamate transporter.[48] It would, however, considering the findings of Rothstein and co-workers,[46] be very interesting to do mutational screening for GLT-1 in ALS patients.

RECEPTOR REGULATED GLUTAMATE UPTAKE

It has recently been shown that transmitter uptake in astrocytes is regulated by surface receptors in both a stimulatory and an inhibitory way.[49,50]

We have shown that chronic opioid administration induces specific plastic changes in the brain, which counteract the processes underlying the acute actions of these drugs.[16]

The knowledge of effects elicited upon chronic receptor agonist administration is only fragmentary. We have previously shown that long term opioid receptor stimulation induces long lasting (plastic) changes within the signal transduction components.[16] Inspired by this, we have recently initiated a study to investigate whether plastic changes could be induced within astroglial transporters in vitro. Preliminary results show that glutamate receptors on astroglial cells regulate the abundance of GLT-1 mRNA in cultured astrocytes. The results suggest that prolonged stimulation of glutamate receptors upregulates GLT-1 mRNA. This suggests that the uptake properties might be under dynamic regulation depending on the glutamatergic synaptic transmission. Increased glutamatergic transmission might therefore upregulate the glutamate uptake capacity, thereby decreasing the risk for overexcitation, self-inhibiting glutamate transport and excitotoxic neuronal damage. Receptor mediated regulation of the glial perisynaptic glutamate transporter could have potential significance for the regulation of neuronal vulnerability in pathological situations such as epilepsy, where neurons are overexcited without severe excitotoxic neuronal death.

We might speculate that a regulated uptake of glutamate is of great significance for the fine tuning of signal transduction. There are several reasons for the plausibility of dynamic regulation of the glutamate uptake. If we assume that synaptic signaling can be executed with different degrees of intensity and that one of the major determinants of synaptic signals is the amount of transmitter released from the presynaptic terminal, then there is either a constant overcapacity in the synaptic uptake systems readily available to deal with excessive presynaptic release or mechanisms that fine-tune the uptake depending on the demand for uptake capacity. If such mechanisms exist, one possibility would be that there are receptor-regulated uptake systems, possibly regulated by the same transmitter as the transported. It is also possible that other agonists, e.g., peptides with actions far from the site of release serve as "super-regulators" of synaptic traffic by this mechanism. The idea of peptides serving as slower overriding regulators far from their site of release has been suggested previously and termed "volume transmission" by Fuxe and Agnati.[51] A mechanism operated via a second transmitter could open the possibility for intervention in order to prevent synaptic overexcitation in situations with elevated levels of extracellular glutamate such as epilepsy or ischemia or even ALS, and might also be associated with induction of neuroprotection by a transient ischemic period prior to a more severe ischemic insult (ischemic conditioning).[52]

A link also seems to exist between astroglial receptors and the uptake of glutamate. This link is interesting since it suggests that the transport of glutamate can be regulated by the presence of a transmitter and therefore the glutamate transport might be within reach for pharmacological intervention.

The coming years will certainly generate more knowledge concerning the role of glia and their transporter systems. This knowledge will most certainly have a broad range of both physiological and pathophysiological implications.

ACKNOWLEDGMENTS

This paper was supported by grants from the Faculty of Medicine, Gteborg University. Göteborgs Läkaresällskap, Svenska Läkaresällskapet, Hjärnfonden, John och Brit Wennerströms stiftelse för neurologisk forskning, Edit Jacobssons Fond. The expert technical assistance of Ann-Marie Ahlborn and Armgard Kling is highly appreciated.

REFERENCES

1. Henn FA, Hamberger A. Glial cell function: Uptake of transmitter substances. Proc Natl Acad Sci USA 1971; 68:2686-2690.
2. Amara SG, Kuhar MJ. Glial transporters. Annu Rev Neurosci 1993; 16:73-93.
3. Kanai Y, Heidiger MA. Primary structure and functional characterization of a high-affinity glutamate transporter. Nature 1992; 360:467-471.
4. Storck T, Schulte S, Hoffman K et al. Structure, expression, and functional analysis of a Na⁺-dependent glutamate/aspartate transporter from rat brain. Proc Natl Acad Sci (USA) 1992; 89:10955-10959.
5. Danbolt NC, Storm-Mathisen J, Kanner BI. A [Na^{2+} + K^+]coupled L-glutamate transporter purified from rat brain is located in glial cell processes. Neuroscience 1992; 51:295-310.
6. Pines G, Danbolt NC, Bjors M et al. Cloning and expression of a rat brain L-glutamate transporter. Nature 1992; 369:464-467.
7. Henn FA, Goldstein MN, Hamberger A. Uptake of the neurotransmitter candidate glutamate by glia. Nature 1974; 249:663-664.
8. Hertz L, Schousboe A. Interactions between neurons and astrocytes in the turnover of GABA and glutamate. GABA neuro-transmission. Brain Res Bull 1980; 52:389-395.

9. Drejer I, Larsson OM, Schousboe A. Characterization of uptake and release processes for D- and L-aspartate in primary cultures of astrocytes and cerebellar granule cells. Neurochem Res 1983; 8:231-243.

10. Hansson E, Eriksson P, Nilsson M. Amino acid and monoamine transport in primary astroglial cultures from defined brain regions. Neurochem Res 1985; 10:1335-1341.

11. Kondo K, Hashimoto H, Kitanaka J-I et al. Expression of glutamate transporters in cultured glial cells. Neurosci Lett 1995; 188:140-142.

12. Murphy S, Pearce B. Functional receptors for neuro-transmitters on astroglial cells. Neuroscience 1987; 22:381-394.

13. Hansson E. Astroglia from defined brain regions as studied with primary cultures. Progr Neurobiol 1988; 30:369-397.

14. Kimelberg HK, ed. Glial Cell Receptors. New York: Raven Press, 1988.

15. McCarthy KD, Salm A, Lerea LS. Astroglial receptors and their regulation of intermediate filament protein phosphorylation. In: Kimelberg HK, ed. Glial Cell Receptors. New York: Raven Press, 1988:1-22.

16. Eriksson PS, Carlsson B, Isaksson OGP et al. Regulation of G-protein mRNA abundancy and cAMP accumulation after long-term opioid incubation in primary cultures of astroglia from the rat cerebral cortex. Mol Brain Res 1992; 16:345-352.

17. Porter JT, McCarthy KD. GFAp-positive hippocampal astrocytes in situ respond to glutamatergic neuroligands with increases in $[Ca^{2+}]_i$. Glia 1995; 13:101-112.

18. Ruzicka BB, Fox CA, Thompsson RC et al. Primary astroglial cultures derived from several rat brain regions differentially express μ, δ and κ opioid receptor mRNA. Mol Brain Res 1995; 34:207-218.

19. Walz W, Hertz L. Comparison between fluxes of potassium and of chloride in astrocytes in primary cultures. Brain Res 1983; 277:321-328.

20. Walz W, Kimelberg HK. Differences in cation transport properties of primary astrocyte cultures from mouse and rat brain. Brain Res 1985; 340:333-340.

21. Usowicz MM, Gallo V, Cull-Candy SG. Multiple conductance channels in type-2 cerebellar astrocytes activated by excitatory amino acids. Nature 1989; 339:380-383.

22. Barres BA, Chun LLY, Corey DP. Ion channels in vertebrate glia. Annu Rev Neuroscience 1990; 13:441-474.

23. Grisar T. Neuron-glia relationships in human and experimental epilepsy: A biochemical point of view. In: Delgado-Escueta AV, Ward Jr AA, Woodbury DM et al, eds. Adv Neurol. Vol 44. New York: Raven Press, 1986:1045-1073.

24. Barron KD, Dentinger MP, Kimelberg HK et al. Ultrastructural features of brain injury model in cat I. Vascular and neuroglial changes and the prevention of astroglial swelling by fluorenyl (aryloxy) alkanoic acid derivate (L644,711). Acta Neuropathol 1988; 75:295-307.

25. Choi DW. Glutamate neurotoxicity and diseases of the nervous system. Neuron 1988; 1:623-634.

26. Rothstein JD, Martin LJ, Kuncl RW. Decreased glutamate transport by the brain and spinal cord in amyotropic lateral sclerosis. New Engl J Med 1992; 326:1464-1468.

27. Rothstein JD, Jin L, Dykes-Hoberg M et al. Chronic inhibition of glutamate uptake produces a model of slow neurotoxicity. Proc Natl Acad Sci (USA) 1993; 90:6591-6595.

28. Lehre KP, Levy LM, Ottersen OP et al. Differential expression of two glial glutamate transporters in the rat brain: quantitative and immunocytochemical observations. J Neurosci 1995; 15:1835-1853.

29. Torp R, Danbolt NC, Babaie E et al. Differential expression of two glial glutamate transporters in the rat brain: an in situ hybridization study. Eur J Neurosci 1994; 6:936-942.

30. Chaudhry FA, Lehre KP, van Lookeren Campagne M et al. Glutamate transporters in glial plasma membranes: highly differentiated localizations revealed by quantitative ultrastructural immunocytochemistry. Neuron 1995; 15:711-720.

31. Sutherland ML, Delaney TA, Noebels JL. Glutamate transporter mRNA expression in proliferative zones of the developing and adult murine CNS. J Neurosci 1996; 16:2191-2207.

32. Privat A, Leblond CP. The subependymal layer and neighboring region in the brain of the young rat. J Comp Neurol 1972; 146:277-302.

33. Rakic P. Guidance of neurons migrating to the fetal monkey neocortex. Brain Res 1971; 33:471-476.

34. Rakic P. Mode of cell migration to the superficial layers of fetal monkey neocortex. J Comp Neurol 1972; 145:61-84.

35. Sturrock RR, Smart IHM. A morphological study of the mouse subependymal layer from embryonic life to old age. J Anat 1980; 130:391-415.

36. Sturrock RR. Cell division in the normal central nervous system. Adv Cell Neurobiol 1982; 3:3-33.

35, Komuro H, Rakic P. Modulation of neuronal migration by NMDA receptors. Science 1993; 260:95-97.

38. Monyer H, Burnashev N, Laurie DJ et al. Developmental and regional expression in the rat brain and functional properties of four NMDA receptors. Neuron 1994; 12:529-540.

39. Lo Turco JJ, Blanton MG, Kriegstein AR. Initial expression and endogenous activation of NMDA channels in early neocortical development. J Neurosci 1991; 11:792-799.

40. Brew H, Attwell D. Electrogenic glutamate uptake is a major carrier in the membrane of axolotl retinal glial cells. Nature 1987; 327:707-709.

41. Schwartz EA, Tachibana M. Electrophysiology of glutamate and sodium cotransport in a glial cell of the salamander retina. J Physiol 1990; 426:43-80.

42. Bouvier M, Szatkowski M, Amato A et al. The glial cell glutamate up-take carrier counterparts pH-changing anions. Nature 1992; 360:471-474.
43. McBean GJ, Roberts PJ. Neurotoxicity of glutamate and DL-threo-hydroxyaspartate in the rat striatum. J Neurochem 1985; 44:247-254.
44. Robinson MB, Djali S, Buchhalter JR. Inhibition of glutamate uptake with L-trans-pyrrolidine-2,4-dicarboxylate potentiates glutamate toxicity in primary hippocampal cultures. J Neurochem 1993; 61:2099-2103.
45. Shaw PJ, Chinnery RM, Ince PG. [³H]D-aspartate binding sites in the normal human spinal cord and changes in motor neuron disease: a quantitative autoradiographic study. Brain Res 1994; 655:195-210.
46. Rothstein JD, Van Kammen M, Levey AI et al. Selective loss of glial glutamate transporter GLT-1 in amyotrophic lateral sclerosis. Ann Neurol 1995; 38:73-84.
47. Rothstein JD, Dykes-Hoberg M, Pardo CA et al. Knockout of glutamate transporters reveals a major role for astroglial transport in excitotoxicity and clearance of glutamate. Neuron 1996; 16:675-686.
48. Meyer T, Lenk U, Kther G et al. Studies of the coding region of the neuronal glutamate transporter gene in amyotrophic lateral sclerosis. Ann Neurol 1995; 37:817-819.
49. Hansson E, Rönnbäck L. Regulation of glutamate and GABA transport by adrenoceptors in primary astroglial cell cultures. Life Sci 1989; 44:27-34.
50. Hansson E, Rönnbäck L. Receptor regulation of the glutamate, GABA and taurine high affinity uptake into the astrocytes in primary culture. Brain Res 1991; 548:215-221.
51. Fuxe K, Agnati LF, eds. Volume transmission in the brain. Novel mechanisms for neural transmission. Adv Neurosci. New York: Raven Press, 1991.
52. Nakata N, Kato H, Liu Y et al. Effects of pretreatment with sublethal ischemia on the extracellular glutamate concentrations during secondary ischemia in the gerbil hippocampus evaluated with intracerebral microdialysis. Neurosci Lett 1992; 138:86-88.

==================== CHAPTER 6 ====================

GLUTAMATE INDUCED ASTROGLIAL SWELLING

Elisabeth Hansson, Fredrik Blomstrand,
Siamak Khatibi and Torsten Olsson

INTRODUCTION

B rain cell swelling, or cytotoxic edema, is of utmost importance in pathology as it represents the first step in a series of events that can lead to destruction of the blood-brain-barrier (BBB) followed by the development of vasogenic edema and increased intracranial pressure. A destruction of the BBB makes it possible for water to pass from the blood to the extracellular (e.c.) space, resulting in the development of vasogenic edema. Generally, cell swelling occurs with no gain of water, but only with a shift of water from the e.c. to the intracellular (i.c.) spaces. As the e.c. space in the brain is comparatively small, even limited changes in cell volume can lead to dramatic changes in the e.c. volume. As long as there is an increase only in the cell volume, the intracranial pressure is not affected. In vasogenic edema,[1] on the other hand, there is a net gain of water in the CNS, with or without parallel cell swelling. The water comes from the outside of the CNS, crossing the BBB. Therefore, in vasogenic edema there is commonly an increased e.c. space.[2] As the brain is enclosed in the inflexible bone, the edema can lead to increased intracranial pressure[3] with disturbed neuronal function and, in the case of prominent edema with severely increased intracranial pressure, the results may be fatal.

ASPECTS OF ASTROGLIAL VOLUME REGULATION

Astrocytes are involved in the regulation of electrolyte concentrations and water volume in the e.c. space of the CNS.[4] The cells have a well-developed capacity to change their volume. One main reason for volume changes is to keep the osmolarity at a constant level both outside and inside the cells. Cell

On Astrocytes and Glutamate Neurotransmission: New Waves in Brain Information Processing, edited by Elisabeth Hansson, Torsten Olsson and Lars Rönnbäck.
© 1997 R.G. Landes Company.

swelling may occur both after a brain injury and under normal conditions, e.g., under intense neuronal activity[5] with changes in the composition of neuroactive substances in the e.c. milieu as a result. Initially, the cells swell at the expense of the e.c. space. The fraction of brain volume that is e.c. space amounts to between 20-27% of the total brain volume.[6,7] The consequences of cell swelling have not yet been completely elucidated. As astrocytes constitute a substantial part of the brain volume, estimated to be some 20%, changes in astroglial cell volume are important for the water re-distribution in brain.[8]

Cell swelling can be attributable to an uptake of osmoles such as Na^+, Cl^-, K^+ or glutamate (Glu) from the e.c. to the i.c. space. The function of the glial cells as a potassium buffering system suggests that excess K^+ in the e.c. space during neuronal activity is transported away from the neurons into the glial cell syncytium. Increased concentrations of external K^+ depolarizes the astrocytes and Cl^- channels are opened. K^+ enters the cells where they are depolarized. This does not necessarily lead to cell swelling. Under physiologic conditions the e.c. K^+ concentrations are controlled at 3 mM. Owing to astroglial uptake and buffering mechanisms, e.c. K^+ levels rarely exceed 12-15 mM. During pathologic events, $[K^+]_e$ increases slowly to 12-15 mM and then suddenly rises to levels of 60-80 mM.[9] During this phase glial swelling is observed,[10] and the active exchange transport of Na^+ and K^+ via Na^+-K^+-ATPase is involved. Volume-sensitive Cl^- channels might also be activated.[11]

Another important mechanism leading to swelling could be transmitter-stimulated carbonic anhydrase activities, such that H^+ and HCO_3^- are created by the hydration of CO_2 and transported out of the cells via the Na^+/H^+ and Cl^-/HCO_3^- carriers. This would lead to an accumulation of NaCl and, therefore, to a net increase in osmolarity, drawing water into the cell.[12] In fact, it seems that an intimate relationship exists between cell volume control, ion fluxes and i.c. pH.[13] Transport models for pH and CO_2 driven swelling of astrocytes have been reviewed and discussed by Kimelberg.[4]

Fig. 6.1. (Opposite page) Schematic drawing of the relation between the development of a brain injury of ischemic type and astroglial swelling. Early after the impairment of the blood flow, there is a lack of energy with a fall in ATP levels. The membrane pumps soon lose their optimal function and the membranes depolarize. E.c. [K+] and [Glu] increase. It is well known that increased [Glu]_e induces astroglial swelling at the expense of a decrease in the e.c. volume. The result is further increases in [Glu]_e and [K+]_e. Other substances, released into the e.c. space, reinforce the development of further increased astroglial volume and a collapse of the e.c. space. A vicious cycle is created including the formation of arachidonic acid, cytokines and free radicals, which are some of the substances known to participate in the development of a brain injury. All the events take place during the early minutes to the first few hours after the impairment of the blood circulation, and if nothing is done to interfere with the process, it leads to disturbed neuronal function and, ultimately, neuronal death.

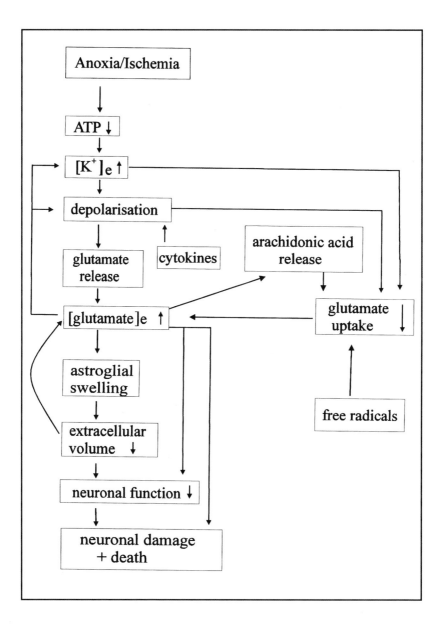

Fatty acids and free radicals can lead to swelling, presumably because they can cause a breakdown of the selective permeability of the membranes leading to a nonselective ion influx. This influx principally involves Na^+ and Cl^- because of the high e.c. concentration of these ions.[14]

The excitatory neurotransmitter Glu[15,16] is rapidly accumulated by astrocytes against its steep i.c./e.c. concentration gradient. Glu-induced cell swelling has been observed in primary astroglial cultures as well as in C6 glioma cells.[8,17] This swelling is gradual and begins immediately after incubating the cells in Glu.[8,18] Pretreatment through blocking the Na^+-K^+-ATPase by ouabain was shown to prevent Glu-induced cell swelling.[8] In addition to the interaction between Glu and its transporters, Glu also stimulates different Glu receptors of which the metabotropic Glu receptors (mGluRs) induce Ca^{2+} release from i.c. stores as well as a Ca^{2+} influx over the plasma membrane.[19,20] An increase of i.c. Ca^{2+} concentrations can lead to the opening of Ca^{2+}-dependent K^+ channels, and to a variety of other Ca^{2+}-dependent phenomena, which could have effects on the cell volume.

Calcium is, in fact, believed to play a fundamental role in cell volume regulation.[21] The swelling of most cells leads to transport changes that seem designed to give rise to shrinkage of the cells back to control levels; a process termed regulatory volume decrease (RVD).[22] The majority of cells shown to have a Ca^{2+}-dependent RVD process are cells in which osmolyte efflux occurs predominantly via K^+ and Cl^- conductances and also via amino acids such as Glu, aspartate and taurine.[23-26] Kimelberg and O'Connor suggested that astroglial swelling in hypotonic media leads to rapid membrane depolarization which opens voltage-operated Ca^{2+} channels.[27,28] E.c. Ca^{2+} enters the cells, leading to increased $[Ca^{2+}]_i$, triggering activation of Ca^{2+} dependent ion channels and the release of K^+ and Cl^- followed by osmotically obliged water, in turn leading to RVD. The time course of swelling and RVD in vitro after exposure to hypotonic medium is faster than the onset of astroglial swelling and its resolution in vivo. This slower rate of swelling is seen in astroglial primary cultures in high $[K^+]_e$ or after increasing the Glu concentration.[29] It has been suggested that calcium must enter the cell to initiate cellular volume regulation. The biological actions of Ca^{2+} can be mediated through several biochemical pathways such as production of secondary i.c. messengers, the exocytic insertion into the plasma membrane of vesicles containing ion channels, and phosphorylation or dephosphorylation of existing transporters.[21] The stretch-activated Ca^{2+} ion channels (SACs)[30] may also be involved.

GLUTAMATE AND ASTROGLIAL SWELLING IN PATHOLOGY

After a stroke or a brain trauma there is an initial energy deficiency with decreased ATP levels at the cellular level (Fig. 6.1). This decrease in the available metabolic energy could lead to reduced activity of energy-requiring ion pumps, especially the Na^+-K^+-ATPase.[10] The result is partial membrane depolarization and an increase in the e.c. K^+ concentration ($[K^+]_e$). Furthermore, membrane depolarizations lead to Glu release with increased e.c. Glu concentrations ($[Glu]_e$). Within minutes after the impairment of the blood flow in a stroke or a brain trauma there is a cellular swelling. Astroglial processes, especially those directed toward blood vessels, increase in volume followed by the cell body swelling.[4,31,32] The result will be a decrease of the volume of the e.c. space and, as this volume is comparatively small in brain, with the cell membranes of different cells being only some 200 nm apart from each other under physiologic conditions, even a slight increase in the astroglial cell volume will result in a prominent decrease of the e.c. volume with further increased $[K^+]_e$ and $[Glu]_e$ as a result. A vicious cycle arises and if the cell swelling progresses and is not inhibited, the e.c. space collapses. Later in the development of the brain injury, swelling of neuronal dendrites can be observed, but swelling of the neuronal cell soma is more limited and swelling of oligodendrocytes is hardly seen.[33] As depicted in Figure 6.1, other factors leading to the disturbed e.c. milieu are the formation of arachidonic acid and free radicals which have been shown to inhibit the astroglial Glu uptake capacity and thus further increase $[Glu]_e$.[34,35] There will be a decrease in pH.[36] Cytokines are also formed, some of which lead to astroglial depolarization[37] with a resultant further decrease in the Glu uptake capacity, acting in the same direction as the above-mentioned events, all with increased $[Glu]_e$ and $[K^+]_e$ as a result.

The described events are well characterized and occur minutes to hours after a brain injury. Later on, there is disturbance and even destruction of the BBB, and water passes from the blood to the e.c. space, leading to the development of vasogenic edema.[2]

All these events are naturally of special importance in pathology, but cell swelling might also play a functional role in normal brain physiology. It can be assumed that variations in $[Glu]_e$, $[K^+]_e$, pH and arachidonic acid concentrations to mention just a few parameters in normal brain activity can affect cell volume and thereby the volume of the e.c. space, with secondary effects on the concentration of substances therein. From the above introduction, the importance of $[Glu]_e$ in astroglial swelling is clear. It has also been demonstrated in many studies.[8,38]

Below, we present some molecular mechanisms underlying Glu-induced swelling, and we demonstrate methods that can be used to dissect these mechanisms at the cellular level. The understanding of these mechanisms is important in knowing how to treat pathological cell swelling pharmacologically. Treatment in the early development of cytotoxic edema might be one way of intervening with and diminishing the severity of the brain damage after a brain injury. However, understanding physiologic changes in cell volume with secondary effects on the e.c. space volume may also be important, as is discussed in the final part of the chapter. Might it be that astrocytes, by changing their cell volume, can affect the concentration and even the composition of neuroactive substances in the e.c. milieu? If so, then the astroglial volume regulation, in addition to its role for the osmotic balance, might be of importance for the regulation of neuronal excitability.

METHODS FOR MEASURING VARIATIONS IN CELL VOLUME

There are several methods for measuring variations in cell volume. For cells left in their normal attached state, i.c. volume can be measured using equilibration with the nonmetabolizable [^{14}C-] hexose 3-O-methyl glucose.[39-42] Two important drawbacks with this method are that large quantities of cells are needed and rapid changes in cell volume cannot be measured. Leakage of the tracer in swollen cells might be a problem. Some other methods have recently been developed to measure rapid cell volume changes.

Kimelberg and co-workers have developed two different methods of measuring cell volume of astroglial cells. The first,[43] is a 3-D technique using high voltage electron microscopy where the volumes are obtained by multiplying the area of each section by its thickness. Recently Kimelberg and co-workers described an electric resistance method to record dynamic changes in cell volume of primary astrocyte monolayer cultures.[29] When the cell volume increases, the volume of the solution within the channel available for resistive current conduction decreases by the same amount.

Kempski, Baethmann and co-workers have used a flow cytometer combined with a Coulter Counter hydrodynamic focusing technique.[44] This technique makes it possible to quantify cell volume changes of 1-2%, and has been especially useful for cells of a homogeneous cell size such as C6 cell lines, where it is also possible to have large cell numbers. A similar method has been used by Pasantes-Morales and colleagues on cultures containing cerebellar granule neurons.[45] Several important physiologic parameters such as ion concentrations, osmolarity, pH, pO$_2$ and temperature can be controlled with this method. However, the cells have to be harvested and their cellular contacts are thereby disrupted. No morphological studies can be performed after the volume measurements are finished.

Tauc and co-workers[46] demonstrated that variations in the signal emitted by the fluorescent probe 2,7-bis(carboxyethyl)-5,6-carboxyfluorescein (BCECF) when excited at its isosbestic point, were directly related to variations in i.c. volume. We have extended this method to measure relative changes in cell volume on single astroglial cells in monolayer together with i.c. transients; in our hands Ca^{2+} or H$^+$. The relative volume changes and parallel Ca^{2+} transients in

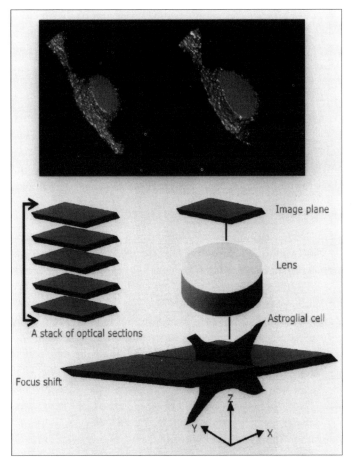

Fig. 6. 2. Simplified principle of the optical sectioning (bottom right). The 3-D image of the astroglial cell is generated from a stack of 2-D images (bottom left).
The 3-D cell reconstructions at the top represent a normal (left) and a swelling (right) astroglial cell. See color figure in insert.

single cells were examined using a microspectrofluorometric system. The cells were loaded with a highly fluorescent, intracellular probe (fura-2/AM). The fluorescence intensity was measured in a delimited zone of the cell. Upon cell swelling, the fluorescence intensity in this delimited zone decreases. The decrease in fluorescence intensity is proportional to the increase in cell volume. The isosbestic point of the probe was used consistently, where the probe is ion-insensitive and the fluorescent signals emitted are related only to the i.c. dye concentration.[18,47] By varying the excitation wavelengths, changes in i.c. Ca^{2+}

transients could be recorded simultaneously with the relative volume variations of the individual cells. We have also extended this method to examine
single cells by using a Fluoromax System. Three, instead of the standard two
excitatory wavelengths are used. Measurements of cell volume are carried out
at the isosbestic point of fura-2/AM. By switching the excitation wavelengths
between the isosbestic point and the Ca^{2+} sensitive wavelengths 340 and 380
nm, simultaneous relative volume changes and $[Ca^{2+}]_i$ can be measured.[18] One
important advantage of this method is that rapid and simultaneous changes in
cell volume and $[Ca^{2+}]_i$ can be measured on intact cells in a monolayer. One
disadvantage is that the method assumes that the cells swell in a uniform way
and that the fluorescent molecules do not redistribute during swelling. Thus, if
the cells do not increase in size uniformly, the changes in fluorescence intensity
will not be proportional to the degree of swelling for all cells.

A computerized 3-D imaging system for the quantification of cell volume is
under development in our laboratory. A series of images is produced from the
microscope by focusing up and down through the specimen. Owing to the large
depth of field in the light microscope,[48] each point of the specimen becomes a
divergent double cone (the 3-D analog of the Airy disc) which contaminates all
the collected 2-D images. Thus each image contains both in-focus information
from the focal plane and out-of-focus information from the neighboring planes
(Fig. 6.2), in the form of a blurring effect on the image. The characteristics of
an optical system can be described by its point spread function (PSF). This
function can be computed (theoretically) or estimated (experimentally). The
out-of-focus removal (deblurring) can be done by using the PSF-function and
is accomplished by traditional image analyses. Developing a suitable deblurring
method is a significant part of our work. The advantages are that 3-D images
make it possible to determine cell volume from 3 dimensions. As compared
with a commercial system, our camera system has substantial sensitivity and
the light exposure is proportionally small. Photo-bleaching and photo-damage

Fig. 6.3. (Opposite page) Schematic drawing of the mechanisms of Glu-induced
volume increase in an astrocyte. Glu interacts with metabotropic Glu receptors
(mGluR) 1 and 5 (=1 in the figure), [where we have used the $mGluR_5$ agonists
1S,3R-ACPD and ibotenate (ibo)] thereby activating PLC and IP_3 and leading to
mobilization of intracellular Ca^{2+} $[Ca^{2+}]_i$ (=2). This, in turn, induces opening of
Ca^{2+} channels and opening of an outward rectifying Ca^{2+} dependent K^+ channel
(=3).
Glu can also interact with mGluR 2,3,4,6 and 7 (=1) (where we have used the
$mGluR_{4a}$ agonist L-AP4) leading to inhibition of adenylate cyclase and decreased
cAMP production. This inhibition of cAMP formation could lead to opening of L-
Ca^{2+} channels and, furthermore, through activation of a G protein ($G_{i\alpha}$), to an
opening of an inward rectifying K^+ channel. There is also activation of the Na^+-K^+-
$2Cl^-$ cotransporter, which seems to be activated by the outward rectifying K^+
channel complex. Na^+-K^+ ATPase is activated according to the figure (=4) as is
also the Na^+-dependent Glu carrier (=5), and Glu is taken up into the cell (=6).

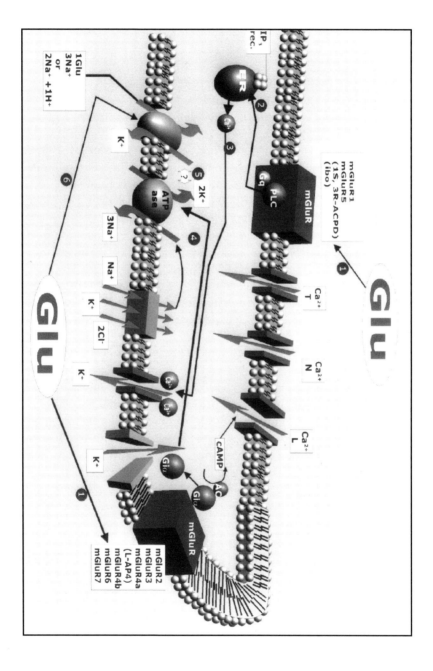

to the cells are reduced. Recording of volume changes in single cells or in several cells at the same time is possible. The disadvantages are, however, that the system requires heavy computational power and the analyses are time-consuming.

MOLECULAR MECHANISMS UNDERLYING GLUTAMATE INDUCED ASTROGLIAL SWELLING

Addition of Glu to astrocytes in cell culture or in cell suspension leads to an immediate cell volume increase,[8,17,18] under normal cultivation conditions. There is, however, at least one part of the swelling process that is reported to continue for longer time periods, up to hours.[44,49] The swelling of astrocytes by Glu is based on an active i.c. accumulation of the amino acid with maximum increases reported to be between 5-18%.[18,50,51] The mechanisms underlying Glu-induced astroglial swelling have been studied using different in vitro model systems, but are far from fully explored. When $[Glu]_e$ increases, the astrocytes accumulate Glu and the cells swell. The swelling is gradual and depends on the amount of Glu in the e.c. space. It is suggested that the astroglial swelling is caused by an osmotically driven transmembrane transport of Glu coupled to the uptake of Na^+ ions that is responsible for the volume increase.[8] The uptake of Glu occurs against a steep i.c. to e.c. concentration difference into the astrocytes, which is energy consuming, and the transport is driven by the electrochemical gradient for Na^+.[50,52] The Glu transport proceeds across the plasma membranes of neurons and glial cells via high- and low-affinity transport systems.[53-55] The net increase of i.c. osmolarity caused by the influx of Na^+ and Glu has been proposed as one mechanism responsible for glial swelling.[8] Inhibition of the Na^+-K^+-ATPase by ouabain, leading to failure of energy supply or sodium transport, prevents Glu-induced astroglial swelling. This suggests that the Na^+-K^+-pump is also involved in the process of astroglial swelling.[56] This might also be the case with the Na^+-K^+-$2Cl^-$ cotransporter, or opening of Cl^- channels.[44] Both e.c. and i.c. Ca^{2+} have been shown to influence cellular volume regulation in different cell types.[21] Actually, Ca^{2+} has been shown to be involved in Glu-induced cell swelling[29,57] as well as calmodulin.[58]

We have studied Glu-induced swelling on astroglial single cells in primary culture.[18,59] We focused on the interaction between Glu and the mGluRs, which activates phospholipase C (PLC), leading to production of inositol 1,4,5-trisphosphate (IP_3). IP_3 mobilizes calcium from the i.c. stores, which is followed by an influx of Ca^{2+} over the cell membrane. Glu was also shown to interact with those mGluRs which inhibit adenylate cyclase and decrease the cyclic AMP production. This inhibition of cyclic AMP formation could lead to an opening of L-Ca^{2+} channels and, through activation of $G_{i\alpha}$, to an opening of inward rectifying K^+ channels (Fig. 6.3). From other cell systems it is suggested that the Ca^{2+}-dependent outward rectifying K^+ channels activate as a compensatory flux of K^+ required for the Na^+-K^+-$2Cl^-$ cotransport.[60] The i.c. accumulation of Glu together with Na^+-ions raises cell osmolarity as an ultimate mechanism of swelling[8] (Fig. 6.3). When the Glu uptake carrier was blocked by dihydrokainate, dihydroaspartate or L-trans-pyrrolidine 2,4-dicarboxylic acid (PDC), the Glu-induced astroglial swelling was only partially inhibited[17] suggesting that the transporter is necessary for a part of the swelling to occur but that its activation does not fully explain the mechanisms underlying the swelling process. Thus the astroglial swelling induced by Glu is not only the result of those now-described processes, but requires another, probably some ion-channel complex for K^+ outflow and Na^+ influx. Chan and Chu[61] found that exposure of astroglial primary cultures to 1mM Glu for 4h caused swelling of the cells, which was inhibited by the noncompetitive NMDA receptor antagonist ketamine. Ketamine was used in high concentrations and it is therefore uncertain whether or not ketamine interacts with the NMDA receptor. In our photometric system we found similar effects on rapid Glu-induced cell swelling.[18] An influx of Na^+ through Glu receptor-coupled ion channels, together with the resultant Ca^{2+} influx and elevated cytosolic Cl^-, may be of importance in astrocyte swelling.[21,28]

CONCLUSIONS AND PERSPECTIVES

Astrocytes have a high capacity to regulate their own cell volume and thereby, indirectly, the volume of the e.c. space. Glu is the major excitatory transmitter in the CNS, but under pathophysiologic conditions it assumes neurotoxic properties.[62] Under physiologic conditions the brain is able to protect itself from the excitotoxic effect of Glu through the rapid uptake of e.c. Glu. During pathophysiologic events such as ischemia, head injury and spreading depression, the e.c. space may be flooded by Glu, and volume control lost.[4,6] The cells have to change their volume, as it is necessary for them to keep the osmolarity at constant levels both outside and inside the cells. The astroglial cells have a high capacity to regulate the homeostasis of ions and amino acids in the interior and exterior milieu. The ionic and amino acid concentrations in the e.c. space are regulated both by the expression of ion channels for Ca^{2+}, Na^+ and K^+ and by the expression of high affinity and high capacity uptake systems for Glu, GABA and taurine. As a single astrocyte may have contact with many neuronal synapses, and, as many astrocytes are linked by gap junctions forming a syncytium, the cells have the capacity to regulate the e.c. concentrations of neuroactive substances in many neuronal systems in parallel, at least under physiologic conditions. Thus, upon astroglial swelling, the distance between neuronal and glial membranes narrows. If we assume that an astrocyte is a sphere with processes and with a diameter of 15–20 µm, then a 10% increase in cell volume corresponds to an increase in the radius of approximately 250 nm. This leads to a state where the cell membranes of astrocytes and neurons come in close proximity of each other. Even if this degree of swelling is seen only in pathologic conditions, the calculation demonstrates how even moderate changes in astroglial cell volume within the overall glial network induce major changes in e.c. volume. Moderate cell swelling might facilitate the transport of neuroactive substances between the cells, while more prominent swelling might cause the e.c. space to collapse. On the other hand, an increase in the e.c. space with an increase in the distance between the membranes involved, might lead to decreased transmission.

With the above discussion in mind, Glu-induced rapid astroglial swelling may have both physiologic and pathophysiologic consequences. Furthermore, it may have consequences for behavior, in the sense that Glu has been implicated in mental processes such as learning and memory. From this point of view it is interesting that Glu-induced astroglial swelling can have effects on the concentrations and transport capacities of the neuroactive substances in the e.c. space with local effects on Glu transmission on the one hand, probably involved in neuronal events such as LTP, and also have implications for neuronal excitability in larger brain areas on the other hand. Our finding that the astroglial cell volume can be changed by receptor stimulation, e.g., via different mGluR:s, raises the question of whether volume changes in the astroglial network could be one physiologic mechanism for control of the e.c. fluid volume. If that is the case, the concentrations of ions and neuroactive and trophic substances in the e.c. space could be regulated in small brain areas. Or, could rapid volume changes within the astroglial syncytium, with secondary pulsating changes of the e.c. space generate transport pathways for e.c. substances? If this is the case, glial mGluR activation could induce changes in the transport and concentration of e.c. messengers. Another possibility is that astroglial swelling leads to narrowing of the astroglial cell membrane in the synaptic regions, causing a morphologically closer interaction between neurons and glia, and economization of the signaling substances.[63] In addition, this mechanism could quite simply protect synaptic regions from substances in the e.c. space.

Further studies are needed to clarify the causes of astrocytic swelling, and to explore the possibilities of therapy for preventing or attenuating this astrocytic response, which may be detrimental to neuronal survival.

ACKNOWLEDGMENTS

Supported by grants from the Swedish Medical Research Council (project no 12X-06812), the Swedish Work Environment Fund (grant no 94-0214), and the Swedish Council for Work Life Research (grant no 95-0231). The skillful technical assistance of Maria Wågberg, Ulrika Johansson, Barbro Eriksson and Armgard Kling was greatly appreciated.

REFERENCES

1. Hossman K. Cortical steady potential, impedance and excitability changes during and after total ischaemia of cat brain. Exp Neurol 1971; 32:163-175.

2. Klatzo I, Suzuki R, Orzi F et al. Pathomechanisms of ischemic brain edema. In: Go TG, Baethmann A, eds. Recent progress in the study and therapy of brain edema. New York: Plenum Press, 1984:1-10.

3. Popp AJ, Feustel PJ, Kimelberg HK. Pathophysiology of head injury. In: Wilkins RH, Rengachary SS, eds. Neurosurgery. 2nd ed. New York: McGraw-Hill, 1995.

4. Kimelberg HK. Swelling and volume control in brain astroglial cells. In: Gilles R et al, eds. Advances in comparative and environmental physiology. Berlin, Heidelberg: Springer-Verlag, 1991; 9:81-117.

5. Ransom BR, Yamate CL, Connors BW. Activity-dependent shrinkage of extracellular space in rat optic nerve: a developmental study. J Neurosci 1985; 5:532-535.

6. Kimelberg HK. Brain edema. In: Kettenmann H, Ransom BR, eds. Neuroglia. New York: Oxford University Press, 1995:919-935.

7. Nicholson C. Extracellular space as the pathway for neuron-glial cell interaction. In: Kettenmann H, Ransom BR, eds. Neuroglia. New York: Oxford University Press, 1995:387-397.

8. Schneider GH, Beathmann A, Kempski O. Mechanisms of glial swelling induced by glutamate. Can J Physiol Pharmacol 1992; 70:S334-S343.

9. Walz W, Hertz L. Functional interactions between neurons and astrocytes. II. Potassium homeostasis at the cellular level. Progr Neurobiol 1983; 20:133-183.

10. Kempski O, Staub F, Schneider G-H et al Swelling of C6 glioma cells and astrocytes from glutamate, high K^+ concentrations or acidosis. Progr Brain Res 1992; 94:69-75.

11. Bausch AR, Roy G. Volume-sensitive chloride channels blocked by neuroprotective drugs in human glial cells (U-138MG). GLIA 1996; 18:73-77.

12. Kempski O, Staub F, Jansen M et al. Molecular mechanisms of glial swelling in acidosis. Adv Neurol 1990; 52:39-45.

13. Kempski O, Gross U, Baethmann A. An in vitro model of cytotoxic brain edema: cell volume and metabolism of cultivated glial and nerve cells. Adv Neurol 1982; 10:254-258.

14. Braughler JM, Hall ED. Involvement of lipid peroxidation in CNS injury. J Neurotrauma 1992; 9:S1-S7.

15. Fonnum F. Glutamate: a neurotransmitter in mammalian brain—short review. J Neurochem 1984; 42:1-11.

16. Greenamyre JT. The role of glutamate in neurotransmission and in neurologic disease. Arch Neurol 1986; 43:1058-1063.

17. Hansson E, Johansson BB, Westergren I et al. Glutamate induced swelling of single astroglial cells in primary culture. Neuroscience 1994; 63:1057-1066.

18. Hansson E. Metabotropic glutamate receptor activation induces astroglial swelling. J Biol Chem 1994; 269:21955-21961.
19. Glaum S, Holzwarth JA, Miller R. Glutamate receptors activate Ca^{2+} mobilization and Ca^{2+} influx into astrocytes. Proc Natl Acad Sci USA 1990; 87:3454-3458.
20. Jensen AM, Chiu SY. Fluorescence measurement of changes in intracellular calcium induced by excitatory amino acids in cultured cortical astrocytes. J Neurosci 1990; 10:1165-1175.
21. McCarthy NA, O'Neil RG. Calcium signaling in cell volume regulation. Physiol Rew 1992; 72:1037-1061.
22. Hoffman EK, Simonsen LO. Membrane mechanisms in volume and pH regulation in vertebrate cells. Physiol Rev 1989; 69:315-382.
23. Kempski O, Chaussy L, Gross U et al. Volume regulation and metabolism of suspended C6 glioma cells: an in vitro model to study cytotoxic brain edema. Brain Res 1983; 279:217-228.
24. Kimelberg HK, Goderie SK, Higman S et al. Swelling-induced release of glutamate, aspartate, and taurine from astrocyte cultures. J Neurosci 1990; 10:1583-1591.
25. Pasantes-Morales H, Schousboe A. Volume regulation in astrocytes: a role for taurine as an osmoeffector. J Neurosci Res 1988; 20:503-509.
26. Pasantes-Morales H, Moran J, Schousboe A. Volume-sensitive release of taurine from cultured astrocytes: properties and mechanism. GLIA 1990; 3:427-432.
27. Kimelberg HK, O'Connor ER. Swelling-induced depolarization of astrocyte potentials. GLIA 1988; 1:219-224.
28. O'Connor ER, Kimelberg HK. Role of calcium in astrocyte volume regulation and in the release of ions and amino acids. J Neurosci 1993; 13:2638-2650.
29. O'Connor ER, Kimelberg HK, Keese CR et al. Electrical resistance method for measuring volume changes in monolayer cultures applied to primary astrocyte cultures. Am J Physiol 1993; 264:C471-C478.
30. Christensen O. Mediation of cell volume regulation by Ca^{2+} influx through stretch-activated channels. Nature 1987; 330:66-68.
31. Bullock R, Maxwell WL, Graham DI et al. Glial swelling following human cerebral contusion: an ultrastructural study. J Neurol Neurosurg Psych 1991; 54:427-434.
32. Klawe C, Volk C, Kempski O. Effects of extracellular acidosis on glial cell intracellular pH: Evidence for a glial spatial H^+-buffering mechanism? In: Hartman A, Yatsu F, Kuschinsky W, eds. Cerebral ischemia and basic mechanisms. Berlin, Heidelberg: Springer-Verlag, 1994:103-110.
33. Van Harreveld A, Fifkova E. Light and electron-microscopic changes in central nervous tissue after electrophoretic injection of glutamate. Exp Mol Pathol 1971; 15:61-81.
34. Barbour B, Szatkowski M, Ingledew N et al. Arachidonic acid induces a prolonged inhibition of glutamate uptake into glial cells. Nature 1989; 342:918-920.

35. Glowinski J, Marin P, Tencé M et al. Glial receptors and their intervention in astrocyto-astrocytic and astrocyto-neuronal interactions. GLIA 1994; 11:201-208.

36. Chopp M, Welch KMA, Tidwell CD et al. Global cerebral ischemia and intracellular pH during hyperglycemia and hypoglycemia in cats. Stroke 1988; 19:1383-1387.

37. Köller H, Sibler M, Pekel M et al. Depolarization of cultured astrocytes by leukotriene B_4. Evidence for the conduction of the K^+ inconductance inhibitor. Brain Res 1993; 612:28-34.

38. Shao Y, Enkvist MOK, McCarthy KD. Glutamate blocks astroglial stellation: Effect of glutamate uptake and volume changes. GLIA 1994; 11:1-10.

39. Kimelberg HK, Frangakis MV. Furosemide-and bumetanide-sensitive ion transport and volume control in primary astrocyte cultures from rat brain. Brain Res. 1985; 361:125-134.

40. Hansson E, Rönnbäck L. Receptor-mediated volume regulation in astrocytes in primary culture. Neuropharmacology 1992; 31:85-87.

41. Schousboe A, Pasantes-Morales H. Role of taurine in neuronal cell volume regulation. Can J Physiol Pharmacol 1992; 70:S356-S361.

42. Bender AS, Neary JT, Norenberg MD. Role of phosphoinositide hydrolysis in astrocyte volume regulation. J Neurochem 1993; 61:1506-1514.

43. Parsons DF, Cole RW, Kimelberg HK. Shape, size and distribution of cell structures by 3-D graphics reconstruction and stereology, I. The regulatory volume decrease of astroglial cells. Cell Biophys 1989; 14:27-42.

44. Staub F, Peters J, Kempski O et al. Swelling of glial cells in lactacidosis and by glutamate: significance of Cl^--transport. Brain Res 1993; 610:69-74.

45. Pasantes-Morales H, Maar TE, Morán J. Cell volume regulation in cultured cerebellar granule neurons. J Neurosci Res 1993; 34:219-224.

46. Tauc M, Le Maout S, Poujeol P. Fluorescent video-microscopy study of regulatory volume decrease in primary culture of rabbit proximal convoluted tubule. Biochim Biophys Acta 1990; 1052:278-284.

47. Eriksson PS, Nilsson M, Wågberg M et al. Volume regulation of single astroglial cells in primary culture. Neurosci Lett 1992; 143:195-199.

48. Sheppard CJR. Depth of field in optical microscopy. J Microsc 1987; 149:73-75.

49. Lehmann A, Hansson E. Morphological effects of excitatory amino acid analogs on primary astroglial cultures. Neurochem Int 1988; 13:105-110.

50. Barbour B, Brew H, Attwell D. Electrogenic glutamate uptake in glial cells is activated by intracellular potassium. Nature 1988; 335:433-435.

51. Kimelberg HK, Pang S, Treble DH. Excitatory amino acid-stimulated uptake of $^{22}Na^+$ in primary astrocyte cultures. J Neurosci 1989; 9:1141-1149.

52. Drejer J, Meier E, Schousboe A. Novel neuron-related regulatory mechanisms for astrocytic glutamate and GABA high-affinity uptake. Neurosci Lett 1983; 37:301-306.

53. Schousboe A. Transport and metabolism of glutamate and GABA in neurons and glial cells. Int Rev Neurobiol 1981; 22:1-45.

54. Hansson E, Eriksson P, Nilsson M. Amino acid and monoamine transport in primary astroglial cultures from defined brain regions. Neurochem Res 1985; 10:1335-1341.

55. Kanai Y, Hediger MA. Primary structure and functional characterization of a high-affinity glutamate transporter. Nature 1992; 360:467-471.

56. Kempski O, Staub F, von Rosen F et al. Molecular mechanisms of glial swelling in vitro. Neurochem Pathol 1988; 9:109-125.

57. Koyoama Y, Baba A, Iwata H. L-Glutamate induced swelling of cultured astrocytes is dependent on extracellular Ca^{2+}. Neurosci Lett 1991; 122:210-212.

58. Bender AS, Neary JT, Blicharska J et al. Role of calmodulin and protein kinase C in astrocytic cell regulation. J Neurochem 1992; 58:1874-1882.

59. Hansson E, Rönnbäck L. Astrocytes in glutamate neurotransmission. FASEB J 1995; 9:343-350.

60. Blatz AL, Magleby KL. Calcium-activated potassium channels. Trends Neurosci Sci 1987; 10:463-467.

61. Chan PH, Chu. Ketamine protects cultured astrocytes from glutamate-induced swelling. Brain Res 1989; 487:380-383.

62. Mayer ML, Westbrook GL. Cellular mechanisms underlying excitotoxicity. Trends Neurosci 1987; 10:59-61.

63. Smith SJ. Do astrocytes process neural information? In: Yu ACH, Hertz L, Norenberg MD et al., eds. Progress in Brain Research. B.V.: Elsevier Science Publishers, 1992; 94:119-136.

CHAPTER 7

CALCIUM WAVE COMMUNICATION WITHIN THE ASTROGLIAL NETWORK VIA GAP JUNCTIONS

Fredrik Blomstrand, Siamak Khatibi, Håkan Muyderman, Torsten Olsson and Lars Rönnbäck

INTRODUCTION

In multicellular organisms, each cell type has to keep its individuality, while still being able to communicate with other cells and cell types to achieve the abilities that have been an advantage for these organisms. Different intercellular communication abilities have been developed for various purposes. Long-range signaling uses neuronal or endocrine mechanisms, while local or regional communication between cells can be achieved by paracrine mechanisms or by direct physical cell-to-cell contact. Diffusion of large molecules between electrically coupled cells was discovered by Kanno and Loewenstein.[1] The diffusion occurred via gap junctions which are aqueous channels that connect cells to each other and thus link the cytoplasms of the connected cells.[2] Gap junctional coupling has been seen in a wide variety of cell types including astroglial cells, where the cells form a functional glial syncytium.[3] Recently, it has become evident that some cell types including astroglial cells communicate intercellularly via complex spatio-temporal calcium fluxes.[4]

Calcium is a ubiquitous intracellular signaling molecule that is tightly regulated by different calcium binding proteins, channels, stores and pumps. The resting level of free intracellular calcium is about 10 to 100 nM, and can increase several fold upon stimulation. The use of intracellular calcium as a cellular messenger molecule has been highly conserved, e.g., it is present for such diverse processes as fertilization events in "primitive" animals to spatio-temporal signaling in primary cultures from the most complex biological structure we know—the mammalian brain. Intracellular calcium participates in the

On Astrocytes and Glutamate Neurotransmission: New Waves in Brain Information Processing, edited by Elisabeth Hansson, Torsten Olsson and Lars Rönnbäck.

control of a wide array of cellular processes, such as gene expression, metabolic activation, motility, contraction and secretion.

Astrocytes use calcium to transduce signals in and between cells. Astroglial cells in primary cultures have been shown to express plasma-membrane bound receptors for many of the known neurotransmitters. In the brain, the neurotransmitters acts as first messengers to the cells, after which this message is transduced to a second messenger. Calcium is one of those second messengers. A common pathway for the generation of a calcium message is the binding of a neurotransmitter or hormone to cell surface receptors and activation of a G protein. The G protein in turn stimulates phospholipase C (PLC) to break down inositol phosphates and generate inositol phosphate metabolites. One of these is inositol-(1,4,5)-tris-phosphate (IP_3), which is known to release calcium from intracellular calcium stores. Depending on the type of stimuli, the calcium that enters the cytosol comes from these intracellular calcium stores or from the extracellular space, or both.

The recent findings that calcium changes propagate from cell to cell in a wave-like fashion via gap junctions is fascinating, and should be studied thoroughly. While the physiological function of the waves is still largely unknown, a little more is known about the cellular mechanisms of these calcium fluxes.

INTRACELLULAR CALCIUM WAVES AND OSCILLATIONS

The development of indicators for free intracellular calcium $[Ca^{2+}]_i$ such as fluorescent probes (e.g., fura-2, fluo-3)[5] and the bioluminescent protein aequorin, has made it possible to perform real time measurements of changes in $[Ca^{2+}]_i$ in living cells. It has been revealed that the $[Ca^{2+}]_i$ rises due to transduction of many different extracellular stimuli are not temporally or spatially uniform over the cell body. Indeed, the $[Ca^{2+}]_i$ changes often appear to initiate in one (or more) part of the cell and then spread throughout the cytoplasm of the cell showing different degrees of oscillatory behavior. Below we focus on intracellular waves and oscillations elicited via the inositol phospholipid cascade.[6] The activation of PLC via tyrosine kinase or G protein linked transduction pathways[7] mediates the breakdown of phosphatidylinositol 4,5-bisphosphate (PIP_2) to IP_3 and diacylglycerol (DAG).[8] The production of IP_3 and the binding to the IP_3-receptor (IP_3R) seems to be the major trigger for release of calcium from intracellular stores. In astrocytes and other nonmuscle cells, the IP_3-sensitive intracellular calcium store is believed to be the endoplasmic reticulum.[9-11] Many different external stimuli have been shown to elicit calcium oscillations in astrocytes. When stimulated with the excitatory amino acid glutamate, astrocytes show oscillatory patterns with various frequencies ranging from 3 to 9 periods per minute.[12,13] Data also show that astrocytic calcium oscillations can occur spontaneously.[14-16] In the same manner intracellular calcium waves have been shown to occur for example after application of glutamate[4] or when mechanically stimulated.[17] The actual oscillation has different parts including the activation of PLC, the binding of IP_3 to its receptor, the release of calcium, removal of excess calcium and the re-release of calcium. It is important to distinguish between intracellular oscillations and waves, and intercellular calcium waves. The latter is also known to exist in astrocytes (see below this chapter). Intracellular oscillations and waves seem to occur independently of $[Ca^{2+}]_i$ in adjacent cells and oscillations can coexist with communicating intercellular waves,[17] indicating different mechanisms between intra- and intercellular calcium waves. The mechanisms underlying intracellular oscillations in astrocytes or in other mammalian cell types are not yet fully understood. Basically the question is whether there are one or two intracellular pools of calcium and whether or not external calcium is required to maintain the oscillatory behavior. There are studies showing distinct differences between spontaneous and agonist triggered calcium changes in astrocytes.[16] Spontaneous oscillations in $[Ca^{2+}]_i$ seem to be insensitive to changes in extracellular calcium concentrations while agonist-induced oscillations are inhibited by calcium free media or exposure to EGTA.[4] This indicates that extracellular calcium is required to maintain these sustained calcium oscillations, favoring a two-pool model of calcium oscillations. At least it seems as intracellular stores are fast depleted and the refilling requires a second store, possible the extracellular calcium. If there are two stores (or more), oscillatory behavior would appear if calcium were being taken up by one pool and then translocated to another from which it could be re-released. In other cells than astrocytes it has been shown that in addition to an IP_3-sensitive pool there is also a ryanodine-sensitive calcium pool. There is evidence that all three known forms of the ryanodine receptor (RYR) exists in the CNS,[18] but it has been difficult to show any relation to glial cells. In 1994, Langley and Pearce[19] discussed the existence of RYR3 on cultured cortical astrocytes. They found that low concentrations of ryanodine could elicit calcium transients while the RYR1 and RYR2 agonist caffeine couldn't, indicating the presence of a noncaffeine sensitive RYR in 60% of their cells. So far this is, to our knowledge, the only work showing calcium transients in astrocytes after stimulation with ryanodine, and there is no other clear evidence for such a non IP_3-sensitive calcium store. In ryanodine- positive cells, a model for "calcium-induced calcium-release" (CICR) has been established, where the calcium is released via the RYR. Functionally one could also call IP_3 mediated calcium release CICR,[20] because the binding of IP_3 to IP_3R has been shown to be inhibited by high or low $[Ca^{2+}]_i$ and stimulated by intermediary concentrations.[21] Of course there is a possibility of a ryanodine-insensitive second calcium pool in astrocytes, but it is yet to be proven. Another question of interest is whether or not IP_3 itself oscillates (Fig. 7.1). In 1991 Meyer

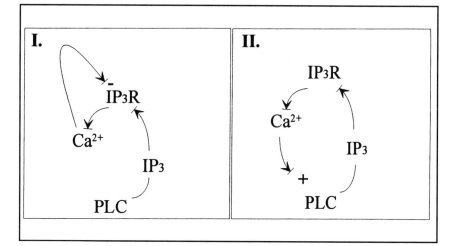

Figure 7.1. Two schematic representations of intracellular Ca^{2+} oscillations in astrocytes. **I.** Requiring sustained levels of IP_3, here the released Ca^{2+} acts via negative feedback on the IP_3-IP_3R complex.[20,21] **II.** A simplification of the ICC model of Ca^{2+} oscillation. Here released Ca^{2+} acts via positive feedback on the regeneration of IP_3.[26]

and Stryer[22] proposed an IP_3-calcium cross-coupling model (ICC) with oscillations of both calcium and IP_3, where an IP_3 mediated calcium release enhances PLC to generate a self-amplifying increase in IP_3 and $[Ca^{2+}]_i$. It seems that a rise in $[Ca^{2+}]_i$ alone is not enough to initiate an oscillatory behavior since a prior activation of PLC is required and the ICC-model predicts an IP_3 diffusion and release of calcium which, in turn, stimulates PLC to the regeneration of IP_3.

Berridge[23] suggests that the oscillations are generated by positive feedback of CICR via IP_3. In cells lacking RYRs, the CICR via IP_3 may be responsible for oscillatory behavior since in cells expressing both RYR and IP_3R the sensitivity to calcium is considerably higher on the IP side. It might be that CICR via RYR is more relevant in situations with higher levels of intracellular calcium.[24] To determine the movement of either IP_3 or calcium, one might imagine that it would be convenient to use the diffusion constant for the substances, but since cytosolic calcium buffering capability is not known, this approach is not useful. There is evidence for a calcium-mediated regeneration of IP_3[7] but it is uncertain if this regeneration is rapid enough to mediate fast oscillation. It may be that a receptor-mediated process or a sensitization of PLC is required for calcium dependent regeneration of IP_3.[25] In addition to the proposed oscillations of IP_3, there are other conceivable explanations for IP_3-mediated calcium oscillations, such as that the release of IP_3 could potentiate its own regeneration by acting on PLC,[26] or that the calcium released by IP_3 interferes with the IP_3 binding to its receptor and temporally inhibiting the IP_3-induced calcium release as described above. When calcium levels then return to resting levels, the inhibition is annihilated and there is a re-opening of the IP_3R channel. This would require a sustained level of IP_3 during the period of oscillation. On the other hand it has been shown that when IP_3 is repeatedly injected into the interior of the cell, the calcium changes are rapidly desensitized,[27] which speaks in favor of the existence of a second non- IP_3 sensitive calcium pool. It has also been shown that during long period of sustained calcium oscillations it is difficult to detect any IP_3 production.[28] In addition to calcium oscillations, the spreading of calcium changes throughout the cytoplasm as waves has been intensively studied over the last years. Intracellular calcium waves in astrocytes can be elicited by externally applied glutamate[4] and mechanical stimulation.[17] These waves travel through the cytoplasm of the cell at 28-42 micrometer/s,[17] showing different behavior in different parts of the cell. There seem to be sub-cellular loci which act as points of amplification, separated by passive diffusion.[29] One important question regarding intracellular waves is whether or not they are actually waves or simple oscillatory loci with different latencies giving the impression of propagating waves. The physiological significance of intracellular calcium waves and oscillations have not yet been fully understood and there will have to be a great deal of work before these secrets are revealed.

ASPECTS ON GLIAL COMMUNICATION AND GAP JUNCTIONS

The abundance of gap junctions in liver and heart encouraged researchers to primarily utilize these tissues for characterization and cloning of the connexin (Cx) protein. This revealed a whole family of proteins[30,31] related by their sequence but differing in molecular weight. Two different connexins, with molecular weights of 26 and 32 kDa respectively were found in the mammalian liver, while in heart the existence of Cx43 was revealed.[32] The rather recent use of polymerase chain reaction (PCR) cloning from genomic libraries has increased the number of connexins to about a dozen, (for review of classes and localization see ref. 33).

Gap junctions are channels bridging the extracellular space between coupled adjacent cells. They have been of great interest during the last 44 years, ever since Weidmann[34] in 1952 showed that the excitation in heart myocytes actually spreads to adjacent cells. About 12 years later, the first report of a similar mechanism in glial cells was given by Kuffler and Potter[35] who observed electrical coupling between glial cells in the leech. In 1964 Kanno and Loewenstein[1] published results claiming that large molecules could pass between electrically coupled cells, indicating that the cells could actually share cytoplasmic substances with each other.[2] The contacts mediating these phenomena became known as gap junctions, on the basis of their appearance in the electron microscope.[36] Here, at the site where the cells were connected, the extracellular space narrowed to a small gap—a gap junction. Gap junctions are expressed in almost every mammalian cell type except erythrocytes, spermatozoa and mature skeletal muscle cells.[33] Although the channel is composed of very different cell types with different tasks and physiological importance, all gap junctions are formed in the same way, providing the cells a direct pathway for exchanging substances less than 1 kDa and not exceeding 2 nm in diameter. These channels are aqueous pores, permitting ions and small organic molecules to diffuse freely from one cell to another, forcing us to consider coupled cells not only as a cluster of individual cells but rather as large functional units, evolutionarily developed to achieve abilities beyond those given for single cells.

THE CENTRAL NERVOUS SYSTEM (CNS) AND GAP JUNCTIONS

Like almost every other mammalian cell, the astrocyte is known to express gap junctional connections with adjacent cells of the same type.[37-39] With the aid of these gap junctions, astrocytes form large functional syncytical structures.[3,40,41] The physiological significance of such multicellular units is still to a large extent unknown, but it is, for example, believed to aid the proposed glial buffering of potassium.[42,43] The probable capacity of buffering other ions such as calcium and the recent discovery of inter- and intracellular calcium waves, makes the glial gap junctions even more interesting. Among glial cells, astrocytes type 1 and oligodendrocytes express gap junctions[37] while microglia, mammalian Müller cells[44] and astrocytes type 2 seem to lack these connections.[45,46] It is noteworthy that low differentiated glioma does not express gap junctions while higher differentiated glial tumors do.[47,48] This could suggest an association of the expression of gap junctions with growth control and degree of differentiation.[2,49] The ability to form functional gap junctions are not restricted to connexins of the same molecular weight. Thus astrocytes can form junctional connections not only with each other, but also with oligodendrocytes, ependymal cells and perhaps even with neurons.[38,41,50] In addition to the fact that one cell type can express more than one type of connexin there are different cell types expressing the same class. For example, both oligodendrocytes and neurons express Cx32, a phenomena that is also seen in cells in the liver, the kidney and the uterus. There are other cells besides oligodendrocytes, neurons and astrocytes expressing connexin in the mammalian brain. For instance, pinealocytes express Cx26 and ependyma express both Cx26 and Cx43.[51] The expression of Cx43 in brain seems to peak in the early postnatal period and to remain at high concentrations thereafter. The expression of Cx43 is not constant throughout the brain. Cx43 mRNA expression is four times higher in cultured astrocytes derived from hypothalamus than from the striatum[52] and it seems to be least expressed in the spinal white matter.[53] The Kd for octanol, a gap junctional uncoupling agent, is significantly lower (188 μM) in astrocytes from the spine than in hippocampal astrocytes, which show the highest degree of coupling with Kd of 654.[54] These findings, together with the fact that the ratio of the phosphorylated and nonphosphorylated forms of Cx43, believed to be related to the functional state of the protein, seems to be constant in all regions suggests that the astrocytic coupling strength varies with brain region.[52,53] These differences can be important as a reflection of various functional requirements in different CNS regions.

GAP JUNCTIONS: STRUCTURE AND PROPERTIES

It is the surprisingly high resistance to proteolytic enzymes and detergents that has made it possible to isolate gap junction proteins.[55] A gap junction channel can be split into two hemi-channels, and it is when one of these is in perfect alignment with another that the channel is formed. The mechanism underlying the assembly is not yet fully understood.[32] These hemi-channels, called connexons[56] have diameters of approximately 2 nm.[57,58] Every connexon, in turn, consists of a hexamer of symmetrical sub-units,[59] six identical membrane spanning proteins—the connexins, (Fig. 7.2). DNA sequencing suggests that the connexin protein crosses the lipid bilayer four times as α-helices, leaving both C and N-terminals on the cytoplasmatic side, exposing two extracellular loops and one intracellular. Bennett and co-workers[32] showed that the greatest variability among the connexins lies in the cytoplasmic domain in general and in the C-terminal in particular. Six connexins (twelve extracellular loops) are thought to associate to form the gap junction channel, lining the pore with one α-helix from each protein. The inside of the pore is probably more hydrophilic than the rest of the protein and may also be somewhat more negatively charged.[60] The electrophysiological properties of gap junctions are revealed today by use of the patch clamp technique. Allowing the resolution of single channel measurements has shown a unitary conductance of about 50-60 pS and a total junctional conductance between the cell pair of 13 nS making an average gap junction site that consists of about 235 functional channels.[61,62]

REGULATION OF GAP JUNCTION PERMEABILITY

Principally there are at least two and possibly three different ways of affecting the conductance of gap junctions:
- modulating the actual state of permeability of the channel itself
- altering the expression of the protein
- degree of compartmentalization of the made protein

The regulation of connexin gene expression is poorly understood, but previous studies have shown a rapid turnover of the protein, with a lifetime of several hours and possible effects of cAMP on the mRNA synthesis.[32]

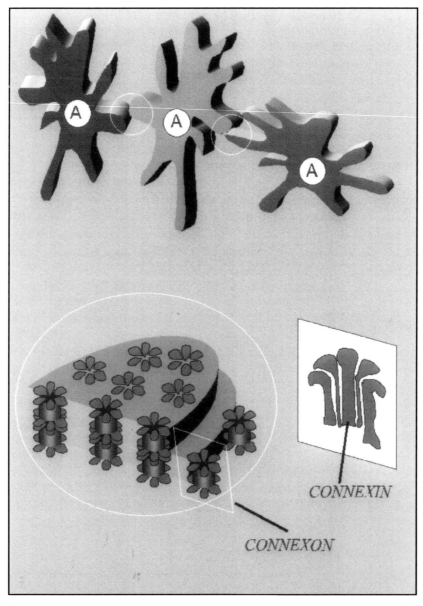

Fig. 7.2. Schematic presentation of the principle of the gap junction channel. Six connexins form a connexon which in perfect alliance with another connexon form the gap junction channel.

There are a number of physiological substances and variables that can influence the permeability of the gap junction channel. The mechanisms are mainly unknown but it has been proposed that the segments forming the wall could be altered in such a way that they mechanically close the channel.[63] This theory is based on electron-microscope studies, suggesting that closed channels appear mechanically disturbed. Chemical agents such as higher alcohols like octanol and heptanol have been shown to block gap junctions.[64] The mechanism is not completely understood but it has been suggested that octanol-induced acidification of the cytoplasm could lower the permeability of gap junctions, possibly resulting in decreased conductivity.[65] It is also shown that if the acidification remains for more than 30 minutes, the decreased conductivity is irreversible.[66] The sensitivity to changes in pH is shown to differ depending on the form of connexin expressed. In the heart, expressing Cx40, 43, 45 and Cx46, the Cx45 channels were closed at an intracellular pH of 6.3, while the Cx43 channels did not close until the acidification reached 5.8.[67] Sensitivity to general anesthetics such as halothane but also CO_2 has been shown experimentally.[68] Second messengers such as cAMP,[32] the activation of PKC[69] and effects of various neurotransmitters such as glutamate and noradrenaline have been shown to be involved in the regulation of gap junction permeability. It is believed that some of the changes in conductance are due to phosphorylation of specific channel sites, mediated, for instance by cAMP. These effects seem to be tissue-specific. Thus an elevation of cAMP increases the junctional conductivity in hepatocytes and myocytes (Cx32 and Cx43) while decreasing conductivity in the uterine muscle, which also expresses Cx43.[32] Increasing intracellular calcium above physiological levels dramatically decreases conductivity,[2] while changes within normal range do not affect gap junctions.[70] An interesting thought was brought forward by Lazrak and Peracchia[71] suggesting that cell injury can induce supraphysiological levels of intercellular calcium, high enough to close the junction thereby preventing the neighboring cells from disturbances of their internal chemistry. Dual voltage clamp studies suggest that gap junction conductivity expresses different degrees of voltage sensitivity depending on which connexin that is expressed.[32] The voltage sensitivity of Cx43 seems to be weaker than of Cx32. This could mean, as suggested by Dermietzel and coworkers,[61] that gap junctions composed of a combination of Cx43 and 32 could allow unidirectional closure of the channel. Concerning the fact that proteins can be stored in the cytoplasm of the cell in a functional or prefunctional state after translation, and considering the relatively long life time of the connexin protein, it is possible that premade protein can be stored and incorporated into the plasmalemma when needed. To our knowledge this has never been proven in astrocytes.

METHODS FOR THE STUDIES OF GAP JUNCTIONS

There are many different ways of gaining knowledge about gap junction properties and their state of opening. The first studies concerning cell-cell coupling were performed using electrophysical methods by applying a voltage gradient across the junctional membrane after inserting a micro-electrode into each of two interacting cells and measuring the current flow. The results indicated that inorganic ions—carrying current—could flow freely from the interior of one cell to another. As described above it then took more than 10 years to show that the physiological coupling was correlated to the presence of the gap junctions in the plasma membrane as shown with electron microscopic techniques. Today, electrical coupling between adjacent cells is usually measured using the dual voltage patch-clamp technique with coupled cell pairs. Voltage clamping of adjacent astrocytes, allowing high spatial resolution, has shown the unitary conductance of a single gap junction channel between astrocytes to be 50-60 pS.[61,62] Injection of a small junction-permeable fluorescent dye has been used to visualize spatial coupling between the cells.[72] An example of such a dye is Lucifer Yellow. Detecting changes in junctional conductance with dye injections can be somewhat difficult because of pitfalls in the evaluation. One factor to consider is the dilution of the dye. A recent method for analyzing and detecting changes in permeability uses laser light to bleach intracellular fluorescent dye molecules and thereafter measuring the time for the dye to diffuse back from adjacent cells.[73] This method is called fluorescence recovery after photo-bleaching (FRAP). Another way to visualize and to a lesser extent to judge junctional coupling is to follow the spread of calcium waves that occurs in, e.g., astrocytes and neurons when they are stimulated either mechanically or by suitable drugs.[4,17] Here it may be difficult to differentiate between pure changes in the state of conductivity and changes in the intracellular calcium homeostasis.

INTERCELLULAR CALCIUM WAVES

Intercellular calcium waves propagating from cell to cell can be induced by mechanical stimulation. This has been studied in some different cell culture types, e.g., epithelial,[74] mixed glial,[17] astrocyte,[69] endothelial[75] and cardial myocyte cultures.[76] The excitatory neurotransmitter glutamate has also been shown to induce intracellular calcium increases that can propagate as calcium waves between astrocytes in cultures or organotypic slices.[4,77-79] There are some differences between mechanically- and glutamate-induced calcium waves, as discussed below.

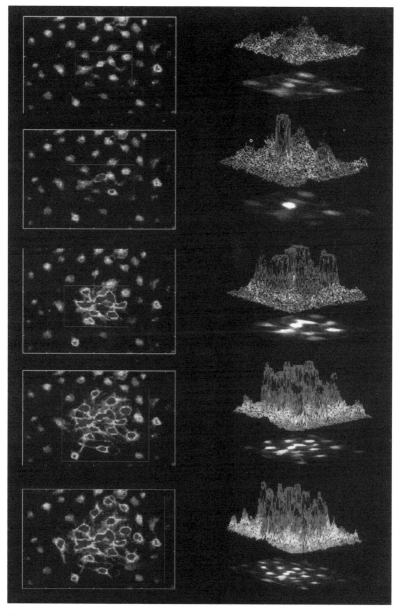

Fig. 7.3. A sequence of pseudocolored images showing a mechanically induced calcium wave in cultured astroglial cells. Time delay between each image was 1.5 seconds. Red color corresponds to high intracellular calcium. On the right are 3-D relief pictures of the intensity changes within the red boxes on left pictures. See color figure in insert.

MECHANICALLY INDUCED CALCIUM WAVES

Mechanically induced intercellular calcium waves in glial cells propagate with an approximate velocity of 15-27 μm/second.[17,80] Figure 7.3 shows a series of images from a mechanically induced calcium wave. The signals for intercellular calcium waves have been shown to travel through gap junctions. Several experimental sets exclude that there is an extracellular factor that transmits the signal of increased calcium from cell to cell. A directional flow of extracellular media could not bias the direction of the mechanically induced calcium waves in epithelial cells[81] and the two uncoupling agents octanol and halothane have been shown to inhibit calcium propagation.[74] A calcium wave propagating through a confluent glial syncytium travels around and not over a disrupted area, indicating that it is a messenger moving within the astroglial syncytium that is responsible for the calcium wave propagation.[69] Further evidence that the wave travels through gap junctions comes from the studies of C6 glioma cells. These cells express very little Cx43 protein and mechanical stimulation results in a calcium increase in a calcium increase in the stimulated cell only that does not propagate to the surrounding cells.[82] Upon transfection with the gene for Cx43, these cells are dye-coupled.[83] Furthermore, mechanical stimulation of these transfected cells induces an intercellular calcium wave, where the extent and rate of the propagation is proportional to the level of Cx43 expression, clearly demonstrating that wave propagation is dependent on passage through gap junctions.[82] There are, however, data that suggest a possible extracellular route for a messenger giving rise to calcium waves.[84,85]

Experimental data indicate that it is the second messenger, IP_3, rather than calcium itself that passes from cell to cell through gap junctions and then releases calcium from intracellular stores via the action on IP_3R. First of all, IP_3 has been shown to diffuse through gap junctions.[86] Iontophoretic injection of IP_3 generated a propagating calcium wave in epithelial cells, similar to the mechanically induced calcium waves in epithelial or glial cells.[74] Loading airway epithelial cells with heparin, an IP_3R antagonist, inhibited the propagation of the intercellular Ca^{2+} waves.[87] Supportive of this, Charles and co-workers showed that thapsigargin, an inhibitor of endoplasmic reticulum Ca^{2+}-ATPases causing leakage of calcium from IP_3 sensitive calcium stores, inhibits intercellular calcium communication.[88] Furthermore, mechanical stimulation of a single astroglial cell in calcium free media generated a propagating wave although the stimulated cell did not respond with increased $[Ca^{2+}]_i$.[17] The reason IP_3 does not give increased $[Ca^{2+}]_i$ in the stimulated cell in calcium-free media is not fully understood, and is discussed elsewhere.[89] In airway epithelial culture it was recently shown that blocking PLC inhibits the spread of mechanically induced calcium waves, indicating that the mechanical deformation of the cell membrane generates IP_3 via stimulation of PLC.[90] It was also shown that neither ryanodine or caffeine affected the calcium levels upon stimulation, further indicating that calcium in a propagating wave is primarily released from IP_3-sensitive calcium stores. Except for the IP_3-induced calcium release, a CICR is thought to enhance propagation. The lack of responsiveness to ryanodine and caffeine and the demonstration of increased IP_3R sensitivity to increased $[Ca^{2+}]_i$ indicates that CICR can occur via IP_3Rs.[91] CICR has been shown to enhance the amplitude of propagating calcium waves in glial cells as well.[88] This was probably via an effect of calcium on IP_3-sensitive or some unknown kind of calcium stores. It is not yet known whether the IP_3 responsible for a propagating wave comes only from the mechanically stimulated cell or if a regeneration of IP_3 occurs along the wave path. Theoretical models based on experimental results in airway epithelial cells and glial cells support the idea that it is IP_3 from the stimulated cell that moves from cell to cell and releases calcium; however it cannot be out ruled that some kind of regeneration of IP_3 occurs along the wave path.[92,93] Our results show that the amplitude decreases with the distance of wave propagation, indicating a diffusion process.[80] However, the relatively long wave propagation in our astroglial cells, sometimes over 8 cells in all directions out from the mechanically stimulated cell, indicates that the IP_3 produced in the stimulated cell might not be enough for this relatively long propagation. It might be that some regenerative process maintains the IP_3 concentration in the propagating wave, possibly some kind of IP_3-induced IP_3 production.[94] The decreasing amplitude could then be due to the diffusion of IP_3 from the stimulated cell in combination with regeneration that is not powerful enough to fully maintain the high concentration of IP_3 propagating out from the stimulated cell. A decreasing $[IP_3]_i$ could result in successively less powerful calcium release and thus a calcium signal amplitude decrease along the wave path.[80]

GLUTAMATE-INDUCED CALCIUM WAVES

Intercellular calcium waves in astroglial cells after chemical stimulation were first described by stimulating the cells with glutamate.[4] Cornell-Bell and co-workers showed that the generation of intercellular calcium waves was concentration dependent, and favored in concentrations of 10 to 100 µM. As in the case of mechanically stimulated calcium waves, a directional flow of extracellular media could not bias the direction of the glutamate-induced calcium waves and treatment with octanol and halothane inhibited the propagation.[78] Glutamate stimulation to astrocytes in primary cultures gives rise to different kinds of response patterns, which could indicate coded information.[95] The glutamate response has been dissected to the contribution of different receptor subtypes, where the metabotropic receptors are responsible for propagation of initial propagating calcium spikes involving IP_3, and the ionotropic receptors are responsible for smoothly propagating regenerative waves involving Na^+/Ca^{2+} exchange.[95] The initial spike is a common response after glutamate stimulation. These spikes were shown to propagate intercellularly at a speed of

400 µm/second. The amplitude and velocity of these spatial spikes were not constant along the propagation route. The smoothly propagating calcium appeared first after several minutes of continuous glutamate stimulation.[78,95] These waves propagated with conserved shape and amplitude and a relative constant velocity of 15 ± 3 µm/second, and disappeared in calcium-free media. Finkbeiner,[78] argues that a short range autocatalytic reaction rather than long range diffusion is responsible for the glutamate-induced wave propagation since in their experiments wave velocity was shown to be relatively constant regardless of the distance propagated. Intercellular calcium waves have also been demonstrated after 5-HT and ATP application to cultured glial cells from the hypothalamic suprachiasmatic nucleus.[12] In summary, this indicates that the mechanisms for these propagations seem to be different, where the mechanically induced waves are arrested for 0.5-1 second at the cell boundaries,[89] which is not seen in glutamate-induced calcium waves.[95] Furthermore, glutamate-induced intercellular calcium waves exhibit latency and propagate longer than the mechanically induced waves, without degradation. They also require extracellular calcium. The mechanically induced calcium waves propagate at higher velocities, exhibit decreasing amplitude and speed along the wave path, and do not seem to require extracellular calcium. However, the fast glutamate-induced propagating spikes may use an IP_3-dependent mechanism similar to the mechanism for mechanically induced calcium waves. A schematic model of intercellular calcium wave propagation is shown in Fig. 7.4.

Modulation of Intercellular Calcium Communication.

The degree of functional coupling is a dynamic process where neurotransmitters may be important regulators. The gap junction conductivity in astroglial cells has been shown to be downregulated by protein kinase C (PKC) activation, increased intracellular calcium and lowered pH[32,65,66,69] and upregulated by cyclic AMP, membrane depolarization and glutamate.[62, 96] 5-HT has been shown to increase $[Ca^{2+}]_i$ in hippocampal neuron-glial cocultures[80] and to hy-

Fig. 7.4. (Opposite page) A schematic model of a possible mechanism for the propagation of mechanically induced calcium waves. The mechanical deformation of the cell membrane is thought to activate PLC leading to an IP_3 production and a subsequent Ca^{2+} release from IP_3-sensitive calcium stores. Ca^{2+} then diffuses throughout the cell and can influence IP_3R sensitivity, where an activation can lead to CICR. However, calcium is highly buffered in the cytosol and its propagation to neighboring cells is probably not very efficient. Instead the most probable intercellular messenger is IP_3, which diffuses through gap junctions and stimulates Ca^{2+} release in the neighboring cells. It is not fully known if any regeneration of IP_3 occurs along the wave path or if all the propagating IP_3 is derived from the stimulated cell. The mechanisms of glutamate-induced intercellular calcium waves upon stimulation of a single cell is to a large extent unknown. See color figure in insert.

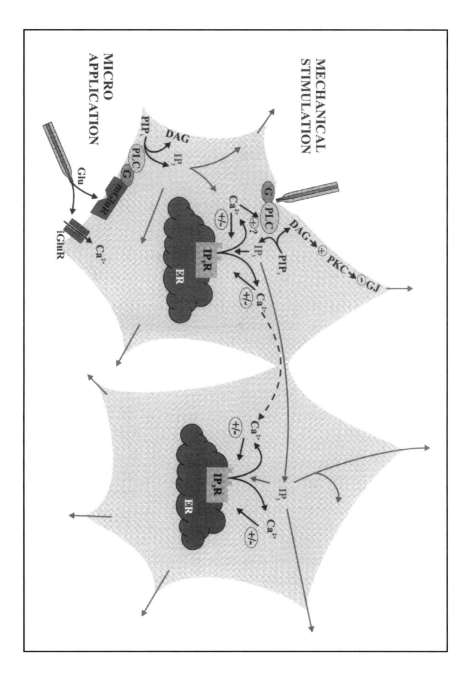

perpolarize cultured astroglial cells from striatum and spinal cord.[97] This effect of 5-HT on the calcium-IP$_3$ system and on membrane potential indicates that 5-HT could affect the communication through gap junctions. In fact, we have recently shown that 5-HT decreases the propagation area and increases the wave rate of mechanically induced calcium waves.[80] When hyperpolarizing the cells with valinomycin[98] or zero $[K^+]_o$,[99] there is a decrease in propagation area similar to what is seen in 5-HT treated cells. Furthermore, the excitatory neurotransmitter glutamate increased the propagation area. This was also seen after the cells were depolarized with 56 mM $[K^+]_o$. These data suggest that the membrane potential could be important for the communication through gap junctions in the astroglial syncytium.

We also have preliminary data suggesting that both transient and prolonged exposure to the α_1-agonist phenylephrine decreases wave propagation drastically. At least two different mechanisms seem to be involved; one PKC dependent mechanism which is seen after prolonged exposure to the drug (t = 20 minutes) and one PKC independent mechanism when the exposure is transient (t < 30 s). After transient exposure the significant decrease in propagation length persists for up to 5 minutes after removal of the drug. This decrease is fully regained within 10 minutes. Both mechanisms are independent of extracellular calcium and can be abolished by blocking the α_1-receptor with selective antagonists. This shows that adrenergic input in vitro can modulate the propagation of mechanically induced calcium waves in astrocytes even if the exposure of the neurotransmitter is transient, giving a fast way to modulate the glial transmission of calcium signals (unpublished results).

MODELING

THE USE OF MODELS

Science relies on relating observations to real world events. In natural science and medicine this process is vital and embraces the concept of models and modeling, the purpose of which is to describe the relations in a consistent manner in which dependencies are preserved and independent parts are disregarded. As a result, much of our knowledge of the real world is expressed in models. In fact, we most often identify, describe and reason about the real world in terms of models. The whole world of statistics has been developed to help in this process and in several branches, extensions to the basic methods are developed to more easily handle particular kinds of observations, e.g., signal analyses and image analyses. Here, we only mention some of the main issues about models and modeling.

The methods are in general generic, that is, they can be used without regard to the origin of the observation. But it is always true that the more we know beforehand about the object, process or events we are studying, the more efficient methods can be used. Thus we can make use of chemical or physical knowledge of parts of biological processes to make the modeling process efficient. Knowledge about the tools and instrument used for observations and recordings are also very useful. There are numerous examples found in scientific reports in which conclusions made about the object studied more reflect the properties of the instrumentation used than of the object itself.

It is a long way from the first observation of a phenomenon to the understanding of the function. In this process a model that describes observations in relation to known facts is most useful.

MODELING ON GLIAL CELLS

The establishment of the existence of Ca^{2+} signaling in glia cells encourages us to seek more insight into its mechanisms to increase the understanding of its functionality. This might be to participate in signal processing in the brain.[22,100,101] These insights must not rely on speculations but must rest on observations and be related to the concept of information processing in the brain at large. In this process modeling is an essential tool and it becomes more important than ever to find a model that will enlighten the role of the glial network.

Models can be categorized into two classes: analytical and mechanistic models. Analytical models are based on observed behavior and are often only loosely connected to the underlying biology. They generally offer more power to related observations and to explaining behavior of phenomena than does a qualitative suggestion. Their disadvantage is that they can be constructed in many different mathematical ways and thus may not show a direct relation to the underlying mechanisms. Mechanistic models are based on a priori knowledge of known mechanisms and parameters. The main advantage of mechanistic model, compared with analytical model, is that they have a more precise power of prediction. However, predictions can be sensitive to variations of earlier parameters in new experiments. Below, without exhaustive mathematical formalism, we describe some mechanistic models of Ca^{2+} signaling and show two model examples which may contribute to a better understanding of the methodology of the spatio-temporal behavior of $[Ca^{2+}]_i$ modeling.

INTRACELLULAR MODELS

The complex spatio-temporal behavior of Ca^{2+} is wave-like in nature[17,100,102-104] and is almost certainly the result of an underlying excitable oscillatory temporal mechanism.[105] Thus construction of all intracellular mechanistic models has been based on a temporal model for oscillations. Several of these models, based on different theoretical models, have been proposed to describe intracellular $[Ca^{2+}]_i$ oscillations in a variety of cells. In accordance with experimental evidence, all the models agree on the initial phase of this process, which is their dependence on inositol $[IP_3]_i$. The models can be categorized into two types, depending on whether they require oscillating $[IP_3]_i$ to drive the oscillations in $[Ca^{2+}]_i$. At present, we are not aware of any way of measuring $[IP_3]_i$ with high temporal resolution, and thus we cannot definitively say whether $[IP_3]_i$ oscillates during receptor activation. However, there are observations that question the significance of feedback to IP_3 production in the generation of Ca^{2+} oscillation in many cell types. For example, experiments in which oscillations were induced using myoinositol-(1,4,5)trisphosphorothioate (IP_3S_3) in place of IP_3 show results that speak against the need of oscillating $[IP_3]_i$ to drive the $[Ca^{2+}]_i$ oscillations.[100,106] Also, the spatio-temporal patterns of $[Ca^{2+}]_i$ are the same regardless of whether IP_3 or IP_3S_3 is used to initiate the oscillations and waves.

The first type of model requires oscillating $[IP_3]_i$ and two examples are :
• the IP_3- Ca^{2+} cross-coupling model of Meyer and Stryer[22]
• the agonist-receptor oscillator model of Cuthbertson and Chay[94]

The second type of model does not require oscillations in $[IP_3]_i$ to drive the oscillations in $[Ca^{2+}]_i$; oscillations in $[Ca^{2+}]_i$ occur for appropriate and constant $[IP_3]_i$. Some examples of the second type are:
• the Ca^{2+}-induced Ca^{2+} release (CICR) model[107]
• the model of Somogyi and Stucki[108]
• the model of DeYoung and Keizer[109]
• the model of Atri,[110] which contains only one intracellular pool of Ca^{2+} that releases Ca^{2+} through the IP_3R. The IP_3R is assumed to be modulated by $[Ca^{2+}]_i$ in a biphasic manner, with Ca^{2+} release inhibited by low and high $[Ca^{2+}]_i$ and facilitated by intermediate $[Ca^{2+}]_i$. The model also separates the time scales of channel activation and inactivation, such that inactivation occurs on a slower time scale.[21]

There is also controversy regarding the mechanism of $[Ca^{2+}]_i$ wave propagation, and a number of qualitative models have been proposed. Almost all the models contain positive feedback but differ regarding mechanisms, and regarding the question of whether Ca^{2+} or IP_3 is the propagating messenger. It has been proposed that the wave is propagated by Ca^{2+} diffusion and then amplified by CICR.[102,107,111] Meyer and Styer[22] propose that the wave is propagated by IP_3 diffusion through a positive feedback mechanism that involves Ca^{2+} activation of PLC. Lechleiter and Clapham[100] and Parys[112] propose that wave propagation is controlled by IP_3-mediated Ca^{2+} release from the IP_3R and is modulated by cytoplasmic concentration and diffusion of Ca^{2+}.

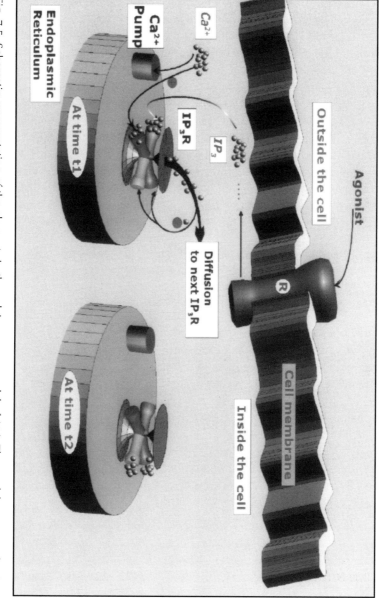

Fig. 7.5. Schematic representation of the elements in the calcium wave model of Atri. The model separates the time scales of channel activation (t1) and inactivation (t2). See color figure in insert.

EXAMPLE OF A ONE-POOL CALCIUM MODEL

A schematic representation of the Atri model[110] can be seen in Figure 7.5. The model contains only one intracellular pool of Ca^{2+} that releases Ca^{2+} through activation of IP_3R. Modeling of the Ca^{2+} flux through the IP_3R is simply a macroscopic representation capturing the essence of other channel models.[109] In fact in the Atri model, modeling of the Ca^{2+} flux is very similar to a simplification of the De Young and Keizer model[109] and IP_3R is modeled in a way similar to that of channel subunits in the Hodgkin-Huxley model of electrical impulse propagation in the nerve axon.[113] In the Atri model, a cell surface receptor is triggered by binding of an agonist, in turn, it mediates the production of IP_3 as well as DAG. Then IP_3 can bind to an IP_3R of an internal Ca^{2+} pool to release Ca^{2+} from this pool. Cytosolic Ca^{2+} can then facilitate or inhibit further Ca^{2+} release, depending on which IP_3R Ca^{2+} binding domain it activates. Ca^{2+} can also be extruded from the cytosol in a $[Ca^{2+}]_i$-dependent manner through reuptake into the pool or pumping to the extracellular medium. Meanwhile, a relatively small amount of Ca^{2+} leaks into the cytosol from outside the cell. The various Ca^{2+} fluxes can be formulated in model balance equations

$$\frac{dC}{dt} = J_{channel} + J_{pump} - J_{leak}, \text{ and}$$

$$\tau_n \frac{dn}{dt} = n(c) - n$$

where c, (in micromolar units) is the concentration $[Ca^{2+}]_i$. The dimensionless variable n is the proportion of IP_3Rs that have not been closed by Ca^{2+}, $J_{channel}$ is the Ca^{2+} flux through the IP_3R , J_{pump} is the Ca^{2+} flux due to the $[Ca^{2+}]_i$-dependent pumping of Ca^{2+} out of the cytosol , J_{leak} is the Ca^{2+} flux due to Ca^{2+} leaking into the cytsol and τ_n is a constant parameter.

For modeling $J_{channel}$, it is assumed that the IP_3R consists of three independent binding domains, each of which may be in an activated or an nonactivated state. Domain 1 binds IP_3, whereas domain 2 and 3 bind Ca^{2+}. The IP_3R will pass Ca^{2+} current only if domains 1 and 2 are activated and domain 3 is nonactivated, and the Ca^{2+} current through the IP_3R is all or nothing. The total Ca^{2+} flux from the internal pool into cytoplasm is controlled by the number of open channels.

The Ca^{2+} current to a concentration flux, $J_{channel}$ is

$$J_{channel} = \frac{N_i P_1 P_2 P_3}{2.f.U}$$

where N_i is the i channel of a given population of N channels. P_1 and P_2 are the probabilities that domains 1 and 2, respectively, are activated. P_3 is the probability that Ca^{2+} is not bound to domain 3 (nonactivated). f is the Faraday's constant. U is the constant assumed volume.

The effect of J_{pump} on the model behavior is small and can be expressed as a simple diffusion equation :

$$J_{pump} = \frac{\gamma C}{k_\gamma + C}$$

Further, the effect of J_{leak} is assumed to be constant.

This example shows that with knowledge of the mechanistic functions of the intracellular environment (from previous experiments) and realistic assumptions, we are able to formulate a model by using some mathematical expressions.

(For detailed presentations and results from simulation of the model see ref. 110.)

INTERCELLULAR MATHEMATICAL MODELS

Although intercellular communication is essential for the coordination of cell function, there are only a few models for the propagation of intercellular calcium waves. On the whole it is difficult to find examples in which changes in cellular events can be directly correlated with the movement of calcium as a second messenger between cells.[86,114,115]

Experimental data show that calcium waves propagate through glial cells generating asynchronous Ca^{2+} oscillations in these cells.[17] The coexistence of intercellular Ca^{2+} waves and asynchronous intracellular Ca^{2+} oscillations indicates that the cellular mechanism responsible for waves and oscillations are different and suggests the existence of an intercellular messenger other than Ca^{2+}, which is widely believed to be IP_3.[74,87,88] This coexistence of propagating Ca^{2+} waves and asynchronous Ca^{2+} oscillations appears to be best explained in terms of two different Ca^{2+} release processes, one mediating the intercellular Ca^{2+} wave and the other amplifying the Ca^{2+} wave and generating Ca^{2+} oscillations. According to current evidence, there are two principal ways in which these release processes may occur.

1. One-pool model:

Ca^{2+} acts as a coagonist on the IP_3 receptor, with a bell-shaped response curve.[21,24,116] In this model, only one intracellular Ca^{2+} pool is needed for Ca^{2+} oscillations and waves.[109] In any given situation, the exact contributions of RYRs, IP_3, Ca^{2+}-gated channels and the internal calcium pools to the Ca^{2+} oscillations remain to be clarified.

2. Two-pool model:

There may be two functionally distinct Ca^{2+} pools, one sensitive to IP_3 and the other to Ca^{2+}.[8,107] IP_3 releases Ca^{2+} from the IP_3-sensitive pool, whereas raised levels of Ca^{2+} in the cytoplasm initiate the release of Ca^{2+}, via RYRs, from the

Ca^{2+}-sensitive pool. This latter process is often called Ca^{2+}-induced Ca^{2+} release (CICR). It should be mentioned that to date there is no clear evidence for the existence of RYRs in glial cells.

Different models for the propagation of intercellular calcium waves, based on the one and two-pool intracellular models respectively, can be constructed and expressed mathematically. But in accordance with experimental evidence, both one-pool and two-pool models have shown that the choice of model for the intracellular Ca^{2+} release processes has little effect on the properties of the intercellular wave. The intercellular movement of IP_3 is considerably more important in the study of the intercellular wave.[92]

EXAMPLE OF TWO-POOL INTRACELLULAR MODEL IN INTERCELLULAR MODELING

The Sneyd model is based on a two-pool model for $[Ca^{2+}]_i$ oscillation, represented in Figure 7.6.[92] This model reproduces the intercellular wave and is able to account for the subsequent Ca^{2+} oscillations in glial cells.[93] The balance equations for the two-pool model are

$$\frac{dC_1}{dt} = in\_flux - extrusion - f(C_1, C_2),$$

$$\frac{dC_2}{dt} = f(C_1, C_2), \text{ and}$$

$$f(C_1, C_2) = uptake - CICR - leak.$$

where C_1 is the concentration of cytosolic calcium, C_2 is the concentration of calcium in the Ca^{2+}-sensitive pool, t is time.

In the construction of the intercellular model three relations are required: a diffusion and degradation process of IP_3, diffusion of cytosolic Ca^{2+} and a more detailed scheme for the release of Ca^{2+} from the IP_3-sensitive pool.

With these relations, the model equations can be modified as

$$\frac{dC_1}{dt} = C_1 diffusion - extrusion - f(C_1 C_2) + IP_3 - dependent\ release,$$

$$\frac{dC_2}{dt} = f(C_1 C_2)$$

$$f(C_1 C_2) = uptake - CICR - leak, \text{ and}$$

$$\frac{dI}{dt} = diffusion\ of\ IP_3 - degradation\ of\ IP_3$$

where C_1 is the concentration of cytosolic calcium, C_2 is the concentration of calcium in the Ca^{2+}-sensitive pool, I is the concentration of IP_3, IP_3-dependent release is a function of I and t is time.

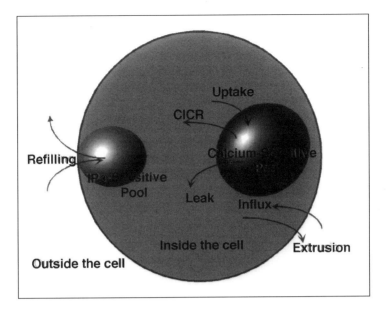

Fig. 7.6. Schematic representation of the elements in the two-pool model of Sneyd.[92] The figure shows calcium refilling of IP_3-sensitive pool and in- and out-fluxes of calcium to respectively from Ca^{2+}-sensitive pool. See color figure in insert.

The movement of IP_3 between cells is suggested to be proportional to the difference in concentration of IP_3 between cells. Numerical solution of the obtained equations shows a qualitative similarity between the model and the experimental results.

The above model was based on a model of intracellular Ca^{2+} wave propagation that relied on Ca^{2+}-induced Ca^{2+} release via RYRs. However, there is no certain evidence of the existence of RYRs in glial cells. The model above has now been modified into a two-dimensional model based only on the kinetic properties of IP_3 receptors and the existence of a single intracellular Ca^{2+} pool.[93] There may be other relations between the pools. The interested reader is referred to Wong and Klassen.[117]

PHYSIOLOGICAL ROLE FOR THE CALCIUM COMMUNICATION WITHIN THE ASTROGLIAL SYNCYTIUM

Intercellular calcium waves are thought to participate in a nonsynaptic communication system in the brain, to which the highly coupled astroglial cells are large contributors. The physiological role for propagating calcium waves in the astroglial syncytium is to a large extent unknown. Stephen Smith has proposed some possible mechanisms by which astroglial calcium waves could modulate the extracellular composition of ions, neurotransmitters and neuromodulators and thereby modulate neural excitability. He discusses the idea that changed astroglial intracellular calcium concentrations due to a propagating wave could influence the action of astroglial potassium channels, calcium channels, calcium-sensitive release and uptake of neuromodulators and neurotransmitters, metabolism, and cell structure, with a changed extracellular composition as a result.[118] A possibility for astrocytes to modulate the extracellular composition and concentration of ions and neuromodulators would mean that the astrocytes might play a more active part in the regulation of neurotransmission and excitability than has previously been thought.

There are indications of signaling going from astrocytes to neurons, via intercellular calcium waves. Induction of intercellular calcium waves in astrocytes using focal electric field potential has been shown to elicit calcium responses in neurons lying on the astrocytes.[119] This signaling probably occurs directly via gap junctions between astrocytes and neurons. In another study astroglial $[Ca^{2+}]_i$ was increased with bradykinin, which induced a release of glutamate from these astrocytes leading to calcium responses in adjacent neurons.[120] Furthermore, mechanically induced calcium waves in astroglial cells of neuronal-glial cocultures have been shown to increase cytosolic Ca^{2+}, to depolarize and to result in bursts of action potentials in neurons lying on astrocytes that were passed by the wave.[121] This effect was mediated by glutamate which was probably released from the astrocytes, leading to a stimulation of ionotropic receptors on the neurons.

Neurons could also influence the potential for astrocytes to communicate intercellularly over large brain areas. In fact, the endogenous arachidonic acid derivative, anandamide, released by neurons, has been shown to block gap-junction communication in cultured striatal mouse astrocytes.[79] This effect on the gap junction status was sensitive to pertussis toxin, a G_i protein inhibitor, indicating that it worked through a specific receptor. Thus, neurons could possibly influence the coupling strength in astroglial cells in vivo. Furthermore, anandamide's blocking effect on gap-junction dye permeability as well as blocking effect on either glutamate or mechanically induced calcium waves in astrocytes show that the gap-junction status is important for both types of propagating waves. Results indicating that the endogenous neurotransmitter serotonin could decrease the astroglial calcium wave communication supports the idea that neurons could influence astroglial cell-cell communication.[80] In this way 5-HT and noradrenaline release, in addition to their direct action on neurons, might modulate synaptic activity in surrounding regions. This would be possible if intercellular astroglial communication in vivo is important for the ion and amino acid composition in the extracellular space.

High potassium and glutamate levels have been shown to increase gap-junction coupling in cultures of astroglial cells.[96] This could be important in the glial contribution to the regulation and termination of high neuronal activity when extracellular glutamate and potassium concentrations are high. Thus, the gap-junctional communication in astroglial cells raises many new questions and ideas about physiology and pathophysiology in the brain. The calcium waves may serve to synchronize and coordinate different cell functions such as the previously proposed glial potassium buffering.[42,43] One interesting observation is that the velocity of the propagating waves in cultured astroglial cells is in a similar range as the velocity of spreading depression (SD). One recent study shows several other similarities between intercellular calcium waves in cultured astrocytes and SD.[50] This study showed that both can be triggered mechanically or by glutamate exposure, both include astrocytes as well as neurons and both are associated with changes in cellular calcium homeostasis. Furthermore, gap junction blockers octanol and halothane inhibit SD in chick retina[50] as well as intercellular calcium waves in mixed hippocampal cultures.[78] The SD required glutamate-induced neuronal depolarization. Neuronal depolarization due to passage of a mechanically induced calcium wave has, in fact, been seen.[121] Our finding that prolonged high extracellular glutamate concentration can increase the propagation of mechanically induced calcium waves in cultured hippocampal astrocytes indicates that glutamate could extend the range of the influence of astrocytes on neurons.

In a longer time perspective the increased calcium concentration due to a propagating wave could have an effect on neuro-glial interaction via differential gene expression. It could result in a changed expression, e.g., of glial glutamate transporters, Cx43 and ion channels. This might be important for the termination of high synaptic activity and potassium spatial buffering. In this way astroglial cells could take part in the regulation of neuronal excitability and thus in brain information processing.

Most studies on astroglial gap junctional communication have been done on cultured cells. One of the important next steps will be to study this communication type in brain slices and intact brain. A very important and to date unanswered question is how far these propagating waves can travel in the intact brain and how tightly regulated they are. If the calcium wave is present and regulated in a controlled and directed way in the brain, the astrocytes could play a more active role in the modulation of neural excitability than has previously been believed.

ACKNOWLEDGMENTS

Supported by grants from the Swedish Medical Research Council (grant no 14x-06005), the Swedish Work Environment Fund (grant no 94-0214), the Swedish Council for Work Life Research (grant no 95-0231), Anna Ahrenbergs Foundation and the Faculty of Medicine, Göteborg University. The skillful technical assistance of Ulrika Johansson, Barbro Eriksson and Armgard Kling was greatly appreciated.

REFERENCES

1. Kanno Y, Loewenstein WR. Intercellular diffusion. Science 1964; 143:959.
2. Loewenstein WR. Junctional intracellular communication: The cell-to-cell membrane channel. Physiol Rev 1981; 61:829-913.
3. Kettenmann H, Orkand RK, Schachner M. Coupling among identified cells in mammalian nervous system cultures. J Neurosci 1983; 3:506-516.
4. Cornell-Bell AH, Finkbeiner SM, Cooper MS et al. Glutamate induces calcium waves in cultured astrocytes: long-range glial signaling. Science 1990; 247:470-473.
5. Grynkiewicz G, Poenie M, Tsien RY. A new generation of Ca^{2+} indicators with greatly improved fluorescence properties. J Biol Chem 1985; 260:3440-3450.
6. Berridge MJ. Inositol trisphosphate and diacylglycerol: two interacting second messengers. Annu Rev Biochem 1987; 56:159-193.
7. Cockcroft S, Thomas GMH. Inositol-lipid-specific phospholipase C isoenzymes and their differential regulation by receptors. Biochem J 1992; 288:1-14.
8. Berridge MJ. Inositol trisphosphate and calcium signalling. Nature 1993; 361:315-325.
9. Berridge MJ, Irvine RF. Inositol trisphosphate, a novel second messenger in cellular signal transduction. Nature 1984; 312:315-321.
10. Streb H, Irvine RF, Berridge MJ et al. Release of Ca^{2+} from a nonmitochondrial intracellular store in pancreatic acinar cells by inositol-1,4,5-trisphosphate. Nature 1983; 306:67-69.
11. Prentki M, Biden TJ, Janjic D et al. Rapid mobilization of Ca^{2+} from rat insulinoma microsomes by inositol-1,4,5-trisphosphate. Nature 1984; 309:562-564.
12. Van den Pol AN, Finkbeiner SM, Cornell-Bell AH. Calcium excitability and oscillations in suprachiasmatic nucleus neurons and glia in vitro. J Neurosci 1992; 12:2648-2664.
13. Nilsson M, Hansson E, Rönnbäck L. Agonist-evoked Ca^{2+} transients in primary astroglial cultures—modulatory effects of valproic acid. Glia 1992; 5:201-209.
14. Salm AK, McCarthy KD. Norepinephrine-evoked calcium transients in cultured cerebral type1 astroglia. Glia 1990; 3:529-538.

15. Nilsson M, Hansson E, Rönnbäck L. Heterogeinty among astroglial cells with respect to 5HT-evoked cytosolic Ca^{2+} responses: A microspectrofluorimetric study on single cells in primary culture. Life Sci 1991; 49:1339-1350.

16. Fatatis A , Russell JT. Spontaneous Changes in Intracellular Calcium Concentration in Type I Astrocytes From Rat Cerebral Cortex in Primary Culture. Glia 1992; 5:95-104.

17. Charles AC, Merrill JE, Dirksen ER et al. Intercellular signaling in glial cells: calcium waves and oscillations in response to mechanical stimulation and glutamate. Neuron 1991; 6:983-992

18. McPherson-PS Campbell-KP. The ryanodine receptor/Ca^{2+} release channel. J Biol Chem 1993; 268:13765-13768.

19. Langley, D, Pearce, B. Ryanodine-induced intracellular calcium mobilization in cultured astrocytes. Glia 1994; 12:128-134.

20. Sanderson MJ, Charles AC, Boitano S et al. Mechanisms and function of intercellular calcium signaling. Mol Cell Endocrinol 1994; 98:173-187.

21. Finch EA, Turner TJ, Goldin SM. Calcium as a coagonist of inositol 1,4,5-trisphosphate-induced calcium release. Science 1991; 252:443-446.

22. Meyer T, Stryer L. Calcium spiking. Annu Rev Biophys Biophys Chem 1991; 20:153-174.

23. Berridge MJ. Calcium Oscillations. J Biol Chem 1990; 265:9583-9586.

24. Bezprozvanny I, Watras J, Ehrlich BE. Bell-shaped calcium-response curves of Ins(1,4,5)P$_3$- and calcium-gated channels from endoplasmic reticulum of cerebellum. Nature 1991; 351:751-754.

25. Harootunian AT, Kao JPY, Paranjape et al. Generation of calcium oscillations in fibroblasts by positive feedback between calcium and IP$_3$. Science 1991; 251:75-78.

26. Meyer T, Stryer L. Molecular model for receptor-stimulated calcium spiking. Proc Natl Acad Sci 1988; 85:5051-5055.

27. Berridge MJ. Inositol trisphosphate-induced membrane potential oscillations in Xenopus oocytes. J Physiol Lond 1988; 403:589-599.

28. Matozaki T, Goke B, Tsunoda Y et al. Two functionally distinct cholecystokinin receptors show different modes of actions on Ca^{2+} mobilization and phospholipid hydrolysis in isolated rat pancreatic acini. Studies using a new cholecystokinin analog, JMV-180. J Biol Chem 1990; 265:6247-6254.

29. Roth BJ, Yagodin SV, Holtzclaw L et al. A mathematical model of agonist-induced propagation of calcium waves in astrocytes. Cell Calcium 1995; 17:53-64.

30. Nicholson BJ, Gros D, Kent SB et al. The Mr 28.000 gap junction proteins from heart and liver are different but related. J Biol Chem 1985; 260:6514-6517.

31. Beyer EC, Paul DL, Goodenough DA. Connexin family of gap junction proteins. J Membr Biol 1990; 116:187-194.

32. Bennett MV, Barrio LC, Bargiello TA et al. Gap junctions: new tools, new answers, new questions. Neuron 1991; 6:305-320.

33. Dermietzel R, Spray DS. Gap junctions in the brain: where, what type, how many and why? Trends Neurosci 1993; 16:186-192.

34. Weidmann S. The electrical constants of Purkinje fibers. J Physiol (Lond.) 1952; 118:348-360.

35. Kuffler S, Potter DD. Glia in the leech central nervous system: physiological properties and neuron-glia relationship. J Neurophysiol 1964; 27:290.

36. Revel JP, Karnovsky MJ. Hexagonal array of subunits in intercellular junctions of the mouse heart and liver. J Cell Biol 1967; 33:C7-C12.

37. Brightman MW, Reese TS. Junctions between intimately apposed cell membranes in the vertebrate brain. J Cell Biol 1969; 40:648-677.

38. Massa PT, Mugnaini E. Cell junctions and intramembrane particles of astrocytes and oligodendrocytes: a freeze-fracture study. Neurosci 1982; 7:523-538.

39. Massa PT, Mugnaini E. Cell-Cell junctional interactions and characteristic plasma membrane features of cultured rat glial cells. Neurosci 1985; 14:695-709.

40. Fischer G, Kettenmann H. Cultured astrocytes form a syncytium after maturation. Exp Cell Res 1985; 159:273-279.

41. Mugnaini E. Cell junctions of astrocytes, ependyma, and related cells in the mammalian nervous system, with emphasis on the hypothesis of a generalized functional syncytium of supporting cells. In Fedoroff S, Vernadakis A, eds. Astrocytes. Vol 1. New York: Academic Press, 1986:329-371.

42. Hertz L. Possible role of neuroglia: Potassium mediated neuronal-neuroglial- neuronal impulse transmission system. Nature 1965; 305:632-634.

43. Orkand RK, Nicholls JG, Kuffler SW. Effect on nerve impulses on the membrane potential of glial cells in the central nervous system of amphibia. J Neurophysiol 1966; 29:788-806.

44. Uga S, Smelser. Comparative study of the fine structure of retinal M(ller cells in various vertebrates. Invest Ophthalmol 1973; 12:434-448.

45. Sontheimer H, Minturn JE, Black JA et al. Specificity of cell-cell coupling in the rat optic nerve astrocytes in vitro. Proc Natl Acad Sci 1990; 87:9833-9837.

46. Belliveau DJ, Naus CC. Cortical type 2 astrocytes are not dye coupled nor do they express the major gap junction genes found in the central nervous system. Glia 1994; 12:24-34.

47. Tani E, Nishiura M, Higashi M. Freeze-fracture studies of gap junctions of normal and neoplastic astrocytes. Acta Neuropathol Berl 1973; 26:127-138.

48. Naus CC, Bechberger JF, Caveney S et al. Expression of gap junction genes in astrocytes and C6 glioma cells. Neurosci Lett 1991; 126:33-36.

49. Klaunig JE, Ruch RJ. Role of inhibition of intercellular communication in carcinogenesis. Lab Invest 1990; 62:135-46.

50. Nedergaard M, Cooper AJL, Goldman SA. Gap junctions are required for the propagation of spreading depression. J Neurobiol 1995; 28:433-444.

51. Dermietzel R, Hwang TK, Spray DS. The gap junction family: structure, function and chemistry. Anat Embryol Berl 1990; 182:517-528.

52. Batter DK, Corpina RA, Roy C et al. Heterogeneity in gap junction expression in astrocytes cultured from different brain regions. Glia 1992; 6:213-21.

53. Nagy JI, Yamamoto T, Sawchuk MA et al. Quantitative immunohistochemical and biochemical correlates of connexin43 localization in rat brain. Glia 1992; 5:1-9.

54. Lee SH, Kim WT, Cornell-Bell AH et al. Astrocytes exhibit regional specificity in gap-junction coupling. Glia 1994; 11:315-325.

55. Hertzberg EL, Disher RM, Tiller AA et al. Topology of the Mr 27,000 liver gap junction protein: Cytoplasmic localization of amino- and carboxyl termini and a hydrophilic domain which is protease-hypersensitive. J Biol Chem 1988; 263:19105-19111.

56. Caspar DLC, Goodenough DA, Makowski L et al. Gap junction structures. I. Correlated electron microscopy and x-ray diffraction. J Cell Biol 1977; 74:605-628.

57. Schwarzmann G, Wiegandt H, Rose B et al. Diameter of the cell-to-cell junctional channels as probed with neutral molecules. Science 1981; 213:551-553.

58. Makowski L. Structural domains in gap junctions: Implications for the control of intracellular communication. In: Bennett M, Spray D, eds. Gap Junctions. New York: Cold Spring Harbor, 1985:5-12.

59. Makowski L, Caspar DL, Phillips WC et al. Gap Junction structures. II. Analysis of the x-ray diffraction data. J Cell Biol 1977; 74:629-645.

60. Neyton J, Trautmann A. Single-channel currents of an intercellular junction. Nature 1985; 317:331-335.

61. Dermietzel R, Hertzberg EL, Kessler JA et al. Gap junctions between cultured astrocytes: immunocytochemical, molecular, and electrophysiological analysis. J Neurosci 1991; 11:1421-1432.

62. Giaume C, Marin P.K., Cordier, J et al. Adrenergic regulation of intercellular communications between cultured striatal astrocytes from the mouse. Proc Natl Acad Sci 1991; 88:5577-5581.

63. Unwin N. The structure of ion channels in membranes of excitable cells. Neuron 1989; 3:665-676.

64. Spray DC, Bennett MVL, eds. Physiology and pharmacology of gap junctions. Annu Rev Physiol 1985; 47:281-303.

65. Pappas CA, Rioult MG, Ransom BR. Octanol, a gap junction uncoupling agent, changes intracellular [H$^+$] in rat astrocytes. Glia 1996; 16:7-15.

66. Anders JJ. Lactic acid inhibition of gap junctional intercellular communication in in vitro astrocytes as measured by fluorescence recovery after laser photobleaching. Glia 1988; 1:371-379.

67. Hermans MM, Kortekaas P, Jongsma HJ et al. pH sensitivity of the cardiac gap junction proteins, connexin 45 and 43. Pflugers Arch 1995; 431:138-140.
68. Mantz J, Cordier J, Giaume C. Effects of general anesthetics on intercellular communications mediated by gap junctions between astrocytes in primary culture. Anesthesiol 1993; 78:892-901.
69. Enkvist MOK, McCarthy KD. Activation of protein kinase C blocks astroglial gap junction communication and inhibits the spread of calcium waves. J Neurochem 1992; 59:519-526.
70. DeMello WC. Cell-to-cell communication in heart and other tissues. Prog Biophys Mol Biol 1982; 39:147-182.
71. Lazrak A, Peracchia C. Gap junction gating sensitivity to physiological internal calcium regardless of pH in Novikoff hepatoma cells. Biophys J 1993; 65:2002-2012.
72. Ransom BR, Sontheimer H. Cell-cell coupling demonstrated by intracellular injection of the fluorescent dye lucifer yellow. In: Kettenman H, Grantyn R, eds. Practical Electrophysiological Methods. New York: Wiley-Liss, 1992:336-342.
73. Lee SH, Magge S, Spencer DD et al. Human epileptic astrocytes exhibit increased gap junction coupling. Glia 1995; 15:195-202.
74. Sanderson MJ, Charles AC, Dirksen ER. Mechanical stimulation and intercellular communication increases intracellular Ca^{2+} in epithelial cells. Cell Regul 1990; 1:585-596.
75. Demer LL, Wortham CM, Dirksen ER et al. Mechanical stimulation induces intercellular calcium signaling in bovine aortic endothelial cells. Am J Physiol 1993; 264:H2094-H2102.
76. Sigurdson W, Ruknudin A, Sachs F. Calcium imaging of mechanically induced fluxes in tissue-cultured chick heart: role of stretch-activated ion channels. Am J Physiol 1992; 262:H1110-H11115.
77. Dani JW, Chernjavsky A, Smith SJ. Neuronal activity triggers calcium waves in hippocampal astrocyte networks. Neuron 1992; 8:429-440.
78. Finkbeiner S. Calcium waves in astrocytes-filling in the gaps. Neuron 1992; 8:1101-1108.
79. Venance L, Piomelli D, Glowinski J et al. Inhibition by anandamide of gap junctions and intercellular calcium signalling in striatal astrocytes. Nature 1995; 376:590-594.
80. Blomstrand F, Khatibi S, Muyderman H et al. 5-HT and glutamate modulate velocity and propagation of intercellular calcium communication in hippocampal astroglial-neuronal primary cultures. (Submitted).
81. Hansen M, Boitano S, Dirksen ER et al. Intercellular calcium signaling induced by extracellular adenosine 5′-trisphosphate and mechanical stimulation in airway epithelial cells. J Cell Sci 1993; 106:995-1004.
82. Charles AC, Naus CCG, Zhu D et al. Intercellular calcium signaling via gap junctions in glioma cells. J Cell Biol 1992; 118:195-201.

83. Naus CC, Zhu D, Todd SD et al. Characteristics of C6 cells overexpressing a gap junction protein. Cell Mol Neurobiol 1992; 12:163-175.

84. Enomoto K, Furuya K, Yamagishi S et al. Mechanically induced electrical and intracellular calcium responses in normal and cancerous mammary cells. Cell Calcium 1992; 13:501-511.

85. Enomoto K, Furuya K, Yamagishi S et al. The increase in the intracellular Ca^{2+} concentration induced by mechanical stimulation is propagated via release of pyrophosphorylated nucleotides in mammary epithelial cells. Pflugers Arch 1994; 427:533-542.

86. Saéz JC, Conner JA, Spray DC et al. Hepatocyte gap junctions are permeable to the second messenger, inositol 1,4,5-trisphosphate, and to calcium ions. Proc Nat Acad Sci 1989; 86:2708-2712.

87. Boitano S, Dirksen ER, Sanderson MJ. Intercellular propagation of calcium waves mediated by inositol trisphosphate. Science 1992; 258:292-295.

88. Charles AC, Dirksen ER, Merrill JE et al. Mechanisms of intercellular calcium signaling in glial cells studied with dantrolene and thapsigargin. Glia 1993; 7:134-145.

89. Sanderson MJ. Intercellular calcium waves mediated by inositol trisphosphate. In: Bock GR, Ackrill K, eds. Calcium, waves, gradients and oscillations. CIBA Foundation Symposium 188. London: Wiley & Sons Ltd., 1995:175-194.

90. Hansen M, Boitano S, Dirksen ER et al. A role for phospholipase C activity but not ryanodine receptors in the initiation and propagation of intercellular calcium waves. J Cell Sci 1995; 108:2583-2590.

91. Marshall IC, Taylor CW. Biphasic effects of cytosolic Ca^{2+} on $Ins(1,4,5)P_3$-stimulated Ca^{2+} mobilization in hepatocytes. J Biol Chem 1993; 268:13214-13220.

92. Sneyd J, Charles AC, Sanderson MJ. A model for the propagation of intercellular calcium waves. Am J Physiol 1994; 266:C293-C302.

93. Sneyd J, Wetton BTR, Charles AC et al. Intercellular calcium waves mediated by diffusion of inositol trisphosphate: a two-dimensional model. Am J Physiol 1995; 268:C1537-C1545.

94. Cuthbertson KSR, Chay TR. Modelling receptor-controlled intracellular calcium oscillators. Cell Calcium 1991; 12:97-109.

95. Kim WT, Rioult MG, Cornell-Bell AH. Glutamate-induced calcium signaling in astrocytes. Glia 1994; 11:173-184.

96. Enkvist MOK, McCarthy KD. Astroglial gap junction communication is increased by treatment with either glutamate or high K^+ concentration. J Neurochem 1994; 62:489-495.

97. Hösli L, Hösli E, Baggi M et al. Action of dopamine and serotonin on the membrane potential of cultured astrocytes. Exp Brain Res 1987; 65:482-485.

98. Åkerman KE, Enkvist MO, Holopainen I. Activators of protein kinase C and phenylephrine depolarize astrocyte membrane by reducing the K$^+$ permeability. Neurosci Lett 1988; 92:265-269.

99. Anderson S, Brismar T, Hansson E. Effect of external K$^+$, Ca^{2+}, and Ba^{2+} on membrane potential and ionic conductance in rat astrocytes. Cell Mol Neurobiol 1995; 15:439-450.

100. Lechleiter JD, Clapham DE. Molecular mechanisms of intracellular calcium excitability in X. laevis oocytes. Cell 1992; 69:283-294.

101. Tsien RW, Tsien RY. Calcium channels, stores, oscillations. Annu Rev Cell Biol 1990; 6:715-760.

102. Girard S, Clapham D. Acceleration of intracellular calcium waves in Xenopus oocytes by calcium influx. Science 1993; 260:229-232.

103. Camacho P, Lechleiter JD. Increased frequency of calcium waves in Xenopus laevis oocytes that express a calcium-ATPase. Science 1993; 260:226-229.

104. Parker I, Yao Y. Regenerative release of calcium from functionally discrete subcellular stores by inositol trisphosphate. Proc R Soc Lond B Biol Sci 1992; 246:269-274.

105. Murray JD. Ch 11-12. In: Mathematical Biology. New York: Springer Verlag, 1989:161-166.

106. Petersen OH, Wakui M. Oscillating intracellular Ca^{2+} signals evoked by activation of receptors linked to inositol lipid hydrolysis: mechanism of generation. J Membr Biol 1990; 118:93-105.

107. Goldbeter A, Dupont G, Berridge MJ. Minimal model for signal-induced Ca^{2+} oscillations and for their frequency encoding through protein phosphorylation. Proc Natl Acad Sci 1990; 87:1461-1465.

108. Somogyi R, Stucki JW. Hormone-induced calcium oscillations in liver cells can be explained by a simple one pool model. J Biol Chem 1991; 266:11068-11077.

109. De Young GW, Keizer J. A single-pool inositol 1,4,5-trisphosphate-receptor-based model for agonist-stimulated oscillations in Ca^{2+} concentration. Proc Natl Acad Sci 1992; 89:9895-9899.

110. Atri A, Amundson J, Clapham D et al. A single-pool model for intracellular calcium oscillations and waves in the Xenopus laevis oocyte. Biophys J 1993; 65:1727-1739.

111. Sneyd J, Girard S, Clapham D. Calcium wave propagation by calcium-induced calcium release: an unusual excitable system. Bull Math Biol 1993; 55:315-344.

112. Parys JB, Sernett SW, DeLisle S et al. Isolation, characterization, and localization of the inositol 1,4,5-trisphosphate receptor protein in Xenopus laevis oocytes. J Biol Chem 1992; 267:18776-18782.

113. Hodgkin AL, Huxley AF. A quantitative description of membrane current and its application to conduction and excitation in nerve. J Physiol 1952; 117:500-544.

114. Brehm P, Lechleiter J, Smith S et al. Intercellular signaling as visualized by endogenous calcium-dependent bioluminescence. Neuron 1989; 3:191-198.

115. Sandberg K, Iida HJ, Catt KJ. Intercellular communication between follicular angiotensin receptors and Xenopus laevis oocytes: medication by an inositol 1,4,5-trisphosphate-dependent mechanism. J Cell Biol 1992; 117:157-167.

116. Iino M. Biphasic Ca^{2+} dependence of inositol 1,4,5-trisphosphate-induced Ca^{2+} release in smooth muscle cells of the guinea pig taenia caeci. J Gen Physiol 1990; 95:1103-1122.

117. Wong AY, Klassen GA. Endothelin-induced electrical activity and calcium dynamics in vascular smooth muscle cells: a model study. Ann Biomed Eng 1996; 24:547-560.

118. Smith SJ. Do astrocytes process neural information? Prog Brain Res 1992; 94:119-136.

119. Nedergaard M. Direct signaling from astrocytes to neurons in cultures of mammalian brain cells. Science 1994; 263:1768-1771.

120. Parpura V, Basarsky TA, Liu F et al. Glutamate-mediated astrocyte-neuron signalling. Nature 1994; 369:744-747.

121. Hassinger TD, Atkinson PB, Strecker GJ et al. Evidence for glutamate-mediated activation of hippocampal neurons by glial calcium waves. J Neurobiol 1995; 28:159-170.

══════ CHAPTER 8 ══════

DOES THE ASTROGLIAL NETWORK PERFORM QUALITATIVE MODIFICATIONS OF NEURONAL MESSAGES?

Hypothesis: Astroglial dysfunction results in an organic psychosyndrome with mental fatigue, decreased capacity for concentration and disturbance of short-term memory.

Lars Rönnbäck and Elisabeth Hansson

INTRODUCTION

Until the early 1980s astroglia were thought of as passive structural bystanders in relation to the neurons, with a metabolic role in neuronal activity. During recent years this picture has changed. Membrane receptors for neurotransmitters, neuropeptides and other neuroactive substances have been identified as well as high affinity, high capacity uptake carriers for glutamate (Glu) and γ–amino butyric acid (GABA). Furthermore, the cells express a large number of ion channels. The astroglial syncytium thus has the properties required to monitor neuronal activity. The syncytium can register neuroactive substances in the extracellular space, the volume of which can be profoundly regulated by the astroglia. The cell syncytium also senses the blood serum composition. After integration of the information obtained within the electrically coupled astroglial network into alterations in Ca^{2+} based excitability or in the membrane potential, the active capacity of the astroglia to clear the extracellular space of Glu and K^+ can be influenced due to the voltage dependence of these carriers and ion channels.

On the basis of some figures, we discuss below whether the astroglia, in addition to their utility or "housekeeping" functions, might have the ability to I) help the neurons in achieving high activity and endurance, II) participate in the regulation of the signal-to-noise ratio for Glu transmission at the single synapse level and III) modulate the neuronal excitability level. As the astroglial

On Astrocytes and Glutamate Neurotransmission: New Waves in Brain Information Processing, edited by Elisabeth Hansson, Torsten Olsson and Lars Rönnbäck. © 1997 R.G. Landes Company.

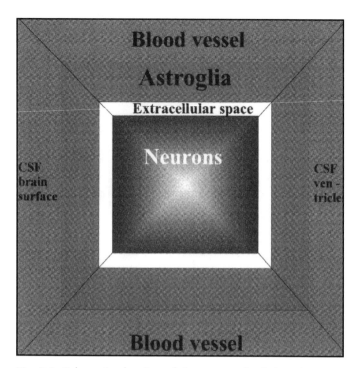

Fig. 8.1. Schematic drawing of the structural relations between astroglia and their environment: neurons, blood vessels, brain surface and ventricles, and contact with the cerebrospinal fluid (CSF). The communication between the astroglia and the neurons occurs through the extracellular space.

network is in contact with many synapses, we put forward the working hypothesis that this syncytium performs qualitative modifications of neuronal information processing and ultimately of the neuronal messages, especially when there are requirements for intense neuronal activity for long time periods.

As a logical consequence, we also put forward the hypothesis that astroglial dysfunction with impairment of the fine tuning of extracellular Glu or K^+ levels might be one pathogenic factor in an organic psychosyndrome with defects in cognitive capacity in mentally demanding situations, requiring high endurance, i.e., mental fatigue, decreased capacity for concentration and secondary impairment of short-term memory, often seen after brain damage, or inflammatory or infectious states in the CNS.

ASTROCYTE ANATOMY, PROPERTIES AND FUNCTIONS

Astrocytes represent a large fraction of the cell population in the CNS. The cells constitute more than 50% of the cell numbers and approximately 20% of the cell volume in the cerebral cortex of higher mammals.[1] (see also chapter 2). Their long processes surround blood vessels and synapses, form a continuous subpial and subependymal layer, surround neuronal surfaces and form a gap junction network with other astrocytes (Fig. 8.1). The figure depicts the strategic position of the astrocytes, situated between the blood vessels and the synapses and neurons, thus with the possibility to protect the neurons from their "surrounding world." However, as Virchow proposed more than 100 years ago, they also provide support for the neurons. The astrocytes and the neurons communicate through the very narrow extracellular space. The gap junctions[2,3] are a prominent feature of astrocytes in the brain and considerable evidence suggests that astrocytes are electrically coupled.[4,5] Recently, it was demonstrated that Glu induces increases in cytoplasmic free calcium, which propagates as waves within the cytoplasm of individual astrocytes and between adjacent astrocytes in confluent cultures.[6,7] (see also chapter 7). The propagating calcium waves within the astrocyte networks may constitute a long-range signaling system within the brain.[8]

In the mature CNS, astrocytes are responsible for K^+ and amino acid homeostasis, preferentially Glu and GABA.[9-11] The cells have a negative resting membrane potential, more negative than that of neurons. A variety of voltage-gated ionic channels, Na^+, Ca^{2+}, K^+ and anion channels, have been demonstrated in recent electrophysiological studies on astroglial primary cultures,[12,13] as well as in various hippocampal preparations.[14,15] The astrocytes possess relatively high K^+ conductance, to which at least five types of K^+-channels contribute (see also chapter 4).

Astroglia have a prominent capacity for Glu clearance from the extracellular space (see chapter 5). The cells express one Na^+-dependent Glu transporter which is electrogenic, that is, for each negatively charged Glu molecule that is taken up, three Na^+ ions (or two Na^+ ions and one H^+ ion) are cotransported into the cell and one K^+ ion is transported out of the cell.[16] This net positive inward flux results in depolarization of the cell membrane. Furthermore, the Glu uptake is strongly voltage-dependent, being smaller at depolarized potentials. Under certain circumstances, the transporter can be reversed, resulting in a release of Glu. It has been shown that such release can be stimulated by raising the extracellular K^+ concentration ($[K^+]_e$), or the intracellular Glu concentration ($[Glu]_i$), $[Na^+]_i$ or by depolarizing the cell membrane.[17] On the other hand, the release of Glu via the transporter is inhibited by rising $[Glu]_e$ or $[Na^+]_e$.[17] Agents such as arachidonic acids,[18] or free radicals[19] inhibit Glu uptake, while some cytokines or leukotrienes,[20] for example, give rise to depolarization of the astroglial cell membrane and, thereby, also prominently interfere with the Glu uptake capacity. Even some metals, e.g., Hg, diminish astroglial Glu uptake.[21] However, the astroglial Glu uptake has been shown to be regulated by adrenergic agonists. Beta-adrenergic agonists diminished the Glu uptake in primary cultures, while α_1-adrenergic agonists increased the Glu uptake.[22]

In addition to neurons, astrocytes are also potential targets for chemical signals from growth factors, hormones and neurotransmitters. It has been well established in many laboratories that the astroglial cells express membrane receptors for most known neurotransmitters.[23,24] (see also chapter 3) As it is important for the body of this chapter, it must be mentioned that astroglia express different Glu receptors (probably of ionotropic or metabotropic types, or both) the presence of which have been demonstrated both in vitro and in vivo.[25-28] It has been demonstrated that Glu depolarizes cultured astrocytes from rat cerebral hemispheres, mediated via receptor activation.[29] However, it is not known to what extent these receptors are expressed on single astroglial cells in the mature nervous system. In culture, a considerable amount of the type 1 astroglial cells respond to Glu with Ca^{2+} transients, which speaks in favor of widely distributed metabotropic Glu receptors (mGluRs) with functioning signal transduction.[25] However, most of those experiments have been performed with bath-application of the receptor agonist, i.e., all cells in the preparation were exposed at the same time. Even when the registrations are from single cells, the responses obtained might originate from other cells within the gap junction coupled cell network. Very few studies are available on the expression of Glu receptors in in vivo preparations.[27]

Recent data have also demonstrated the astroglial cell population to be potentially important recipients of adrenergic input.[30,31] (see also chapter 3). Beta[1] receptors, coupled to the cyclic AMP/adenylate cyclase system, seem to be expressed to a greater extent on astroglial cells than on neurons.[32] The other adrenergic receptors are expressed on both astroglia and neurons, and there seems to be an interaction between these receptors on the astrocytes and the capacity to modulate second messenger processes (see chapter 3). The adrenergic system seems primarily to be involved in the energy metabolism of astroglia[33] but it has also been shown that adrenergic stimulation regulates amino acid uptake[22] (see above). The suggestions that in addition to neurons, astroglia are an important target for noradrenaline (NA)[30] is important, as the central noradrenergic system is intimately involved in determining both the level of neuronal

Fig. 8.2. (Opposite page) Schematic drawing of a synapse region with pre- and postsynaptic (presyn and postsyn) structures and a blood vessel, surrounded by astroglial processes. An inhibitory axon terminates at the presynaptic terminal. Neuroactive substances, visualized by black dots in the figure, are transported in the extracellular (e.c.) space. This space has been calculated to constitute approximately 20-25% of the total brain volume. Astroglia regulate the extracellular concentration of ions and amino acids by two principal mechanisms, namely: I) by the activation of ion channels and amino acid high affinity, high capacity uptake carriers and II) by changing the extracellular volume secondary to changes in the cell volume.

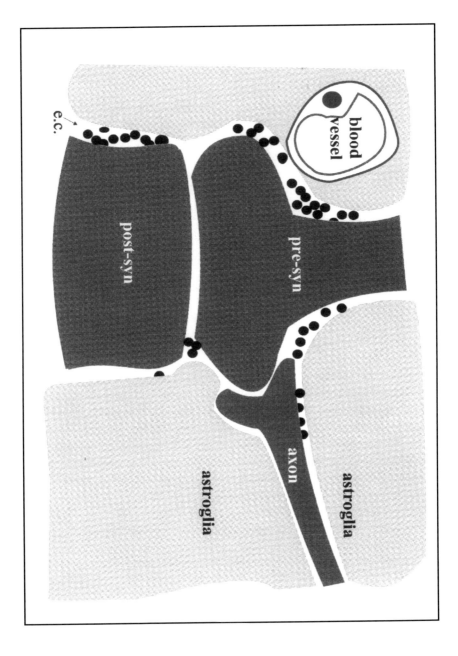

excitability and the pattern of activity they generate in the cortical systems. Furthermore, the noradrenergic system is thought to play an important role in attention processes and in responses to stress.[34] There is also some data which indicates that astroglia might be targets even for the long-distance transported 5-HT in the cerebral cortex (see chapter 3). There are intimate interactions between the signal transduction systems of 5-HT and those of adrenergic receptor systems (see chapter 3).

Astrocytes have a pronounced capacity to regulate their own cell volume.[35] (see chapter 6) As the distance between the astroglial and neuronal membranes is small, even limited changes in astroglial cell volume give rise to proportionally large effects on the extracellular space volume, with dramatic effects on the concentration of substances therein. In summary, astroglia appear to have a prominent capacity to regulate the concentration of neuroactive substances in the extracellular space, both by modulating the uptake of substances and by regulating the extracellular volume.[36] It seems that astroglia in various brain regions differ concerning their sets of receptors, uptake carriers and ion channels, mostly due to the requirements of their neuronal partners. This was demonstrated in the early 1980s.[37-41] The early studies were performed in tissue culture, with the drawbacks of a culture system concerning maturation of the cells.

ASTROGLIA HAVE THE CAPACITY TO SENSE AND MODULATE GLUTAMATE NEUROTRANSMISSION

ASTROGLIA AND THE GLUTAMATE SYNAPSE

According to the traditional view the Glu synapse consists of a pre- and a postsynaptic terminal, two membranes separated by a 20 nm wide space. The electrically transmitted signal is transferred into a chemical signal by the release of neurotransmitters from the presynaptic terminal. The interaction of the transmitter with the Glu receptors in the postsynaptic membrane transfers the chemical message into changes in the membrane potential of the postsynaptic

Fig. 8.3. (Opposite page) Astroglial monitoring of synaptic activity. Same synapse structures as in Figure 8.2. The synapse is now active with the release of glutamate (Glu). Glu interacts with astroglial metabotropic Glu receptors (mGluRs), the activation of which induces the formation of inositoltrisphosphate (IP$_3$) and a Ca^{2+} transient in the astroglial cytoplasm giving rise to Ca^{2+} oscillations or waves. K$^+$ and Glu, released from the neuron, are actively taken up by the astroglia and induce astroglial depolarization which spreads rapidly within the gap junction coupled astroglial cells. These substances also induce a volume increase (swelling) of the astroglial cell, with the result that the astroglial and neuronal cell membranes approach each other. The astroglia, now active, are illustrated with a darker shade than in Figure 8.2.

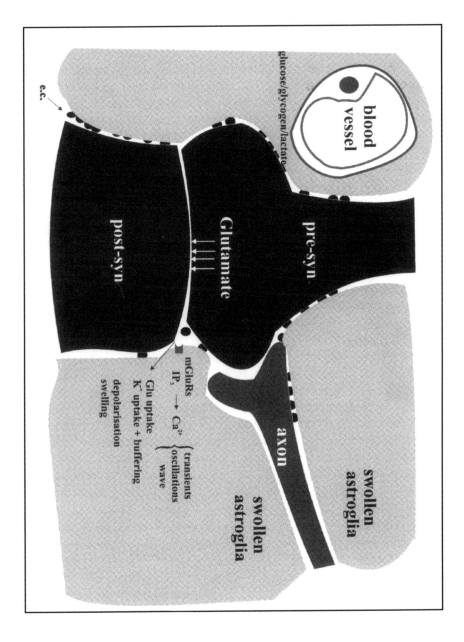

cell and, in addition, leads to the activation of signal transduction systems within that cell.

Recent research has demonstrated that the Glu synapse is not as simple a structure as was previously thought. It was shown that Glu-releasing nerve terminals are close to astrocytic membranes. The extracellular space between the neuronal and the glial membranes is approximately 200nm. In view of this anatomic arrangement and in the light of the characteristics and properties of astrocytes presented above and in previous chapters, the neurotransmitters interact not only with the synaptic membranes but also with the membranes of the astroglial processes (Fig. 8.2). Receptor stimulation of the astroglial cell leads to activation of second messengers, ion channels, intracellular metabolic pathways and changes in cell volume. The extracellular concentrations of Glu and K^+ formed during neuronal activity are removed by the astroglial network. Furthermore, the astrocytes provide metabolic support to the neurons and facilitate neurotransmission by producing the precursors of the neurotransmitters, e.g., the GABA/Glu shunt with glutamine production.[42]

ASTROGLIA MONITOR, INTEGRATE AND MODULATE SYNAPTIC ACTIVITY

We will now put together data from the literature and results from our own laboratory to try to formulate an image of some of the mechanisms underlying the astroglial monitoring of synaptic activity, the integration of information within the linked and electrically coupled network of the gap junction and finally to present some view of the astroglial influence on the excitability level of synapses (Figs. 8.3-8.6).

Astroglia register synaptic activity (Fig. 8.3)

When the action potential reaches the presynaptic region, the neuronal depolarization induces the release of K^+ into the extracellular space. Glu is released from the presynaptic terminal and when it interacts with the postsynaptic membrane receptors there is neuronal depolarization resulting in an increased level of $[K^+]_e$ around the postsynaptic region. These increased extracellular K^+ levels are recognized by the astroglial membranes and in view of the high astroglial capacity to remove K^+ from the extracellular space, the astroglial K^+ uptake serves to get the neuronal membrane ready for a new action potential, thus enabling rapid synaptic signaling. One might ask whether the glial cell is just a sink for K^+ which is pumped back to the neuronal compartment within the same synapse, or if K^+ is redistributed within a single astroglial cell or within the astroglial syncytium. It was shown during the mid-1960s that K^+ is transported within the astroglial gap junction coupled syncytium and released at places where there is lower neuronal activity.[43-45]

When $[Glu]_e$ increases, owing to release of Glu from the presynaptic terminal, the activation of astroglial mGluRs[46,47] induces the formation of inositol-

1,4,5-trisphosphate (IP$_3$) which, in turn, leads to the mobilization of intracellular Ca^{2+}, the formation of Ca^{2+} oscillations and/or Ca^{2+}-"waves", that travel within the affected cell and probably to other cells. Even the adenylate cyclase/cAMP system is activated with stimulation and/or inhibition, depending on the receptor subtype activated. Glu is actively taken up together with Na$^+$ and H$^+$ and the Glu/GABA shunt transforms Glu to glutamine. The [Glu]$_e$ might increase if glial Glu uptake capacity is reduced, secondary to astroglial depolarization, increased [K$^+$]$_e$ and arachidonic acid release due to neuronal Glu receptor stimulation.[48] These factors might cause an increase in the amount of time spent by Glu in the synaptic space. The question of whether or not the astroglial Glu uptake is of importance for Glu transmission has been discussed. Owing to the anatomical location, the presynaptic Glu uptake carriers might be important for the reuptake of presynaptically released Glu. However, it has been estimated that astroglial Glu carriers have enough capacity to remove all Glu released from the presynaptic site.[9] Under any circumstances, the arrangements with astroglial Glu uptake carriers acting as an effective "vacuum cleaner" in the synaptic region demonstrate that the high capacity and high affinity Glu uptake may make intense synaptic transmission for long time periods possible, and with a high signal-to-noise ratio. Furthermore, the inherent electrogenicity of the transporter causes a membrane depolarization that slows the uptake. Clearly, maximum efficiency of Glu uptake would be obtained if the extent of depolarization could be minimized during the uptake process. Activation of the various K$^+$ channels could reduce the depolarization. One interesting possibility is that the activation of mGluRs, which results in the liberation of Ca^{2+} from internal stores, could lead to activation of Ca^{2+}-dependent K$^+$ channels which, in turn, would serve to clamp the membrane potential to a range most conducive to Glu buffering during repetitive synaptic activity.[49] In the long-term depolarized astroglia, e.g., after a brain injury with a deteriorated metabolic state and an accompanying increase in [K$^+$]$_e$, the Glu uptake capacity will be profoundly decreased. This will result in a pathophysiological situation of increased [Glu]$_e$, astroglial depolarization and astroglial swelling, with an accompanying collapse of the extracellular space.

The astroglial membrane will be depolarized due to increased [K$^+$]$_e$ and [Glu]$_e$. If the neuronal activity is intense, the astroglial cell increases in volume, leading to a decrease of the extracellular space. Such a decrease of the extracellular volume might affect the concentration of substances (including the Glu concentration) therein. The volume regulation of the astroglia with secondary effects on the extracellular space is probably important for the dynamics of the neurotransmission. If we assume that the distance between the astroglial and neuronal membranes in the vicinity of the synapse is in the order of 200 nm, then a 10% increase in the astroglial volume would result in an average increase

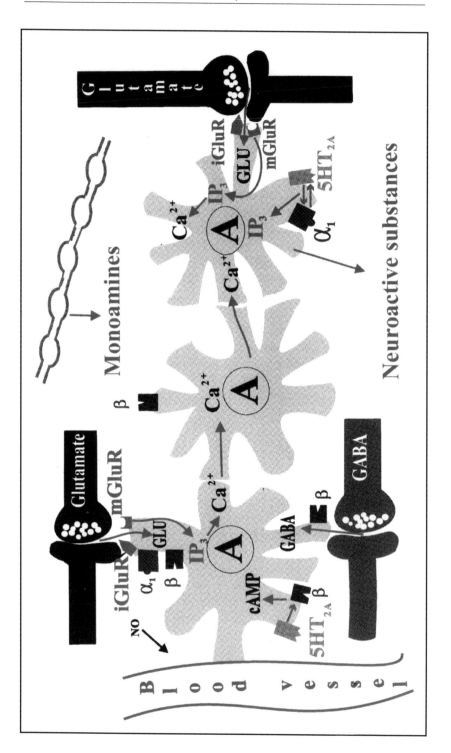

in the astroglial cell diameter to make the cell membranes come into close contact. In the experimental situation, 100μM Glu has been shown to cause a 10% increase in cell volume.[25] In the cell culture experiments, the whole cell is exposed to the amino acid and furthermore, there are no limits to cell swelling. For these reasons, results from the in vitro experiments could not be transferred to the in vivo situation per se. Yet it can be stated that small changes in the astroglial volume results in a prominent effect on the extracellular space volume and thereby on the concentration of substances therein. It can be asked if volume changes by the astroglia with secondary effects on the time spent by Glu in the synaptic region may be one cause of the long-term-potentiation (LTP) mechanism being initiated. It seems important to go on with experiments demonstrating the probable role of astroglia in LTP initiation.[50,51] Furthermore, it seems of utmost importance to look at Ca^{2+} signaling, changes in membrane potential and probable alterations in cell volume within the gap junction coupled astroglial network after the elicitation of LTP within one synaptic region.

Astroglia integrate the information from synapses, from other astroglia and from the extracellular milieu (Fig. 8.4)

Astroglial mGluRs activation initiates Ca^{2+}-mediated signaling to other astrocytes through gap junctions (see chapter 7). This signaling system makes use of intracellular mediators that convey messages which, in turn, diffuse throughout the glial syncytium. In this way, the system represents signaling

Fig. 8.4. (Opposite page) Schematic presentation of the astroglial capacity to integrate signals and information from synapses, from the blood serum composition and from the extracellular milieu within the astroglial syncytium. The figure shows three astrocytes (=A) sharing gap junctions and forming part of a network. Astrocytic processes extend toward Glu-ergic and GABA-ergic synapses and toward a blood vessel. The astrocytes possess ionotropic and metabotropic Glu receptors (iGluRs and mGluRs) and membrane receptors for monoamines. Such substances modulate energy metabolism, ion channels, membrane properties, second messengers and amino acid uptake carriers. Interactions between the second messengers cAMP/ adenylate cyclase and inositolphosphate (IP) are indicated. Glial Glu and GABA uptake carriers are shown. The arrangement with astroglial membranes encapsulating the Glu synapse makes it probable that Glu signaling induces the IP_3 formation and an intracellular Ca^{2+} release. Ca^{2+} transients are formed and propagate as waves or oscillations from cell to cell via the gap junctions. This Ca^{2+} signaling in the astroglial network might serve among others to open Ca^{2+}-activated K^+ channels, thus inducing an immediate hyperpolarization of the astroglial membrane, but, if the signaling is persistent for some time, there will be a depolarization of the astroglial syncytium and also a decreased Glu uptake capacity.
The figure also indicates the formation of nitric oxide (NO) after Glu stimulation and the probable astroglial interaction with the microcirculation, owing to the demands of neuronal activity (see text). Furthermore, the probable astroglial synthesis and release of neuroactive substances (S100, NGF, etc.) due to neuronal activity is presented. See color figure in insert.

probably based on frequency-coded signals. Compared with the neuronal action potential, this Ca^{2+} propagation is slow, but as far as is seen from experiments in in vitro systems, the Ca^{2+} signaling is of a long-range type. Ca^{2+} dynamics have also been observed in in situ preparations within electrically stimulated hippocampal brain slices.[52] The possible information provided by the astroglial Ca^{2+} signaling has been summarized by Smith[8] to be a regulation of Ca^{2+} dependent K^+ channels, a regulation of Ca^{2+} channels, synthesis and release of neuroactive substances, changes in shape of the astroglial cells with secondary effects on the extracellular space and effects on astroglial Glu and GABA carriers. Furthermore, Ca^{2+} signaling has been proposed to affect astroglial NO synthesis (see below) and to trigger the mobilization of carbohydrate energy stores. All these effects are of great importance in terms of the astroglia supporting the neurons and modulating neuronal activity.

Furthermore, the astroglial gap junction linked syncytium can allow for the transport of ions and small molecules such as K^+, Ca^{2+}, inositolphosphates, cAMP, etc. The astroglial membrane potential has been shown to influence the degree of opening of the gap junctions, where depolarization increases and hyperpolarization decreases lucifer yellow spreading from astrocyte to astrocyte via gap junctions. Other parameters that influence on the permeability of gap junctions between astroglial cells in culture are the phosphorylation degree, $[Ca^{2+}]_i$, cAMP and pH (see chapter 7). Thus, prerequisites exist for a pronounced K^+ redistribution within the astroglial network.[53] The signaling within the astroglial network also consists of variations in membrane potential in the coupled network. It is well known that the Na^+ dependent Glu uptake carrier is electrogenic and strongly voltage-dependent. It is also well known that the K^+ uptake capacity is voltage dependent, the membrane potential in the astroglial network thus being of utmost importance to these astroglial cell functions. The clearance of K^+ ions from the interstitial space by spatial buffering helps maintain an environment in which neurons can fire at high frequency.[54]

Fig. 8.5. (Opposite page) Probable modulation by astroglia of synaptic excitability. The figure shows the synapse structures presented in Figure 8.2. It is indicated that astroglial depolarization with a K^+ outflow nearby the presynaptic site (=1 in the figure) can lead to presynaptic depolarization with increased transmitter release. Similarly, astroglial depolarization at the postsynaptic site (=2) can induce a relative depolarization of the postsynaptic membrane and increased excitability. A decrease in the $[Ca^{2+}]_e$ concentration can lead to diminished neurotransmitter release (=3) from the presynaptic site and also to decreased excitability of the postsynaptic membrane. Astroglial swelling (=4) leads to a decrease in extracellular (e.c.) volume and thereby an increase in the concentration of ions and amino acids, with consequent changes in neuronal excitability. The astroglial function as an energy supporter for the neurons is indicated as glucose is taken up from the blood, stored as glycogen and transferred to the neuron as lactate and other usable fuel for the neuron.

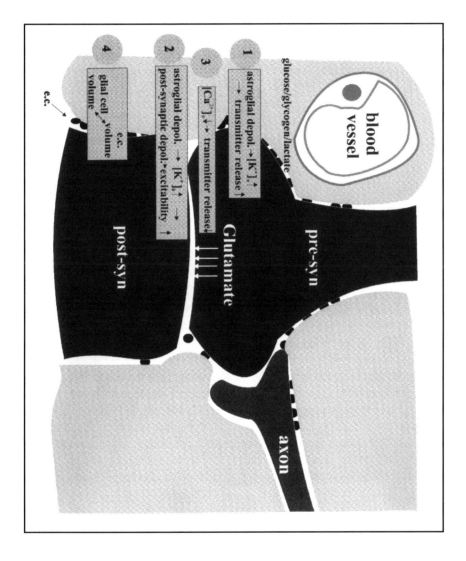

Similarly, information is received from other astrocytes, reflecting for instance the activity of other synaptic regions. In addition, the astrocyte can be affected by extracellular mediators such as monoamines, that reach the cells via "volume transmission."[55] NA and 5-HT can regulate energy metabolism and NA can also affect astroglial Glu and GABA uptake. Such mediators could even operate directly on the astroglial ion channels (e.g., Ca^{2+}) and thereby affect the extracellular Ca^{2+} levels, probably within small limits under physiological conditions. Under specific circumstances, however, they could modulate transmitter release.

It can be assumed, as already proposed by Kettenmann and co-workers in 1983,[56] that the astroglial cells form a functional syncytium which might integrate the information obtained from synapses, the composition of blood and the composition of the extracellular space to serve specific functions including the regulation of amino acid carriers, ion channels, synthesis and release of neurotrophic factors and modulation of the membrane potential of the electrically coupled syncytium.

Astroglia modulate the excitability of the neuronal synaptic membranes (Fig. 8.5)

Below, we describe how alterations in the astroglial membrane potential in the vicinity of the synaptic membranes can modify neuronal excitability.[5,57] An astroglial depolarization in the vicinity of the presynaptic terminal with a resultant increase in the $[K^+]_e$ can give rise to relative depolarization of the presynaptic membrane and consequent increased transmitter release. In the case of Ca^{2+}-dependent transmitter release, $[Ca^{2+}]_e$ is of importance. Even here the astroglial process might have some role to play, as the cell expresses different Ca^{2+} channels, both voltage-dependent and voltage-independent, thereby having the capacity to regulate the $[Ca^{2+}]_e$.[58] It should be emphasized that all these events are dynamic, being regulated by different mechanisms. Thus, it has been demonstrated that if $[Ca^{2+}]_e$ decreases critically due to, e.g., astroglial uptake, neurons will become more excitable.[59,60] Furthermore, Housely and Stanley[61] demonstrated already in the beginning of the '80s that a pronounced increase in $[Ca^{2+}]_i$ could result in a progressive closure of gap junctions and loss of spatial buffering with a reduced ability of the astroglial syncytium to relocate K^+ and other ions removed from active regions. Thus, Ca^{2+} interchange between neurons and astroglia might be one mechanism for the regulation of neuronal excitability.[57]

An astroglial depolarization in the vicinity of the postsynaptic membrane may lead to a depolarization of the postsynaptic membrane, thereby increasing the probability of an action potential being elicited, i.e., increased neuronal excitability. Neuronal firing in the mammalian motor cortex has, in fact, been

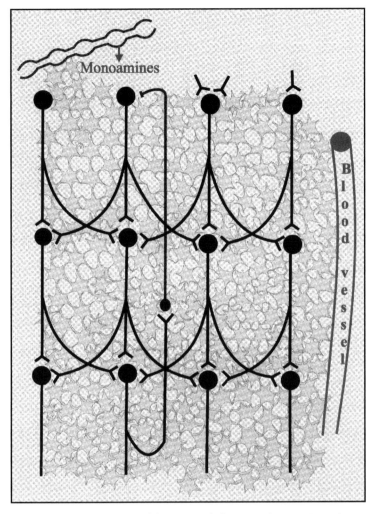

Fig. 8.6. An extended view of those astroglial-neuronal interactions shown in Figure 8.4. The astroglial network forms the background. Glu-ergic neurons (large cell bodies) and an inhibitory neuron (small cell body) is shown. Monoamine varicosities and a blood vessel are demonstrated. With this anatomical sketch and with the properties and functions of the astroglia presented in this chapter and in this book, it can be imagined that the astroglial network, by its capacity to monitor its environment and to integrate the information obtained, can modulate the neuronal excitability level in many neuronal systems simultaneously. The astroglia are probably active partners of the neurons and should be considered an active component in the neuronal circuits. See color figure in insert.

demonstrated to increase when neighboring glial cells were experimentally depolarized in the presence of either Na^+ or Li^+.[62] It is interesting that K^+ can be redistributed within the astroglial network from regions with high neuronal activity into regions with a lower activity. The changes in $[K^+]_e$, determined by neuronal release, astroglial clearance and redistribution, are another way by which astroglia and neurons can communicate. In this context it should be remembered that astrocytes exhibit a K^+-induced, non-Ca^{2+}-dependent release of Glu which can exert effects on neuronal Glu receptors, thus forming a basis for excitability control. By these, and probably other mechanisms astroglia have the capacity to modulate neuronal excitability.[63,64] Astroglial cells might even participate in LTP mechanisms (see above). They can synthesize and release arachidonic acid which has been shown to induce a long term, activity-dependent enhancement of synaptic transmission in the hippocampus.[65] As astroglial cells exhibit a considerable plasticity in response to neuronal signals, long-term changes in astroglial cell properties might give rise to changes in synaptic function. In this context, it is interesting to note that glial fibrillary acidic protein (GFAP)-null mice, created using gene targeting in embryonic stem cells, displayed enhanced LTP (of both population spike amplitude and excitatory postsynaptic potential slope) compared to control mice. It was thus demonstrated that a primary defect in astrocytes influences neuronal excitability.[66]

The astroglial network in integrated neuronal circuits (figs. 8.4 and 8.6)

Taking the astroglial heterogeneity concerning membrane receptors, amino acid transporters, ion channels and the differential capacities of the cells to synthesize and release neuroactive substances[37-40,67] into consideration, it is tempting to postulate that these cells can dynamically modulate the ionic and amino acid compositions of the extracellular space. The anatomy of the astroglial cell makes it possible for one cell to have contact with many synaptic regions, with other astroglial cells forming a syncytium and also with blood vessel walls. Thus, the basis for an extra neuronal, astroglial, system is formed with the capacity to intimately collaborate with neurons and to modulate neuronal excitability, preferentially by changing extracellular Glu, K^+ and Ca^{2+} concentrations simultaneously with changes in the extracellular volume attributable to changes in cell volume. To complete the picture of the role of astroglia in neuronal circuits and in neuronal information processing, some supplementary examples from areas which have not been discussed in this book are given below: The role of astroglia as providers of neurotrophic factors, the role of astroglia in energy supply to the neurons and the role of the astroglial-neuronal collaboration for the regulation of the local microcirculation.

I). If we add the capacity of the astrocyte to synthesize and release neuroactive substances to the characteristics and properties mentioned, it seems probable that astroglia send extracellular signals to other cells in the nervous system, including neurons and other glia.[54,63,64] Two examples are: S100 is an astrocyte enriched protein, isolated in the mid-1960s by Blake Moore. Already in the early 1970s the protein was found to bind Ca^{2+}.[68] Behavioral experiments by Hydén and collaborators[69] in the late 1960s and early 1970s demonstrated that the protein increased in central structures, such as hippocampus, septum and amygdala, of the brain after different training situations regarding learning new behavior. During recent years it has been demonstrated that a subunit of the S100 protein has a trophic effect,[70] probably directed toward the 5-HT neurons.[71] From the data available it might be speculated as to whether the S100 protein, and of course also other Ca^{2+} binding proteins such as calmodulins,[72] increase in amount in the astroglial network, owing to intense neuronal activity, as is the case in a training situation, in order to bind the Ca^{2+} released from the Ca^{2+} waves. The S100 protein has been shown to be secreted to the extracellular space, where it probably has a trophic effect, serving as one component in the rebuilding of neurites and synapses. Could it be that S100 is one molecule of importance in the transformation of neuronal electrical activity into more stable neuronal structures after neuronal rebuilding? Do we in fact have some explanation for the role of S100 in the formation of a stable long-term memory from the electrical short-term memory, as was suggested by Hydén? Another example of the role astroglial networks play in integrated neuronal function might be the demonstrated synthesis and secretion from astroglia of the nerve growth factor (NGF) after astroglial β receptor stimulation.[73,74] In this case, increased neuronal activity, preferentially mediated by volume transmission, can give rise to the release of neuroactive substances from the astroglia that have effects on neuronal rebuilding and plasticity. These are just a few examples of intimate neuronal-astroglial interaction where astrocytes actively support the neurons in rebuilding processes.

II). Another important aspect of neuronal-astroglial collaboration which is not addressed in this book is the astroglial energy supply to the neurons. It is well known that brain glycogen is stored predominantly in astrocytes. It has been shown that both NA and 5-HT can evoke glycogenolysis and that noradrenergic control of glycogen metabolism is exerted through both α- and β-receptors.[75,76] Furthermore, increased extracellular K^+ was found to increase astroglial glycogenolysis.[77] It has also been found that β-receptor activation stimulates glucose uptake into astroglial cells[78] and that NA stimulates oxidative metabolism in astrocytes but not in neurons in culture.[79] Magistretti and co-workers[80,81] suggested that the activation of the noradrenergic system together with vasoactive intestinal peptide (VIP)ergic neurons causes potentiated cyclic AMP and glycogenolytic responses that produce metabolic "hot spots" in the cerebral cortex to cope with local increases in neuronal activity.

III). A third example of an intimate neuronal-astroglial collaboration is one where even the cerebral blood microcirculation is included. Nitric oxide (NO) has been suggested as a candidate for such a neuronal-astroglial-blood vessel mediator. NO is produced after Glu stimulation even in astroglia[82] and might increase blood flow in response to increased neuronal activation. Thereby the basis exists for an astroglial/neuronal control of the local microcirculation.

The picture of the astrocyte evolving here is of a cell that can sense multiple stimuli (via both membrane receptors in the vicinity of synapses and long-range signaling within the astroglial syncytium) and produce integrated responses. The effectors can produce additive, synergic or inhibitory effects on astrocyte signal transduction systems. With the probable specialization of the astrocytes concerning membrane receptors, carriers and synthesis capacity of neuroactive substances in mind, the astroglial syncytium might constitute an extraneuronal system with the capacity to sense and support neuronal activity and modulate neuronal excitability. Interestingly, this cell syncytium has the capacity to modulate the excitability levels of many neuronal systems simultaneously.

Can the astroglia alter the neuronal message? If the questions refer to the substance of the message, the probable answer is no. Neuronal activity is extremely rapid and specific. The neuronal networks have well-developed capacities to direct their messages by altering their levels of excitability, among others, by activation of inhibitory feed-back systems. The astroglial network, on the other hand, should be seen as a cell syncytium interlinking the neuronal systems and with the capacity not only to passively support, depending on the requirements of the neuronal activity. Furthermore, the astroglial network might modulate and synchronize, neuronal activity on the basis of information from the "outer world," i.e., from other parts of the brain and from the blood composition. The astroglial syncytium probably has the capacity to integrate all this information in order to act as a fine tuner to optimize the quality of the neuronal message according to the requirements made, and possibilities given, from the outer and inner milieu of the brain. The concept of "actively working supporters" might be a proper descriptor of our present view of the astroglial network.

FROM CELL TO BEHAVIOR

ASTROGLIAL CELL DYSFUNCTION AND AN ORGANIC PSYCHOSYNDROME WITH COGNITIVE DEFECTS

In the previous section we put forward the thought that astroglia might reinforce the quality of high performance neuronal information processing especially when there are requirements for high endurance. If this is true, then

Table 8.1. Typical symptoms in the astheno-emotional disorder

fatigue during prolonged mental activity
stress intolerance
decreased simultaneous capacity
decreased concentration capacity, sometimes with secondary deficiency of
    short-term memory
headache from intense and prolonged mental activity
lability with irritability
emotional instability
sensitivity to sound and sometimes even light

astroglial dysfunction with a resulting impairment of the fine tuning astroglial Glu and K⁺ clearance from the extracellular milieu might result in an impairment of rapid neuronal signaling over longer time periods, especially when many neuronal systems are active at the same time. In this section we ask whether such an impairment in neuronal support might be one pathogenic mechanism for the mental fatigue and problems with concentration and short-term memory often seen after brain damage. The symptoms of this organic psychosyndrome, the astheno-emotional or neurasthenic syndrome are specific, whereas the underlying causes are diverse, ranging from all kinds of brain damage, injury, vascular destruction, infectious or inflammatory disease, to heavy psychological burdens such as deep anxiety or stress.

As stated in the introduction to this book, we cannot tackle the pathogenesis of an organic psychosyndrome with a purely reductionistic approach, using knowledge about cellular mechanisms and intercellular communication. Instead, we must have a holistic view, or better, to apply both a holistic as well as a reductionistic view. We also have to pay attention to the hierarchic organization of the brain. We therefore begin this section by describing the typical clinical symptoms, after which we ask ourselves what brain region and what cell systems might be affected. In doing so we try to gain insight into the requirements for reaching a reasonable pathogenesis at the cellular level. At the same time, we utilize the knowledge from the earlier chapters of this book in order, using a reductionistic approach, to pile layer on layer of knowledge to form a whole concerning the requirements for cellular communication and information processing in the brain, and to explain the pathogenesis of the symptoms.

THE ASTHENO-EMOTIONAL DISORDER—SYMPTOMS AND ASPECTS OF PATHOGENESIS

The astheno-emotional symptoms, classified according to Lindqvist and Malmgren,[83] are summarized in Table 8.1. These symptoms relate to higher cortical brain functions, and they appear during stressful situations, or when the patient needs a high capacity for patience and concentration. Moreover, the symptoms only arise when the patients have the prerequisites for mental activity. Thus, the patients are often disturbed by these symptoms during their rehabilitation from focal brain damage, e.g., a stroke or a traumatic brain injury; which often makes the rehabilitation more difficult. The symptoms may even arise in the absence of focal tissue destruction, e.g., after a concussion or a viral meningitis, with no other neurological symptoms. Furthermore, the astheno-emotional symptoms may appear in the early stages of degenerative brain diseases, such as dementias, or in inflammatory diseases, such as multiple sclerosis (MS). They can develop even in situations of massive and long-term anxiety and stress, and consequently can be induced by psychological disturbances. If the syndrome has been induced by an organic brain lesion, the symptoms may be aggravated by secondary mental stress and anxiety. Thus the astheno-emotional disorder might represent a state where organic brain lesions and psychological mechanisms induce similar effects on mental capacity.

What part(s) of the brain is (are) affected? The symptoms, per se, do not seem to arise from one local or specific brain region. Probably larger cortical regions are involved. These areas include structures dealing with cognitive processes ("higher cerebral cortical functions"), sensory input and processing of information into a memory. Probably parts of the hippocampus, the limbic system, the temporal lobes and parts of the frontal lobes are involved in the generation of the symptoms.

Fig. 8.7. (Opposite page) Scheme of proposed mechanisms underlying the astheno-emotional disorder. Various pathogenic conditions (=1 in the figure) induce increased neuronal excitability, astroglial depolarization and/or decreased astroglial K^+ and Glu clearance from the extracellular (e.c.) space (=2a-c). The results are slightly increased $[K^+]_e$ and $[Glu]_e$ levels (=2d), and a decreased signal-to-noise ratio for Glu neurotransmission (=2e) with a resultant decrease in the possibilities for distinct activation of many neurons simultaneously and for long time periods (=2f). According to our hypothesis this is the neurochemical basis of the astheno-emotional disorder (=3) with a decreased cognitive capacity. Secondary anxiety and stress (=4) often appear due to perceived decreased cognitive capacity, and this anxiety and stress further increase the neural excitability. The excitability level in the cerebral cortex might be reported by the selective projection from the basal frontal lobe to the locus coeruleus (LC) and the raphe nuclei, with a decrease in cortical NA and 5-HT release (=6). The astroglial depolarization seen in 2b leads to the synthesis of substances with inhibitory effects on the neurons (=5), such as taurine, GABA and opioids and also to an increased pH_i and a decreased pH_e, in turn leading to decreased neural activity (=7). This, in turn, forms one part of the astheno-emotional disorder and furthermore, might participate in the development of depression (=8). If the states 2f and 7 are present for long time, the result may be synaptic rebuilding (=9) and the formation of a long-term astheno-emotional state (=10).

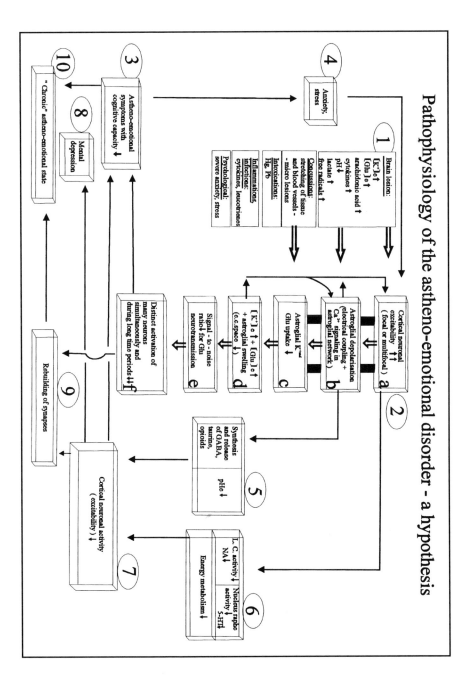

Pathophysiology of the astheno-emotional disorder - a hypothesis

The underlying cause of the symptoms seems to be a decreased capacity for rapid and precise activation of many neuronal pathways, in parallel and over longer time periods. Glu is the most frequently distributed excitatory neurotransmitter in the brain and Glu-ergic neurons are widely distributed in the hippocampus, the frontal cortex and in regions associated with sensory functions, e.g., the superior colliculus and the cochlear nucleus.[84] Glu is removed from the extracellular space around synapses by high affinity uptake into both neurons and astroglia, while astroglia are considered the main site for active Glu uptake (see above and chapter 5). The pathogenic mechanisms might be a disturbance in the Glu transmission, probably in many Glu synapses in parallel and with a decreased signal-to-noise ratio for the transmitter.

At the cellular level, the symptoms do not seem to require any specific neuronal lesion. Neither does there seem to be a single or specific neuronal pathway that totters; there merely seems to be an insufficiency in the precise and simultaneous activation of many excitatory synapses and especially when long-term activation is required. How could this be and from what cellular system in the brain are the symptoms derived?

According to the presentation above, the astroglial cells interact dynamically with neurons, and both sense and support synaptic transmission.[5,47,54,57,63,64] The anatomy of the astroglial cells, their formation of an electrically-coupled syncytium within which there is a long-distance, slow-speed transfer of information, together with their well-developed capacity for cell volume regulation and an indirect and pronounced influence on the extracellular volume, all make it probable that this syncytium modulates the neuronal extracellular environment and regulates the excitability of many neuronal systems in parallel.

IS THE ASTHENO-EMOTIONAL DISORDER CAUSED BY AN IMPAIRMENT IN THE FINE TUNING OF ASTROGLIAL GLUTAMATE AND K+ EXTRACELLULAR CLEARANCE?

PRESENTATION OF PROBABLE PATHOGENIC MECHANISMS OF THE ASTHENO-EMOTIONAL DISORDER (FIG. 8.7)

In a uni- or multifocal brain lesion (1 in Fig. 8.7), a pathophysiologic cascade is developed very rapidly and this cascade includes decreased ATP levels which lead to an increase in $[K^+]_e$, [Glu], arachidonic acid, astroglial swelling with collapse of the extracellular space, and further increases in the concentrations of the above-mentioned substances (see chapter 6). In addition, cytokines, leukotrienes, lactate and free radicals are formed and are released into the extracellular space, and there is also a drop in pH level.[85] In infectious or inflammatory diseases, there is production and release of cytokines and leukotrienes. In contusion or concussion, there is a distension of tissue and blood vessels with secondary microlesions and astroglial swelling.[86] The substances produced or released in these states increase neuronal excitability (excitatory amino acids) with a secondary astroglial depolarization[87] and a resultant inhibition of Glu and K^+ clearance from the extracellular space (2a-c in Fig. 8.7). The glial depolarization is spread in the astroglial network because of the electrical coupling and the Ca^{2+}-signaling within the network, with effects on the membrane potential over larger brain regions. Some agents, some cytokines for example, induce a primary astroglial depolarization[20] while others, arachidonic acid and free radicals, primarily inhibit Glu uptake.[18,19] An increased neuronal excitability, an astroglial depolarization and a decrease in astroglial removal of extracellular $[K^+]$ and [Glu] all operate together with a resultant astroglial swelling, a secondary decrease of the extracellular space, and increased extracellular concentrations of K^+ and Glu (2d in Fig. 8.7). This will be the case as long as the underlying causes are present. The level of $[Glu]_e$ will be dependent on the extent to which the pathophysiological process is driven.

If the state described above persists with increased $[Glu]_e$, then the signal-to-noise ratio for the Glu transmission will decrease (2e in Fig. 8.7), tentatively leading to difficulties in distinct activation of Glu neurons, at least for longer time periods (2f in Fig. 8.7). According to our hypothesis, this is the mechanism underlying the symptoms of the astheno-emotional disorder (3 in Fig. 8.7).

In addition, the pathophysiological situation described above, if long-term, gives rise to a decrease in neuronal cortical activity (7 in Fig. 8.7). This may be achieved by two mechanisms: the first one local (5 in Fig. 8.7), including the production of an increased inhibitory tonus mediated by astroglial production and release of taurine, GABA and opioids,[88-92] and the second a pH mediated decrease of neuronal excitability.[93,94] In addition there is a selective projection, identified at least in animals, from the basal part of the frontal lobe to the LC and the raphe nuclei, and probably also to the periaqueductal gray (PAG) region.[95] It has been proposed that increased cortical neuronal excitability is signaled to these regions. From PAG, there is a release of opioids directed to the locus coeruleus (L.C.) and from there communication to the raphe nucleus. The overall result of long-term, high cortical excitability, would be a decrease in the release of NA and 5-HT (6 in Fig. 8.7). It is interesting to note here that this decrease in cortical activity in some situations can lead to depression, which, in fact often develops after brain lesions.[96-98] Notwithstanding, it can sometimes be difficult to differentiate between the astheno-emotional disorder and a depressive state.

The hypothesis describes how increased nerve cell activity, owing to either a focal brain lesion or to demanding long-term mental activity with anxiety and stress and with a depolarization within parts of the astroglial network, can lead to the development of the astheno-emotional disorder. It also follows that this hypothesis can explain how organic brain damage can generate symptoms similar to those arising from psychologically-induced overload. It also explains why severe anxiety and stress can increase astheno-emotional symptoms primarily induced by an organic brain process.

If the hypothesis is correct, the symptoms might be relieved by pharmacological reinforcement of the astroglial Glu uptake capacity, e.g., by inducing a slight hyperpolarization of the astroglial network, thereby increasing Glu-clearance from the extracellular space. It is interesting to note that in some experimental preparations low-dose β-adrenergic or 5-HT receptor agonists, adenosine, or even histamine (H_1) receptor agonists hyperpolarize astroglia.[99-101] Furthermore, our findings of an increased astroglial Glu uptake by adrenoreceptor activation[22] might indicate that specific treatment could be developed.

How to Prove or Reject the Hypothesis

The search for pathogenic mechanisms underlying an organic psychosyndrome with impairment of cognitive functions is an extremely challenging task. On the one hand, difficulties with concentration and short term memory, stress intolerance and headache in mentally demanding situations are very specific human problems. This means that there are no animal models and that the experiments required are difficult to carry out with animal models. On the other hand, the pathogenesis of the symptoms is difficult to study in humans, as there are no indications of destruction or injury in any specific brain region or neuronal pathways or systems. As the patients perform well in nonstressful situations, especially if they can work slowly with breaks, there merely seems to be a functional disturbance in the neuronal networks preferentially affecting those brain regions or systems where cognitive functions are processed. This is one of the reasons we have selected a dysfunction of the astrocyte network, with its normally supportive functions toward the neurons, as a probable pathogenic factor for the symptoms to appear. Since we have no animal models, one way to proceed would be to apply a reductionistic as well as a holistic view of the problem. The reductionistic direction might include studies at the cellular or multicellular level, preferentially in three dimensions, e.g., tissue slices, to attempt to map the role of the astroglial network in maintaining a high Glu-ergic signal-to-noise ratio and its possibilities of modulating neuronal excitability levels. As the events described are dynamic, the experiments would require vast computer capacity in order to follow many different astroglial parameters: Ca^{2+} excitability, K^+ buffering, membrane potential, changes in cell volume, changes in pH, etc., to extrapolate what role the astroglial network might play in neuronal information processing. The experiments will be especially demanding when these dynamic systems are manipulated pharmacologically which, in fact, might be an additional way of gaining insight into the mechanisms studied and thereby into the functions of the astroglia in brain information processing.

Another direction of research might be to illuminate the importance of the astroglial gap junction coupling in the "functional" syncytium. Such experiments can be performed in cell and tissue cultures and in animals, and should be directed toward blocking the expression of the connexin proteins or pharmacologically manipulating the gap junction proteins both structurally and functionally. One important prerequisite regarding our present hypothesis is that there is communication between individual astroglial cells, and that the network is coordinated in a functionally integrated cell mass.

Going to the clinical approach, imaging techniques on the intact brain will be of importance, especially when they can be combined with labeling of tracers for the visualization of dynamic events at the cellular/multicellular level. Many problems exist at present: labeling of ions and amino acids, resolution at the cellular level, identification of astroglia in the intact brain, etc., but hopefully the technological development will allow such types of experiments to be performed in the not too remote future. This would make it possible to follow astroglial functions in the intact CNS and study effects of astroglial dysfunction, e.g., after brain damage. Furthermore, pharmacological manipulations of the astroglial network will give new insights into neuronal-astroglial interactions. The hypothesis presented might appear correct, but probably a lot of new knowledge will show that the collaboration between neurons and astrocytes is far more complicated than thought at present. Under any circumstances, and even if our present thoughts turn out to be completely incorrect, it is important to continuously fill in the gaps between the few already known pieces of information with hypotheses and thoughts, to try to prove or preclude their accuracy to be able to go further and try to understand the inner secrets of the brain. Our current knowledge makes it seem probable that the interactions and collaborations between astroglia and neurons are of utmost importance even for the "highest" cortical functions: concentration, memory formation and probably also behavior. Even if the supportive role of the astroglia most probably will be shown to exist, it seems probable that the "support" will appear much more active than was previously thought.

SUMMARY AND FUTURE DIRECTIONS

Astroglia constitute an electrically coupled gap junction-linked syncytium with Ca^{2+} excitability in the cell network. The astrocytes, situated between the blood and the neurons, have the capacity to sense and integrate synaptic activities from many synapses simultaneously. They can register the composition of the extracellular milieu and also the serum composition concerning neuroactive substances. Through the synchronizing of the membrane potential and the

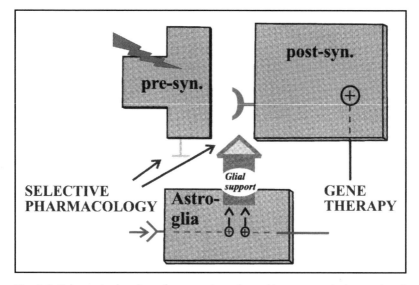

Fig. 8.8. Schematic drawing of a synaptic region with presynaptic (presyn) and postsynaptic (postsyn) membranes and an astroglial process. The figure indicates future possibilities to develop selective pharmacology and/or somatic gene therapy directed against the astroglia to reinforce dysfunction of the astroglial neuronal support.

Ca^{2+} excitability within the coupled astroglial network, the Glu uptake capacity of the cells can be regulated as well as the K^+ uptake and K^+ buffering abilities. In summary astroglia might support the neurons in achieving high signal-to-noise ratio, high activity and high endurance of the Glu synaptic transmission in one or several neuronal systems. Future studies must be designed to test these thoughts including our hypothesis that astroglial dysfunction is an important component in the pathogenesis of an organic psychosyndrome, the astheno-emotional syndrome with cognitive fatigue. Such studies must include experimental as well as clinical projects. In the experimental situation, many events such as membrane potential, K^+ uptake and buffering, Glu uptake, pH regulation and astroglial cell swelling should be registered simultaneously, and thus give a dynamic view of the possibilities of the astroglial syncytium to integrate with and probably modulate neuronal functions on the synaptic level, depending on the surrounding milieu of the astrocytes. The possibilities of registering what effects different components of brain damage may have on the functions of the astroglial network might be even more important. Might one result be decreased neuronal support in their processing of specific and distinct information of high quality in many synapses simultaneously and over long periods of time? Future research might aim at developing therapy directed against dysfunctions of the astroglial as well as against the neuronal networks. When molecular techniques allow the identification of receptors and ion channels specific to astroglia, selective pharmacology could be used to reinforce the astroglial neuronal support in the form of, e.g., Glu or K^+ clearance from the extracellular space. Probably more far away, somatic gene therapy might be used to induce the production of new or enhance the production of existing neuroactive or trophic substances within the astrocyte network, to alter neuronal excitability and participate in neuronal rebuilding processes. Maybe we will be able to increase our therapeutic arsenal and treat even organic psychosyndromes and probably other diseases in the nervous system by specific interactions with the astroglial cells (Fig. 8.8).

ACKNOWLEDGMENTS

This work was supported by grants from the Swedish Medical Research Council (project No. 14X-06005), the Swedish Work Environment Fund (Grant No 94-0214), the Swedish Council for Work Life Research (Grant No 95-0231), The 1987 Foundation for Research on Stroke, the John and Brit Wennerström's Foundation for Neurologic Research, the Rune and Ulla Amlöv's Foundation for Neurological and Rheumatological Research and the Edit Jacobson's Foundation. The authors want to thank Professor Holger Hydén for valuable comments on the manuscript. The skillful technical assistance of Ulrika Johansson, Barbro Eriksson and Maria Wågberg is greatly appreciated. We specially want to thank Armgard Kling who performed computer drawing of all the figures.

REFERENCES

1. Peters A, Palay SL, Webster de FH (eds.). The fine structure of the nervous system: Neurons and their supporting cells. 2nd ed. Philadelphia: WB Saunders, 1991.
2. Dermietzel R, Hertzberg EL, Kessler JA et al. Gap junctions between cultured astrocytes: immunocytochemical, molecular, and electrophysiological analysis. J Neurosci 1991; 11:1421-1432.
3. Dermietzel R, Spray DC. Gap junctions in the brain: where, what type, how many and why? Trends Neurosci 1993; 16:186-192.
4. Ransom BR, Kettenmann H. Electrical coupling, without dye coupling, between mammalian astrocytes and oligodendrocytes in cell culture. GLIA 1990; 3:258-266.
5. Barres BA. New roles for glia. J Neurosci 1991; 11:3685-3694.
6. Cornell-Bell AH, Finkbeiner SM, Cooper MS, Smith SJ. Glutamate induces calcium waves in cultured astrocytes: long-range glial signaling. Science 1990; 247:470-473.

7. Cornell-Bell AH, Finkbeiner SM. Ca^{2+} waves in astrocytes. Cell Calcium 1991; 12:185-204.

8. Smith SJ. Do astrocytes process neural information? In: Yu ACH, Hertz L, Norenberg MD et al, eds. Progress in Brain Research. B.V.: Elsevier Science Publishers, 1992; 94:119-136.

9. Hertz L. Functional interactions between neurons and astrocytes. I. Turnover and metabolism of putative amino acid transmitters. Progr Neurobiol 1979; 13:277-323.

10. Walz W. Role of glial cells in the regulation of the brain ion microenvironment. Prog Neurobiol 1989; 33:309-333.

11. Kimelberg HK, Norenberg MD. Astrocytes. Sci Am 1989; 260:66-76.

12. Barres BA, Chun LLY, Corey DP. Ion channels in vertebrate glia. Annu Rev Neurosci 1990; 13:441-471.

13. Sontheimer H. Astrocytes, as well as neurons, express a diversity of ion channels. Can J Physiol Pharmacol 1992; 70:223-238.

14. Sontheimer H, Waxman SG. Expression of voltage-activated ion channels by astrocytes and oligodendrocytes in the hippocampal slice. J Neurophysiol 1993; 70:1863-1873.

15. Duffy S, MacVicar BA. Potassium-dependent calcium influx in acutely isolated hippocampal astrocytes. Neurosci 1994; 61:51-61.

16. Brew H, Attwell D. Electrogenic glutamate uptake is a major current carrier in the membrane of axolotl retinal glial cells. Nature 1987; 327:707-709.

17. Szatkowski M, Barbour B, Attwell D. Nonvesicular release of glutamate from glial cells by reversed electrogenic glutamate uptake. Nature 1990; 348:443-446.

18. Barbour B, Szatkowski M, Ingledew N, Attwell D. Arachidonic acid induces a prolonged inhibition of glutamate uptake into glial cells. Nature 1989; 342:918-920.

19. Volterra A, Trotti D, Tromba C, et al. Glutamate uptake inhibition by oxygen free radicals in rat cortical astrocytes. J Neurosci 1994; 14:2924-2932.

20. Köller H, Siebler M, Pekel M, Muller HW. Depolarization of cultured astrocytes by leukotriene B_4. Evidence for the induction of a K^+ conductance inhibitor. Brain Res 1993; 612:28-34.

21. Brookes N. Specificity and reversibility of the inhibition by $HgCl_2$ of glutamate transport in astrocyte cultures. J Neurochem 1988; 50:1117-1122.

22. Hansson E, Rönnbäck L. Receptor regulation of the glutamate, GABA and taurine high-affinity uptake into astrocytes in primary culture. Brain Res 1991; 548:215-221.

23. Kimelberg HK, ed. Glial Cell Receptors. New York: Raven Press, 1988.

24. Hösli E, Hösli L. Receptors for neurotransmitters on astrocytes in the mammalian central nervous system. Progr Neurobiol 1993; 40:477-506.

25. Hansson E. Metabotropic glutamate receptor activation induces astroglial swelling. J Biol Chem 1994; 269:21955-21961.

26. v Blankenfeld G, Enkvist K, Kettenmann H. Gamma-aminobutyric acid and glutamate receptors. In: Kettenmann H, Ransom BR eds. Neuroglia. New York: Oxford University Press, 1995:335-345.

27. Porter JT, McCarthy KD. GFAp-positive hippocampal astrocytes in situ respond to glutamatergic neuroligands with increases in $[Ca^{2+}]_i$. GLIA 1995; 13:101-112.

28. Steinhäuser C, Gallo V. News on glutamate receptors in glial cells. Trends Neurosci 1996; 19:339-345.

29. Sontheimer H, Kettenmann H, Backus KH et al. Glutamate opens $Na^+ \div K^+$ channels in cultured astrocytes. GLIA 1988; 1:328-336.

30. Stone EA, Ariano MA. Are glial cells targets of the central noradrenergic system? A review of the evidence. Brain Res Rev 1989; 14:297-309.

31. Lerea LS, McCarthy KD. Neuron-associated astroglial cell express β- and $α_1$-adrenergic receptors in vitro. Brain Res 1990; 521:7-14.

32. Salm AK, McCarthy KD. Expression of beta-adrenergic receptors by astrocytes isolated from adult rat cortex. GLIA 1989; 2:346-352.

33. Magistretti PJ, Sorg O, Martin J-L. Regulation of glycogen metabolism in astrocytes: Physiological, pharmacological, and pathological aspects. In: Murphy S, ed. Astrocytes, Phramacology and Function. New York: Academic Press, 1993:243-265.

34. Grant SJ, Aston-Jones G, Redmond Jr E. Responses of primate locus coeruleus neurons to simple and complex sensory stimuli. Brain Res Bull 1988;21: 401-410.

35. Kimelberg HK. Swelling and volume control in brain astroglial cells. In: Gilles R et al, eds. Advances in comparative and environmental physiology. Berlin, Heidelberg: Springer-Verlag, 1991; 9:81-117.

36. Nicholson C. Extracellular space as the pathway for neuron-glial cell interaction. In: Kettenmann H, Ransom BR, eds. Neuroglia. New York: Oxford University Press, 1995:387-397.

37. Schousboe A, Divac I. Differences in glutamate uptake in astrocytes cultured from different brain regions. Brain Res 1979; 177:407-409.

38. Hansson E. Primary astroglial cultures. Aspects of morphology, biochemistry and transmitter metabolism. Thesis. Göteborg University. 1982.

39. Hansson E. Regional heterogeneity among astrocytes in the central nervous system. Neurochem Int 1990; 3:237-245.

40. Wilkin GP, Marriott DR, Cholewinski AJ. Astrocyte heterogeneity. Trends Neurosci 1990; 13:43-46.

41. Lee SH, Kim WT, Cornell-Bell AH et al. Astrocytes exhibit regional specificity in gap-junction coupling. GLIA 1994; 11:315-325.

42. Schousboe A. Transport and metabolism of glutamate and GABA in neurons and glial cells. Int Rev Neurobiol 1981; 22:1-45.

43. Orkand RK, Nicholls JG, Kuffler SW. Effect of nerve impulses on the membrane potential of glial cells in the central nervous system in amphibia. J Neurophysiol 1966; 29:788-806.

44. Orkand RK. Signalling between neuronal and glial cells. In: Sears TA, ed. Neuronal-glial interrelationships. Heidelberg: Springer-Verlag, 1982:147-158.

45. Orkand RK. Glial-interstitial fluid exchange. Ann NY Acad Sci 1986; 481:269-272.

46. Teichberg VI. Glial glutamate receptors: likely actors in brain signaling. FASEB J 1991; 5:3086-3091.

47. Hansson E, Rönnbäck L. Astrocytes in glutamate neurotransmission. FASEB J 1995; 9:343-350.

48. Glowinski J, Marin P, Tencé M et al. Glial receptors and their intervention in astrocyto-astrocytic and astrocyto-neuronal interactions. GLIA 1994; 11:201-208.

49. Jensen AM, Chiu S-Y. Astrocyte networks. In: Murphy S, ed. Astrocytes, Pharmacology and Function. New York: Academic Press, 1993:309-330.

50. Sastry BR, Maretic H, Morishita W et al. Modulation of the induction of long-term potentiation in the hippocampus. Adv Exp Med Biol 1990; 268:377-386.

51. Wenzel J, Lammert G, Meyer U et al. The influence of long-term potentiation on the spatial relationship between astrocyte processes and potentiated synapses in the dentate gyrus neuropil of rat brain. Brain Res 1991; 560:122-131.

52. Dani JW, Chernjavsky A, Smith SJ. Neuronal activity triggers calcium waves in hippocampal astrocyte networks. Neuron 1992; 8:429-440.

53. Gardner-Medvin AR. Analysis of potassium dynamics in mammalian brain tissue. J Physiol 1983; 335:393-426.

54. Cooper M. Intercellular signaling in neuronal-glial networks. BioSystems 1995; 34:65-85.

55. Fuxe K, Agnati LF. Two principal modes of electrochemical communication in the brain: volume versus wiring transmission. Adv Neurosci 1991; 1:1-9.

56. Kettenmann H, Orkand RK, Schachner M. Coupling among identified cells in mammalian nervous system cultures. J Neurosci 1983; 3:506-516.

57. Laming PR. Do glia contribute to behavior? A neuromodulatory review. Comp Biochem Physiol 1989; 94A:555-568.

58. Eriksson PS. Opioid receptors on neural cells in primary cultures. Thesis. Göteborg University. 1992.

59. Ward AA. Physiological basis of chronic epilepsy and mechanisms of spread. In: Delgado Escueta AV, Wasterlain CG, Treiman DM et al, eds. Advances in Neurology. Vol 34. Status Epilepticus. New York: Raven Press, 1983:189-197.

60. Somjen GG. Interstitial ion concentration and the role of neuroglia in seizures. In: Wheal HV, Schwartzkran PA, eds. Electrophysiology of Epilepsy. New York: Academic Press, 1984:303-341.

61. Housley MB, Stanley KK. Dynamics of Biological Membranes. Chichester: John Wiley, 1982.

62. Grossman RG. Glial-neural interactions studied with intracellular injections of ions into cortical glia. In: Tower DB, Franck G, Hertz L, eds. Dynamic Properties of Glial Cells. Oxford: Pergamon Press, 1978:105-113.

63. Nedergaard M. Direct signaling from astrocytes to neurons in cultures of mammalian brain cells. Science 1994; 263:1768-1771.

64. Parpura V, Basarsky TA, Liu F, et al. Glutamate-mediated astrocyte neuron signaling. Nature 1994; 369:744-747.

65. Williams JH, Errington ML, Lynch MA et al. Arachidonic acid induces a long term activity-dependent enhancement of synaptic transmission in the hippocampus. Nature 1989; 341:739-742.

66. McCall MA, Gregg RG, Behringer RR et al. Targeted deletion in astrocyte intermediate filament (GFAP) alters neuronal physiology. Proc Natl Acad Sci USA 1996; 93:6361-6366.

67. Martin DL. Synthesis and release of neuroactive substances by glial cells. GLIA 1992; 5:81-94.

68. Calissano P, Moore BW, Friesen A. Effect of calcium ion on S-100; a protein of the nervous system. Biochemistry 1969; 8:4318-4326.

69. Hydén H, McEwen BS. A glial protein specific for the nervous system. Proc Natl Acad Sci USA 1966; 55:354-358.

70. Yang Q. Localization of S-100β in the nervous system—new indications for a trophic function. Thesis. Göteborg University 1996.

71. Azmitia EC, Griffin WST, Marshak DR et al. S100β and serotonin: a possible astrocyte-neuronal link to neuropathology of Alzheimer's disease. In: Yu ACH, Hertz L, Norenberg MD, Syková E, Waxman SG, eds. Neuronal-astrocytic interactions. Implications for normal and pathological CNS function. Progress in Brain Research 1992; 94:459-474.

72. Bender AS, Neary JT, Blicharska J et al. Role of calmodulin and protein kinase C in astrocytic cell regulation. J Neurochem 1992; 58:1874-1882.

73. Furukawa S, Furukawa Y, Satoyoshi E et al. Regulation of nerve growth factor synthesis/secretion by catecholamine in cultured mouse astroglial cells. Biochem. Biophys Res Commun 1987; 147:1048-1054.

74. Schwartz JP, Mishler K. β-Adrenergic receptor regulation, through cyclic AMP, of nerve growth factor expression in rat cortical and cerebellar astrocytes. Cell Mol Neurobiol 1990; 10:447-457.

75. Cambray-Deakin M, Pearce B, Morrow C et al. Effects of neurotransmitters on astrocyte glycogen stores in vitro. J Neurochem 1988; 51:1852-1857.

76. Subbarao KV, Hertz L. Effect of adrenergic agonists on glycogenolysis in primary cultures of astrocytes. Brain Res 1990; 536:220-226.

77. Cambray-Deakin M, Pearce B, Morrow C et al. Effects of extracellular potassium on glycogen stores of astrocytes in vitro. J Neurochem 1988; 51:1846-1851.

78. Hsu CC, Hsu CS. Effect of isoproterenol on the uptake of ^{14}(C)glucose into glial cells. Neurosci Res 1990; 9:54-58.

79. Subbarao KV, Hertz L. Noradrenaline induced stimulation of oxidative metabolism in astrocytes but not in neurons in primary cultures. Brain Res 1990; 527:346-349.

80. Magistretti PJ, Schorderet M. VIP and noradrenaline act synergistically to increase cyclic AMP in cerebral cortex. Nature 1984; 308:280-282.

81. Sorg O, Magistretti PJ. Vasoactive intestinal peptide and noradrenaline exert long-term control on glycogen levels in astrocytes: blockade by protein synthesis inhibition. J Neurosci 1992; 12:4923-4931.

82. Murphy S, Minor RL, Welk G et al. Evidence for an astrocyte-derived vasorelaxing factor with properties similar to nitric oxide. J Neurochem 1990; 55:349-351.

83. Lindqvist G, Malmgren H. Organic mental disorders as hypothetical pathogenetic processes. Acta Psychiatr Scand 1993; 88:Suppl 373: 5-17.

84. Cotman CW, Monaghan DT, Ottersen OP, Storm-Mathisen J. Anatomical organization of excitatory amino acid receptors and their pathways. Trends Neurosci 1987; 10:273-280.

85. Chopp M, Welch KMA, Tidwell CD et al. Global cerebral ischemia and intracellular pH during hyperglycemia and hypoglycemia in cats. Stroke 1988; 19:1383-1387.

86. Bullock R, Maxwell WL, Graham DI et al. Glial swelling following human cerebral contusion: an ultrastructural study. J Neurol Neurosurg Psych 1991; 54:427-434.

87. Kimelberg HK, O'Connor ER. Swelling-induced depolarization of astrocyte potentials. GLIA 1988; 1:219-224.

88. Shain W, Madelian V, Martin DL et al. Activation of beta-adrenergic receptors stimulates release of an inhibitory transmitter from astrocytes. J Neurochem 1986; 46:1298-1303.

89. Philibert RA, Rogers KL, Allen AJ et al. Dose-dependent, K^+ stimulated efflux of endogeneous taurine from primary astrocyte cultures is Ca^{2+}-dependent. J Neurochem 1988; 51:122-126.

90. Kimelberg HK, Goderie SK, Higman S et al. Swelling-induced release of glutamate, aspartate, and taurine from astrocyte culture. J Neurosci 1990; 10:1583-1591.

91. Negro A, Tavella A, Facci L, et al. Interleukin-1b regulates proenkephalin gene expression in astrocytes cultured from rat cortex. GLIA 1992; 6:206-212.

92. Low KG, Allen RG, Melner MH. Differential regulation of proenkephalin expression in astrocytes by cytokines. Endocrinol 1992; 131:1908-1914.

93. Chesler M, Kraig RP. Intracellular pH of astrocytes increases rapidly with cortical stimulation. Am J Physiol 1987; 22:R666-R670.

94. Ransom BR. Glial modulation of neural excitability mediated by extracellular pH: a hypothesis. In: Yu ACH, Hertz L, Norenberg MD, Syková E, Waxman SG, eds. Neuronal-astrocytic interactions. Implications for normal and pathological CNS function. Progress in Brain Research 1992; 94:37-46.

95. Arnsten AFT, Goldman-Rakic PS. Selective prefrontal cortical projections to the region of the locus coeruleus and raphe nuclei in the rhesus monkey. Brain Res 1984; 306:9-18.

96. Jorge RE, Robinson RG, Arndt SV, et al. Depression following traumatic brain injury: a 1 year longitudinal study. J Affective Disorders 1993; 27:233-243.

97. Andersen G, Vestergaard K, Riis JO, Lauritzen L. Incidence of poststroke depression during the first year in a large unselected stroke population determined using a valid standardized rating scale. Acta Psychiatr Scand 1994; 90:190-195.

98. Mayberg HS. Frontal lobe dysfunction in secondary depression. J Neuropsychiatr Clin Neurosci 1994; 6:428-442.

99. Walz W, Schule WR. Ionic mechanism of a hyperpolarizing 5-hydroxytryptamine effect on leech neuropile glial cells. Brain Res 1982; 250:111-121.

100. Hösli L, Hösli E, Baggi M et al. Action of dopamine and serotonin on the membrane potential of cultured astrocytes. Expl Brain Res 1987; 65:482-485.

101. Ogura A, Amano T. Serotonin-receptor coupled with membrane electrogenesis in a rat glioma clone. Brain Res 1984; 297:387-391.

INDEX